KT-165-525

OFFICE FOR
NATIONAL
STATISTICS

Health Inequalities

Decennial supplement

edited by:

Frances Drever
Statistician, Office for National Statistics

Margaret Whitehead
Visiting fellow at King's Fund Policy Institute and Karolinska Institute, Sweden

COLLEGE OF RIPON AND
YORK ST. JOHN

RIPON CAMPUS LIBRARY

REFERENCE
COLLECTION

Series DS No. 15

19 MAY 2024

150133

London: The Stationery Office

College of Ripon & York St. John

3 8025 00353439 6

© Crown copyright 1997

ISBN 0 11 620942 9

Requests to produce any contents from this
publication should be addressed to Copyright
Enquiries, Marketing and Customer Services,
Office for National Statistics, Zone B1/4,
1 Drummond Gate, London SW1V 2QQ.
Telephone 0171 533 5674

Contents

Tables and Figures

Chapters 6-13: all tables and figures refer to
England and Wales

Chapter 10 Male mortality from major causes of deaths

Chapter 11 Mortality trends using the Longitudinal Study

Acknowledgements

The editors wish to thank the many colleagues in the Office for National Statistics who have helped in the preparation of this report. We are indebted to the authors of the individual chapters, together with many people who have prepared additional data and offered their advice and guidance. Special thanks go to Julia Bunting and the socio-economic and geographic team for the many long hours they have put in so enthusiastically to deliver the volume ahead of time. We have received valuable advice from the independent referees listed in Appendix C and from colleagues at the Department of Health. Professor Finn Diderichsen has helped to guide us expertly through the international evidence.

We are grateful to the following copyright holders for kind permission to reproduce material from their publications in this volume. Göran Dahlgren (Figure 1.1); Vladimir Shkolnikov (Table 4.1); World Health Organisation (Figure 4.5); Swedish National Board for Health and Welfare (Figure 4.6); International Journal of Epidemiology (Figure 4.7); Institute of Health, City of Barcelona (Figure 4.8); BMJ Publishing Group (Figure 4.9).

Foreword

This volume continues the tradition started in the middle of the last century, by this office, of presenting a major analysis and review of mortality in this country every ten years - the so-called 'decennial supplements'. With the first such review, William Farr, who compiled the statistics, presented his report in the form of a Letter to the Registrar General, in which he guided the reader through the major findings of the analysis and discussed the implications for the public health. Foremost among his concerns was to shed light on the socio-economic and environmental conditions of the day and their influences on health, as illustrated by the extract below.

While we can't hope to match William Farr's prose, the intention in this current volume has been to produce a report in the same spirit of openness and social inquiry. The presentation of very complex analyses has been simplified as much as possible, although the detailed data are available in electronic form for anyone wishing to study them further. To aid interpretation of the analyses, social commentaries on a number of related issues have also been included.

This report is timely, with several national initiatives now underway to inquire into social differences in health. Together with the other decennial supplements in this current series - *Occupational Health* (1995), *The Health of Our Children* (1995) and *The Health of Adult Britain* (1997) - we hope that *Health Inequalities* will provide much needed information on the current patterns and trends in the population's health in this country.

KAREN DUNNELL
Director of Health and Demographic Statistics

Letter to the Registrar General from William Farr, 1875

"There is a relation betwixt death and sickness: and to every death from every cause there is an average number of attacks of sickness, and a specific number of persons incapacitated for work. Death is the extinction of pain. There is a relation betwixt death, health, and energy of the body and mind. There is a relation betwixt death and national primacy: numbers turn the tide in the struggle of populations, and the most mortal die out. There is a relation betwixt the forms of death and moral excellence or infamy...There is finally a relation betwixt death and the mean lifetime of man...The laws of life are of the highest possible interest, even if the knowledge of those laws gave men no more power over the course of human existence than the meteorologist wields over the storms of the atmosphere, or the astronomer over the revolutions of the heavens. But all human laws precede under the belief that the lives of individuals and of communities can within certain limits, be regulated for good or for evil."

Part One

Wider perspectives on health inequalities

Health inequalities: setting the scene

Frances Drever and Margaret Whitehead

'The primary object is to determine what the death toll is at the several ages, and what the causes of the loss of life are, under different circumstances.

Armed with this golden bough, we may enter the gloomy kingdom of the dead, whither have gone in twenty years nine thousand, thousand English children, fathers, mothers, sisters, brothers, daughters, sons ... each having left memories not easily forgotten; and many having biographies full of complicated incidents. Here, fortunately for this inquiry, they appear divested of all colour, form, character, passion, and the infinite individualities of life: by abstraction they are reduced to mere units undergoing changes as purely physical as the setting stars of astronomy or the decomposing atoms of chemistry; and as in those sciences so in this, the analysis of the elementary facts observed in their various relations to time and place will shed new light on the more complicated phenomena of national life'.

William Farr. Letter to the Registrar General on the mortality in the registration of districts of England during the years 1861–70.[1]

A key responsibility

Evidence on socio-economic factors and their involvement in ill health and death are presented in the sixteen chapters of this volume, together with two technical appendices and an accompanying electronic disk giving more detailed data analyses. Why should the Office for National Statistics (ONS) publish a whole volume concerned with this issue in 1997?

The above extract, from a report by the first superintendent of statistics, shows that socio-economic influences have been the concern of the office responsible for registering deaths since its inception in 1837. William Farr clearly believed that it was the responsibility of the national office not just to record deaths, but to uncover underlying linkages which might lead to the prevention of disease and suffering in the future.

Today, socio-economic factors are still an important focus for public health at local, national and international levels. Along with every other member state of the European Region of the World Health Organisation (WHO), Britain is committed to the European Health For All Strategy, which has as its first target:

Target 1: Equity in health: By the year 2000, the differences in health status between countries and between groups within countries should be reduced by at least 25 per cent by improving the level of health of disadvantaged nations and groups.[2]

The monitoring of progress towards this target is part of the strategy and every country in Europe has agreed to collect relevant information to fulfil this responsibility. This volume brings together a number of important analyses to help inform the debate on equity both here and abroad.

Major influences on health

The social and economic environments in a country contain key influences on the population's health and well-being. Figure 1.1 illustrates the many determinants of health.[3] Some, such as age, gender and genetic make-up, are fixed and little can be done to change them. Others range from individual behaviours, through psychosocial and community influences, to living and working conditions, and beyond these to the broader

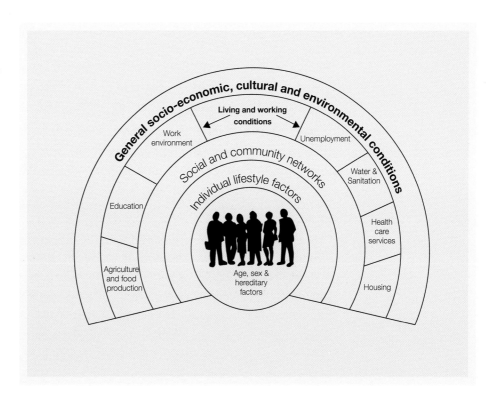

macroeconomic environment. These different layers of influence do not operate in isolation, but interact in complex relationships. They are all potentially amenable to change.

Figure 1.1 shows that medical care provided by health services is just one factor of many concerned with the state of a nation's health, and not necessarily the most important from a public health perspective. Over the century social and economic factors have made the largest contribution to the striking improvement observed in the overall health of the population (see Chapter 2).

The trends in both infant and adult mortality tell a story of a fairly steady improvement over the decades of the 20th century. Life expectancy in England and Wales has increased from 52 years for men and 55 years for women in 1910[4] to 74 years and 79 years respectively in 1994.[5] Over the same period infant mortality has fallen from around 105 per thousand[6] to six per thousand.[7] Throughout this century, however, different sections of society have benefited to different extents. Differentials in health can be observed across the social groups within the population, with a gap of five years in life expectancy at birth between men in Social Classes I/II and IV/V (see Chapter 6). Infant mortality rates also show substantial differences across the social spectrum (see Chapter 7).

When weighing the evidence on what are the most likely explanations for the observed differentials, the Department of Health's Variations subgroup concluded in 1995 that:

> *'It is likely that cumulative differential exposure to health damaging or health promoting physical and social environments is the main explanation for the observed variations in health and life expectancy, with health related social mobility, health damaging or health promoting behaviours, use of health services, and genetic or biological factors contributing'.[8]*

This points the way towards the priority areas for action if these health differences are to be reduced.

Monitoring these differentials has been an important part of the work of the General Register Office since it was founded in 1837, as illustrated in Chapter 2. Furthermore, there has been a tradition of commenting on the analyses of deaths, particularly in the ten-yearly reviews of deaths published as decennial supplements to the Registrar General's annual reports.[9] These supplements, issued every ten years since 1851, make use of data from each census to update population estimates for calculating mortality rates for different groups in society.

In the study of social inequalities in health, the most frequently used indirect indicators of social and economic circumstances are a person's occupation, education or income.[10] These indicators attempt to capture the less tangible aspects of social organisation, for example those concerned with social ranking or standing in the community or economic power. Because occupation is the only socio-economic information that is recorded routinely at the census and at birth and death registration in Britain, classifications based on occupation are more commonly used in mortality analyses here. Occupation is also recognised as a powerful determinant of income and life chances in general.

Only a very broad classification of occupations was attempted at the first census of 1801. By 1851 a more refined industrial classification was developing.[11] This classification was in use until 1911 when the Registrar General first introduced a social class scheme. Originally this consisted of eight classes, five of which were 'designed to represent as far as possible different social grades',[12] and three based on separate industries. This scheme was first used to analyse the fertility of married men in each occupation and occupational infant mortality rates.

By 1921, the three industrial groupings had been integrated into the five main social classes, which were used to examine both infant and adult male mortality. Analyses for women by social class were not included in the statistics until the publication of the 1931 decennial supplement. This included analyses for both single women by their own social class and married women by their husband's social class.

There was no census in 1941 due to World War II, but the series resumed in 1951 when a new revision of occupations was introduced. The 1971 supplement introduced several new types of analyses, including calculations of life expectancy by social class, and the assessment of social class gradients by country of birth.

The Office of Population Censuses and Surveys (OPCS), now the Office for National Statistics (ONS), Longitudinal Study also began in 1971. This took a one per cent representative sample of the population of England and Wales from the census and subsequently linked information from birth, marriage, death and cancer registrations and censuses to those individuals. The sample is constantly updated with new LS members. This provides much greater detail on socio-economic characteristics of the individuals and has been used to study, for example, women and older people's mortality by alternative measures of social position.[13]

The social class analysis centred on the 1981 Census was, by comparison, rather sparse, apart from a detailed analysis of children by social class.[14] The adult mortality was presented as microfiche tables without commentary.[15] In contrast, for the 1990s this volume has been given over in its entirety to the examination of the issue of health and the socio-economic environment.

About this volume

There are three main parts to this volume. The first, Chapters 1 to 4, contains discussions which help to set the scene for the subsequent analyses. Chapter 2 gives an historical perspective, looking back to what is known of life and death over the millennium, and the recurring debates on such themes as hunger and poverty, overcrowding and blighted opportunities. Chapter 3 gives a review of more recent social and economic trends including changes since World War II in population, family and household structure, working and living conditions, national income and its distribution. Chapter 4 provides an international perspective, reviewing the latest evidence on inequalities in health across Europe and North America, to help place the British situation in the context of developments elsewhere.

Part Two, Chapters 5 to 13, presents analyses of mortality by social class and other socio-economic indicators for the years around the 1991 Census. Following a description of methods used, see Chapter 5, current socio-economic patterns and trends are analysed for different stages in life, starting with life expectancy at birth in Chapter 6. Infant and childhood mortality are covered in Chapter 7 and trends in all-cause mortality in adult men in Chapter 8. The mortality differences of first-generation migrants and social class is explored in Chapter 9 for all-cause mortality and for major disease groups. Chapter 10 goes on to provide a detailed breakdown of about 50 causes of death by social class for adult men aged 20 to 64.

Chapters 11, 12 and 13 draw on data from the Longitudinal Study to cast further light on the mortality patterns for men and with a special focus on women and elderly people. Chapter 11 presents evidence of social class trends from a 22-year follow-up of LS members, Chapter 12 covers the issue of unemployment and mortality, and Chapter 13 uses the alternative socio-economic indicators of housing tenure and car access. As well as offering insight into sections of the population not covered by analyses in earlier chapters, they also provide much evidence that the patterns in mortality seen using the social class schema persist when alternative socio-economic measures are used.

Part Three of the volume contains chapters which go beyond mortality to look at morbidity and *Health of the Nation* priority areas. Areas of morbidity relating to children are contained in Chapter 14. Chapter 15 looks at adult morbidity, lifestyles and health service use. Finally, Chapter 16 draws together the conclusions from the volume and looks to the future.

The body of the volume has been designed to be accessible to a wide lay readership, as well as to a professional audience. The more technical descriptions of how the analyses were carried out have been placed in two appendices at the end of the book. Many of the summary figures and tables in this volume have been derived from more comprehensive databases. Much of the more detailed information is available on electronic media accompanying this volume.

This volume has benefited greatly from comments on earlier drafts made by a panel of independent referees as well as by internal advisers. A list of the independent referees is given in Appendix C. During the peer review process, each chapter was reviewed by at least four external and three ONS referees. Their comments were much appreciated, and were taken on board wherever possible. However, responsibility for any defects or errors rests with the authors of each chapter, not with the referees or with ONS.

References

1 Registrar General's Decennial Supplement to the 35th Report, 1861–70. General Register Office, 1875.

2 WHO (1991) *A Strategy for Health for All: Revised Targets*. Copenhagen, World Health Organisation.

3 Dahlgren, G and Whitehead, M (1991) *Policies and Strategies to Promote Social Equity in Health*. Stockholm, Institute for Futures Studies.

4 Devis, T (1990) The expectation of life in England and Wales, *Population Trends;* 60: 23–24.

5 Office for National Statistics (1997) Table 12, *Population Trends,* 87, Spring 1997; The Stationery Office, 1997.

6 Registrar General's 73rd Annual Report, 1910. General Register Office 1912.

7 Office for National Statistics (1997) Table 8, *Population Trends,* 87, Spring 1997: The Stationery Office, 1997.

8 Department of Health (1995) *Variations in Health: What can the Department of Health and the NHS do?* London, HMSO.

9 Nissel, M (1987) *People Count. A History of the General Register Office*. London, HMSO.

10 Kunst, A and Mackenbach, J (1995) *Measuring Socio-economic Inequalities in Health*. Copenhagen, World Health Organisation.

11 Armstrong, W (1972) The use of information about occupation. In: Wrigley, E (ed.) *Nineteenth-century society: essays in the use of quantitative methods for the study of social data*. Cambridge, Cambridge University Press.

12 Registrar General's 74th Annual Report, 1911. General Register Office, 1913.

13 Goldblatt, P (ed.) (1990) *Longitudinal Study: Mortality and Social Organisation, 1971–1981*. Series LS no. 6. London, HMSO.

14 Office of Population Censuses and Surveys (1988) *Occupational Mortality: Childhood Supplement 1979–80, 1982–83*. Series DS no.8. London, HMSO.

15 Office of Population Censuses and Surveys (1986). *Occupational Mortality 1979–80, 1982–83 – Decennial Supplement*. Series DS no. 6. Part II Fiche Tables. London, HMSO.

2 | Life and death over the millennium

Margaret Whitehead

Summary

This chapter discusses what is known about life and death over the last thousand years, covering late medieval to early modern times; the 19th century, a time of great agitation for social reform and a transformation of public health; and the 20th century.

Over the millennium the chances of survival have improved beyond recognition.

The nature of diseases has been transformed; whereas for the first 900 years of the millenium infectious diseases were among the major killers, during the 20th century, at least in the western world, chronic degenerative diseases have become more prominent.

Inequalities in health have been a recurring theme throughout the centuries. There is relatively firm evidence of substantial social inequalities in mortality in 17th century Geneva, and other parts of Europe and Britain in the 18th century. Throughout the 19th and 20th centuries evidence has continued to emerge of differentials in health between different population groups.

Health in the late 20th century is still greatly influenced by the prevailing social and economic conditions, and there remain large differentials in the health of different groups of the population.

William Farr's work at the General Register Office in the 19th century, linking mortality statistics with the wider causes of death, has been credited with laying the foundations of epidemiology, medical statistics and the study of occupational mortality.

Over the last 150 years successive Registrar General's Decennial Supplements have analysed mortality in England and Wales in relation to social and economic circumstances. These analyses have played a vital role in informing social policy, and have influenced the development of public health in this country and internationally.

These reports have been used to understand the influences on health of the recurring historical themes of hunger and famine; poverty and overcrowding; the pollution and squalor of urbanisation and industrialisation.

Introduction

Approximately every ten years over the last 150 years, the Registrar General for England and Wales has issued a Decennial Supplement (DS) analysing in detail socio-economic factors and mortality over the decade. As we near the end of this millennium, an unparalleled opportunity arises to look back and take stock, not only over the past ten years, but over the century and even further back, to what is known of life and death in this country over the millennium.

It is particularly appropriate that the Office for National Statistics (ONS) should do this, because the data it has produced and used so effectively have been at the very centre of the great debates about the causes of disease and death and how public health might be improved. So, for example, the long series of mortality trends from the General Register Office (GRO) has been used to understand the influences on health of the recurring historical themes of hunger and famine, poverty and overcrowding, the pollution and squalor of urbanisation and industrialisation, and the hazardous conditions under which men, women and children have worked over the centuries. Many of these analyses have not sat on shelves gathering dust, but have been used, sometimes hot off the press, to inform and stimulate social policy and public works.

Furthermore, the way the analyses were carried out for the early reports has had an enduring influence on the direction the whole field of public health has taken both in this country and internationally.

With such a rich historical record, only a limited selection of issues can be covered in this chapter. For this overview the time-span has been divided into three main periods: from the beginning of the millennium in 1000 AD to the first census of 1801 – covering late medieval and early modern times; 1800 to 1900 – a period that witnessed feverish agitation for social reform and a transformation in public health; and finally the 20th century. Within these periods, scientific and social debates are highlighted to which data from the Registrar General's office have made a major contribution. The chapter ends where the rest of the book begins – in the closing decades of this century.

Living and dying in late medieval England

For the early part of the millennium the Doomsday book of 1086 AD provides the first reliable marker for the population. Chambers has drawn up population estimates for England for the early centuries of this period based on old tax returns, the Hearth Tax records, subsidy rolls and parish registers. From these documents the population of England has been estimated as 1.75 million in 1086, trebling to 4 million by the mid-1300s, before suffering a severe decline, possibly as much as a 50 per cent reduction between the years 1348–75. This was followed by a century of stagnation before a recovery, which began to accelerate dramatically towards the end of the 1600s, as shown in Figure 2.1.[1] There are indications that there was also a halt, or even decline, in population between 1620 and 1700.[2]

From the mid-16th century onwards more quantitative evidence is available, not only on population numbers but also births and deaths. These came from studies of christenings and burials from parish registers, which were established from 1538 onwards, and from Bills of Mortality kept by parish clerks, recording the number of deaths and their causes in each parish. More recently detailed back projection modelling from thousands of parish registers around England and family reconstitution studies have helped fill in the evidence.

Figure 2.2 shows the birth and death rates for England and Figure 2.3 the expectation of life from 1541 onwards, from Wrigley and Schofield's reconstruction work[2] and from the Registrar General's records for more recent years.

For nearly 200 years from 1541, the underlying death rate remained in the region of 30 per 1,000 population, although it was subject to violent swings. There were mortality crises in England about every five years up until 1700, but then these gradually subsided. A period of rising birth rates and declining death rates coincided by 1781, resulting in the observed rapid up-surge in population, which more than doubled – from 5 to 11 million – by 1800.[2] The increase in birth rate, through earlier and more widespread marriage, made the largest contribution to the observed population growth.

From Figure 2.3 it can be seen that life expectancy, although subject to erratic swings, remained basically at around 34 years for nearly 250 years, and only began to show a clear rising trend after 1780, reaching 36 years by 1801. A more rapid rate of increase did not occur until the end of the 19th century.

FIGURE 2.1

Population of England, 1100–1871

Source: Chambers[1] for years 1100–1540: Wrigley and Schofield[2] for 1541 onwards

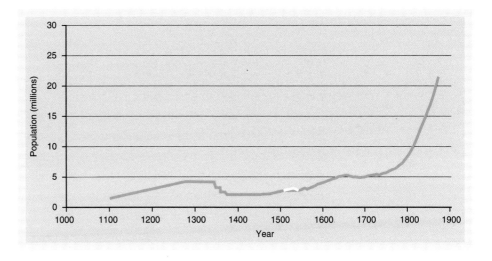

FIGURE 2.2

Crude birth rate and crude death rate

England, 1541–1994

Source: Wrigley and Schofield: Office for National Statistics

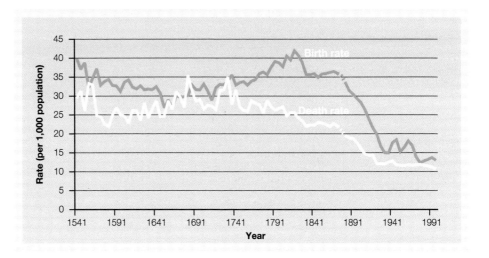

FIGURE 2.3

Life expectancy at birth
England, 1541–1994

Source: Wrigley and Schofield; Office
for National Statistics

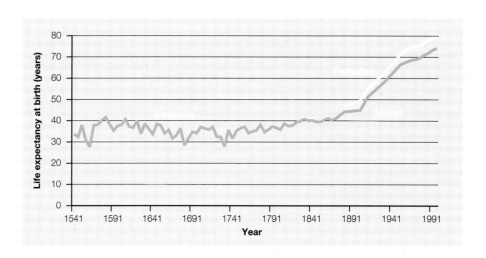

Pestilence and famine

What caused these fluctuating trends? Up to the 16th century assessments concerning fertility, birth rates, mortality and its causes are highly speculative. There seems no doubt, however, that food shortages and epidemics of infectious diseases were dominant features of these early centuries and the major causes of the high death rates. The early rise in the population up to the 1280s has been attributed to the absence, or at least rarity, of epidemics, so that life expectancy and fertility were high. The catastrophic fall in population coincided with the onset of the Black Death in 1348, coupled with a succession of epidemic outbreaks of other infectious diseases thought to include smallpox, typhus, cholera, and dysentery.[1]

By comparing annual mortality with records of harvests for the preceding year, it is clear that some mortality crises were also caused by food shortages. Famines could cause the mortality rate in a locality to treble or quadruple. For instance, an analysis of infant mortality and the wheat price index, a measure of the availability of food, in Penrith (Cumbria) from 1557–1812 found clear oscillations in infant mortality synchronised with the oscillations in the wheat price index. Examination of the ten years before and after the famine of 1623, showed that pregnancies when food prices were high were associated with subsequent severe infant mortality.[3]

After what seems to have been a decade of particular crises in terms of famine and pestilence, the English government introduced a Dearth Policy in 1527 aimed at controlling famine whenever the harvest failed.[4] This was a first attempt to assess the population in need and to search out the supply of grain to ensure that it was brought to the market, where it was to be offered first to the poor in small quantities. The policy had modest success in distributing scarce grain more equitably, but it was ineffective in regulating the market to improve the geographic distribution of food. It has been claimed, however, that the whole process left a valuable legacy, encouraging the careful measurement of social and economic phenomena, and gradually making people aware of social deprivation and changing perceptions of the entitlements of the poor.[4] After 1623, there were no signs of major crises involving harvest failures followed by high mortality over a whole region, though there were still reports of localised famine and misery.[4]

The relationships between mortality, food shortages, disease and population growth turned out to be more complex than originally envisaged. There was an idea circulating at the end of the 1700s that life had to be this cruel: that famine and disease were necessary evils to control the population numbers and that market forces operating on wages and food prices played their part.[5] Ironically, at about the same time as this theory was formally published in England and was rapidly gaining ground, developments in the country were disproving it. Fundamental changes in agriculture in the 18th century, involving more intensive farming methods and the introduction of new crops, made it possible to produce food at a greater rate than ever before. Production thus kept pace with the needs of a growing population. At the same time, marked improvements in transport systems, including the construction of a vast network of canals, led to improved distribution of food produced by these new methods.[6] The issue was no longer whether there was enough food in the country to sustain the population, but whether everyone had sufficient means to obtain it.

Was there inequality in the face of death?

Given the main theme of this book, the key question arises of whether there were substantial inequalities in death rates and chances of survival between different sections of the population in this early period, and if not, when did such inequalities emerge? Opinion is split on this question. Commentators such as Antonovsky argue that class differences in life expectancy prior to the 18th century were relatively limited because:

> 'given a society which, though it manages to survive, does so at or near what might be called a rock-bottom level of life expectancy, one is not likely to find great differences among the strata of that society'.[7]

Mackenbach, in his study of late medieval death dances, conversely argues that:

> 'It is nevertheless difficult to believe that higher placed persons did indeed have the same survival chances as the majority of the population in the 14th and 15th centuries',

given that the richer families would be at less risk of dying from food shortages, less risk from overcrowding and poor housing, and were better able to escape to other places when epidemics threatened, rather than be confined to 'pest houses', which was the fate of the poor in many places.[8]

The problem is that most comparisons are made between ruling families (kings, queens, dukes and duchesses) for whom there are more complete records of births and deaths, and estimates of mortality for the population of a country as a whole are drawn from much more fragmentary evidence. However, the ruling families were a highly atypical group. They appeared to have had their own unique health hazards, over and above those faced by the more prosperous, but non-aristocratic sections of a population. In a study of British ducal families for example, male members of these families in the 14th and 15th century were found to have a very high incidence of death from violence, as not only civil wars, but also power struggles leading to executions for treason were fairly frequent. The gap in life expectancy between male and female members of these families was greatly reduced once violent deaths were excluded.[9]

Rarely is it possible to compare the experience of the mass of poor people with that of more representative sections of the richer classes before the 18th century. One of the earliest studies of this kind is of occupational class mortality in Geneva in the 17th century. This showed that there was already a well-established health divide in the city at that time, with life expectancy of the highest occupational class standing at 36 years, compared with 18 years for the lowest class.[10] By the 18th century, there is more evidence of socio-economic inequalities in mortality from around Europe. Peller, for example, compared the survival rates for Europe's ruling families with those for the inhabitants of the city of Vienna. He found that, by 1752–5, survival rates for the ruling families were far ahead of those for the Viennese population in general, as shown in Table 2.1. Differences were particularly large in the post-neonatal period, with a mortality rate of 106 per 1,000 for the ruling families compared with 331 per 1,000 for the Viennese population.[11] Berlin church registers provide further evidence of wide mortality differentials across the social spectrum in the city in the 18th century.[12]

In Britain an indication of different mortality experience for subsections of the population can be glimpsed from pre-18th century records. In the relatively poor parish of St Botolph's in London in 1583–99, of every 100 babies born only 30 survived to the age of 15.[13] In contrast, in British ducal families in the years 1480–1679, 69 out of 100 babies born survived to age 15.[9] John Graunt, writing in 1662, estimated from the London Bills of Mortality that of 100 babies born in London at that time 40 survived to age 16.[14] Graunt detected greater mortality in London than in the countryside, which he put down to environmental pollution in the city, as the extract from his book in Box 2.1 illustrates.

As illustrated in Table 2.2, evidence of social inequalities in mortality in Britain in the 18th century comes from studies of British ducal families and peasant villagers from around the country. The less favoured lowland villages appeared to have particularly high mortality. In Wrangle, Lincolnshire for example, right up to the last decade of the 18th century, 27 per cent of those baptised died before the age of one, 39 per cent before the age of five and 60 per cent before the age of 21.[1] By the close of the century, the existence of social inequalities in health was being recognised in contemporary writing:

> *'The people in a civilised state may be divided into many different orders; but, for the purpose of investigating the manner in which they enjoy or are deprived of the requisites to support the health of their bodies and minds, they need only be divided into two classes, viz. the rich and the poor'.*
> Hall (1805).[15]

In summary, relatively firm evidence of substantial social inequalities in mortality goes back to the 17th century in Geneva, and to the 18th century in other parts of Europe and Britain. Traces of evidence from the 16th and 17th centuries in Britain add support to what can only be speculation that differentials in death, as in life chances, existed at these earlier times.

TABLE 2.1

Survival of children in Europe, 1752–5

Source: Peller[11]

	Of 1,000 born alive in 1752–5 number surviving		
	1st year of life	5th year of life	15th year of life
Europe's ruling families	847	723	664
Viennese population	590	413	359

Box 2.1 Extract from John Graunt 1662. On mortality in country and city.

(70)

faintly afferted in the former Chapter, that the Country is more *healthfull*, then the City, That is to fay, although men die more regularly, and lefs *per Saltum* in *London*, then in the Country, yet, upon the whole matter, there die fewer *per Rata* ; fo as the Fumes, Steams, and Stenches above-mentioned, although they make the Air of *London* more equal, yet not more *Healthfull*.

13. When I confider, That in the Country feventy are Born for fifty eight Buried, and that before the year 1600 the like happened in *London*, I confidered, whether a City, as it becomes more populous, doth not, for that very caufe, become more *unhealthfull*, I inclined to believe, that *London* now is more *unhealthfull*, then heretofore, partly for that it is more populous, but chiefly, becaufe I have heard, that 60 years ago few *Sea-Coals* were burnt in *London*, which now are univerfally ufed. For I have heard, that *Newcaftle* is more *unhealthfull* then other places, and that many People cannot at all endure the fmoak of *London*, not onely for its unpleafantnefs, but for the fuffocations which it caufes.

14. Suppofe, that *Anno* 1569 there were 2400 fouls in that Parifh, and that they increafed by the *Births* 70, exceeding the *Burials* 58, it will follow, that the faid 2400 cannot double under 200. Now, if *London* be lefs *healthfull* then the Country, as certainly it is, the *Plague* being reckoned in, it follows, that *London* muft be doubling it felf by generation in much above 200 : but if it hath encreafed from 2 to 5 in 54. as aforefaid, the fame muft be by reafon of tranfplantation out of the Country.

The

TABLE 2.2

Mortality of infants and young people, 1739–79

Source Chambers[1]

	% of deaths among recorded baptisms	
	under 5 years	under 21 years
British dukes (Hollingsworth, 1965)	20	27
Bedfordshire peasants (fairly prosperous) (Tranter, 1966)	24	31
Lincolnshire peasants (Chambers, 1972)	39	60

The 19th century is now recognised as a pivotal time for public health in Britain, with a major break appearing in the pattern that had prevailed for most of the millennium. At the beginning of the century, the population began a sustained and steep increase, followed in the second half by a dramatic drop in mortality. By the close of the century the start of a sustained rise in life expectancy could also be seen, as illustrated in Figures 2.1–2.3.

These remarkable trends were inextricably bound up with attempts to deal with the two major social problems of the 19th century – the growing numbers of people in poverty and the adverse consequences of industrialisation. Why the public health movements sprang up in the way they did, and the subsequent course of population health, cannot be fully understood without reference to these wider social and economic trends.[16]

Social and economic trends

The agricultural revolution in the 18th century had involved more intensive farming in a successful bid to expand production to feed the growing population. It had, however, entailed fencing off, or enclosing a great proportion of what had previously been common lands, to make bigger, separate fields for private landowners. Huge numbers of people were made destitute in rural areas as they lost entitlement to the land they had farmed at a subsistence level. This threw the existing local systems for supporting the poor into crisis, as each community was responsible for the paupers resident in its own parish. One result was widespread rioting in agricultural areas in the first half of the 19th century. Another was unrest among the ratepayers at having to foot the bill for poor relief.

At the same time the growth of industrial factories and transport systems was creating the demand for an army of mobile workers, willing and able to move to where the factories were concentrated. The New Poor Law Act of 1834 was designed to solve several of these problems in one go. It created a national system of poor relief in place of the many local systems. This was structured to reduce expenditure by restricting entitlement to poor relief and, at the same time, spurring the able-bodied poor to take work by cutting off support and exposing them to hardship. It also took away the previous restrictions on the mobility of rural workers so that they were freer to go to the cities where the factories were facing a severe labour shortage.

The ensuing mass movement from rural areas to the towns generated severely health-damaging circumstances which required attention in their own right. The English social reformers of the day at first concentrated on the environmental effects of industrialisation and pressed for improvements in physical living and working conditions. It was only later that they became more vocal about why people continued to be poor and in bad health.

The way in which statistical data on health were collected and presented was important in stimulating developments. At times, the campaigns for public health improvements took on the characteristics of moral crusades. The skill of the protagonists in presenting their case, as illustrated later, greatly influenced subsequent events and legislation.

'Healthy Districts' and the annual sacrifice of lives

The population of many towns in England doubled from 1801 to 1831, then doubled again in the next 20 years.[17] As people flocked to the towns to find work unprecedented overcrowding, occupational hazards, air pollution and faecal contamination of the water supply were the inevitable result.

Conditions were ripe for the spread of disease and disability, but at first these conditions were hidden from the view of the prosperous. However, in 1838 and 1839 the Poor Law Commissioners, set up to review the working of the New Poor Law, submitted reports to the Home Secretary with evidence from medical inspectors for poorer parts of London:

> *'While systematic efforts on a large scale have been made to widen the streets, to remove obstructions to the circulation of free currents of air, to extend and perfect the drainage and sewerage, and to prevent the accumulation of putrefying vegetable and animal substances in the places in which the wealthier classes reside, nothing whatever had been done to improve the condition of the districts inhabited by the poor. These neglected places are out of view, and are not thought of; their condition is known only to the parish officers and the medical men whose duties oblige them to visit the inhabitants to relieve their necessities and to attend to the sick ... Such is the filthy, close and crowded state of the houses, and the poisonous condition of the localities in which the greater part of the houses are situated from the total want of drainage, and the masses of putrefying matters of all sorts which are allowed to remain and accumulate indefinitely ... Yet in these pestilential places the industrious poor are obliged to take their abode; they have no choice ... by no prudence of forethought on their part can they avoid the dreadful evils of this class to which they are exposed'.* Smith (1839)[18]

The Commissioners used their returns for poor relief to illustrate 'the final results of that suffering'. For example, they reported that in Bethnal Green and Whitechapel Districts alone, of 77,000 recorded paupers in 1838, 14,000 had been attacked with fever and 1,300 had died from those attacks. They were careful to point out that the rest of the community suffered too, as disease spread to all districts out of the slums.[18]

This report, presented to parliament, stimulated the setting up of an inquiry headed by the Poor Law Commissioners, into sanitary conditions in the whole of Great Britain. The inquiry's findings, published in 1842 under the title *General Report on the Sanitary Conditions of the Labouring Population of Great Britain*,[19] immediately went into common circulation. About 100,000 copies of the report were distributed and in turn resulted in the setting up of a Royal Commission specifically on the health of large towns.[20,21]

The evidence in these three 1840s' reports was compelling and stimulated an array of other influential publications, including a devastating indictment by Frederick Engels,[22] which swelled popular pressure for public health reform. On the sanitary conditions in the country as a whole, the Poor Law Commissioners concluded:

> *'The annual loss of life from filth and bad ventilation is greater than the loss from death or wounds in any wars in which the country has been engaged in modern times'.* Chadwick (1842)[19]

From the *Health of Towns* inquiry came graphic descriptions of living conditions and resulting mortality. Conditions in the cellars of Liverpool illustrate the plight of people in towns in that period. According to evidence collected by the Medical Officer for Health (MOH) WH Duncan, by 1841 some 22,000 people lived in 7,000 subterranean cellars. Each cellar measured about 10 or 12 feet square and was sometimes less than six feet in height. Many were three or four feet below the level of the street, but each was home to three or four people. Such dwellings contained no light, no heat or ventilation, no sanitation or running water – except for the surface water and raw sewage that flowed down into them from the street level, lingering perpetually in the walls and the floors.[23] Duncan pointed out that there were 1,800 excess deaths per year in the poorer districts of Liverpool compared to the prosperous ones:

> *Should not this simple fact be sufficient to arouse the attention and stimulate the exertions of the most indifferent? It is calculated that about 1,500 lives are annually lost by ship wreck on the British coast, and not a single wreck occurs without exciting a large amount of public sympathy. These lives are lost by the decrees of providence, by causes which perhaps no human foresight could avert; and yet we look idly on, while on a spot of that coast less than two square miles in extent, hundreds of our fellow townsmen perish yearly, by causes which in a great measure it is within our power to remedy or remove.*
> Duncan (1844)[23]

Table 2.3 was published in the *Lancet* in 1843.[24] This not only showed much higher mortality in towns than in rural districts, but also illustrated the enormous differentials which existed in average age at death between different sections of the communities – a gap of 30 years between gentry and labourers in Bath, for instance.[24] The figure of 15 for average age at death of labourers in Liverpool was truly shocking, helping to create feelings of guilt that more was not being done about the situation. Such estimates were, of course, inaccurate, failing to take account of the differing age-structure of different classes, but were still highly effective as a political tool in provoking action on sanitary reform.

The commissioners for the inquiry into the health of towns were keen to stress that this was something that could be corrected:

> *'we are desirous to remove the injurious impression that a great amount of excess disease and death in the country is due to causes, which cannot in a considerable degree be removed by legislative enactments when earnestly enforced ... we must express our opinion that the efficient execution of the law will tend to reduce sickness and disease, and so far increase the means of the poor.'[21]*

They quoted evidence of studies before and after improvements which showed that increased facilities for the removal of refuse and sewage were followed rapidly by a marked improvement in health for the residents and a reduction of the mortality rate for the district (first report of *Health of Towns* 1844).[20]

A characteristic of this period was the setting up of many voluntary associations in response to these revelations including 'The Health of Towns Association', 'The Association for Promoting Cleanliness among the Poor', 'The Association for

District	Gentry and professional	Farmers and tradesmen	Labourers and artisans
Rural			
Rutland	52	41	38
Urban			
Bath	55	37	25
Leeds	44	27	19
Bethnal Green	45	26	16
Manchester	38	20	17
Liverpool	35	22	15

Improving Dwellings of the Industrious Classes', and 'The Society for the Improvement of the Conditions of the Labouring Classes'.[25]

From its inception in 1837, the General Register Office under the influence of the 'compiler of abstracts' William Farr, entered into and influenced this debate. In 1841 the Registrar General instructed the local registrars in London to carry out special surveys to identify 'unhealthy' and 'healthy' streets or parts in their district and to report on the sanitary conditions, density of populations, occupations, food supplies and heating (or lack of it) in the different areas and to compare them.[26]

From the very first annual reports, William Farr used the national data to test and prove the hypothesis that towns were more unhealthy than country districts, and that there was a relationship between the population density in different locations and the mortality rate. He mapped the pattern of death by age and cause, and used these as a rapid monitoring system for epidemics, such as the 1847 influenza outbreak and the cholera outbreaks in 1848 and 1849 in London. John Simon, MOH for the City of London, was supplied every week by Farr with the latest returns of deaths in London. He used these to brief the Privy Council the next day. These weekly returns, and sometimes daily returns, were also used in a collaborative effort by Farr, Simon and John Snow to track down the source of cholera to contaminated water supplies in 1854.[27]

The idea of taking the 'healthiest districts' as a standard, up to which the rest should theoretically be able to rise, was developed further by William Farr and used very effectively to press his point. Table 2.4, derived from the first Decennial Supplement covering 1851–61, illustrates his calculation of the 'annual sacrifice of children's lives in 151 unhealthy districts in the kingdom'. He calculated that almost 65,000 children's lives were lost each year unnecessarily in these 'unhealthy' districts and questioned how this could be tolerated:

> *'the children of the idolatrous tribe who passed them through the fire to Moloch scarcely incurred more danger than is incurred by children born in several districts of our large cities ... a strict investigation of all the circumstances of the children's lives might lead to important discoveries, and may suggest remedies for evils of which it is difficult to exaggerate the magnitude'.*
>
> Farr (1864)[28]

Results of these efforts can be seen in the Public Health Act of 1848. Various public works gradually ensured safe water, sewage and housing. Even so, some of the progress

TABLE 2.4

'Annual sacrifice of children's lives in 151 [unhealthy] districts in the kingdom.' 1851–60

Source: Adapted from William Farr[28]

Take 28 'healthy districts' as standard:

Average annual rate of mortality in children under 5 as percentage of that population	=	3.35%

In 151 'unhealthy' districts:

Annual rate	=	8.01%
Observed numbers of deaths at 8.013%	=	111,494
Expected numbers if 'healthy district' rate of 3.348% applied	=	46,585
Annual sacrifice of children's lives		64,909

was gained at the expense of other possible developments in the social and economic environment of 19th century Britain.

Poverty and health debates

Although these sanitary reforms started to improve the physical living and working conditions of large sections of the population, many reformers still held back from pressing for tackling poverty itself. This was seen as something out of their control. Reformers were probably realistic in calculating that politically it was more feasible to press for cleaning up filth and stench, with immediate benefits for all sections of the population. The importance of destitution and poverty in exacerbating death and disease was therefore not highlighted in England until later in the century.

While the battle for sanitary reforms was being waged, the devastating effects of the New Poor Law were unfolding and proving hugely unpopular. In 1834 the New Poor Law abolished money payments to able-bodied paupers. Instead these people were offered entry into a 'workhouse', where they would live and work under very harsh regimes. Workhouses were intended as a safety net for the sick and old so that no one should starve, but the able-bodied would be 'subjected to such courses of labour and discipline as would repel the indolent and vicious'.[29]

Outrage and debate over the effects of this new policy rumbled on for the rest of the century, and the effects on health and hunger were at the centre of many of these debates. Just how sensitive an issue it was has been illustrated by an argument between Edwin Chadwick and William Farr in 1839 over the GRO mortality statistics. Letters exchanged between the two men have been analysed by the American historian, Christopher Hamlin, and centre around the question: Could you starve to death in England in 1839?[30]

William Farr's first analysis of the causes of death was published in 1839 and attributed 63 deaths to 'Starvation', with the comment: 'Hunger destroys a much higher proportion than is indicated by the registers in this and in every other country, but its effects, like the effects of excess, are generally manifested indirectly, in the production of diseases of various kinds'.[31]

At the time, the Poor Law Commission was being accused on all sides of 'starvation' of the poor, and Chadwick, as the Secretary to the Commission, was sensitive to what he saw as Farr's further attack on the policy. Chadwick argued that, with the workhouse provision, there could be no deaths from lack of food and questioned the basis of the GRO statistics.[30] Farr was searching for a wider classification that would take in causes of deaths, not just diseases. His definition of starvation was much wider than hunger: 'While few die from the absolute want of food many die, or drag on a miserable existence upon insufficient, innutritious diet'.[32] Farr quoted new evidence that the workhouse diet provided only three quarters of the daily minimum requirement. Agricultural labourers had an even poorer diet providing only half the daily requirement. Chadwick responded that people did live on the workhouse diet and even saved enough for drink, and that the excuse of hunger (in the official statistics) must be disallowed.[33]

Farr retorted it was beyond doubt that 'if the quantity of provisions and supply of food to the great mass of the population could be augmented, the mortality would be reduced'.[34] The public controversy ended with Chadwick accusing Farr of speculation.[30]

It highlights, however, a debate which is still going on about how the wider social and economic determinants of health can be incorporated into prevailing ideas on disease and death.

It was only towards the end of the 19th century that sufficient evidence had accumulated and was finally filtering through that many people in the country did not have enough money for a nutritious diet or decent housing. Growing agitation about slum conditions stimulated the setting up of a Royal Commission on the Housing of the Working Classes in 1884. This showed convincingly that wages for thousands of hard working families were too low for the rents of even inadequate, unhealthy dwellings.

Some of the leading public health reformers started to speak out as the century wore on. Persistently high infant mortality, which was not declining with the adult death rates, was one indication that all was not well. John Simon, reviewing the progress made in sanitary reform of the century, stressed:

> *'Be done what may under the Sanitary Acts to banish from the dwellings of the poor all worst degrees of uncleanliness and overcrowding, the conditions remains, that scanty earnings can buy but scantily of the necessaries and comforts of life ... Question, how the house-accommodation of the poorer labouring classes may be rendered such as humane persons would wish it to be, is therefore necessarily in great part (to) question how far poverty can be turned into non-poverty, how far the poor can be made less poor'.*
>
> Simon (1890)[25]

The 20th century

As Figures 2.2 – 2.4 illustrate, the striking improvement in some of the health indicators for the population as a whole has continued throughout the 20th century. While the marked decline in adult death rates began in the last two decades of the 19th century, infant mortality was slower to show a significant improvement, and did not really start a major decline until around 1910. Since 1910, however, deaths in infancy have fallen from around 105 per 1,000 live births to below 7 per 1,000 by 1995 (see Figure 2.4). Maternal mortality was even slower to follow the downward trends, and it was not until the late 1930s that a real reduction in the rates began.[35,36]

These overall figures mask the very different experiences of the constituent parts of the population. Throughout the 20th century, evidence has continued to emerge of differentials in health between different groups in the population, causing concern or indifference depending on the political and social climate of the time.

The overall figures also mask a profound change in the nature of the health problems experienced. Whereas for the first 900 years of the millennium infectious diseases were among the major killers, during the 20th century chronic degenerative diseases, such as coronary heart disease and cancers, have become more prominent. These, together with deaths due to 'external causes', including accidents, violence and suicide, make up the bulk of deaths as we near the end of the millennium.[37]

It may therefore seem ironic that infectious disease is again posing new threats to health in the last two decades of the millennium, not least with the emergence of HIV/ AIDS. While it does not yet register as a major cause of death at the population level in Britain, the impact of HIV/AIDS on subgroups within the population is already significant. For example in younger age groups, when death rates are at their lowest,

FIGURE 2.4

Trends in infant mortality,
by social class England
and Wales, 1911–1971

Source: Registrar General (1978)[f]

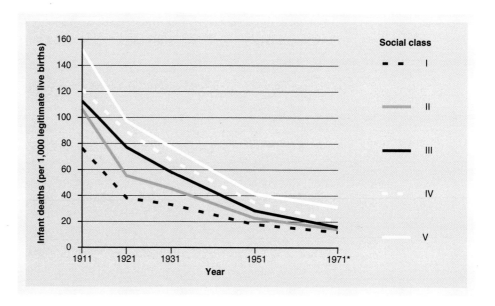

AIDS, suicides and accidents now account for the major proportion of deaths.[38] In some parts of the world, poorer social groups are already hardest hit by HIV/AIDS. There are prospects of a similar socio-economic profile emerging in Britain in the new millennium.

These 20th century developments raise questions about the main causes of the observed health trends and about the fate of different socio-economic groups in the process. This last section takes a closer look at some of these issues and the developments in measuring and monitoring that have accompanied them.

Why has mortality declined?

What were the major contributory factors in the dramatic mortality decline in Britain experienced in the second half of the 19th century, continuing into the 20th? More precisely, how much of the improvement can be attributed to improved medical care, how much to the public health sanitary reforms, and how much to the general rise in living standards and the improved nutrition that brought about?

It has been possible to examine these questions in much more depth in the last few decades with the help of the Registrar General's returns by age and cause of death for the whole period from 1837 to the present day. The DSs compare these data with information on the different subgroups of the population recorded at each census to calculate age-specific, cause-specific death rates for the country.

The interpretation of the trends has been the subject of heated debate. Thomas McKeown in his seminal work, analysed the DS data covering the period 1838 to the early 1970s and concluded that curative medicine was responsible for very little of the decline in mortality for most diseases in the 19th century and only really began to make a contribution for very specific conditions in the second half of the 20th century.[39] The rising standard of living, the most significant feature of which was improved nutrition, was assessed as a major contributor to the decline. He also concluded, from an examination of the causes of diseases and their modes of transmission (air-borne, water-borne etc.), that the sanitary measures of the second half of the 19th century could only have accounted for about a quarter of the observed fall in mortality. Rising nutritional standards could have been responsible for about a half of the decline.[39,40]

Some of McKeown's conclusions have been challenged by the historian Simon Szreter.[41] He argues that, in his eagerness to downgrade the contribution of curative medicine, McKeown has minimised the role of public action in general, not just clinical care. One of Szreter's main arguments is that life expectancy showed a considerable rise between 1750 and 1820, but then stagnated for the next 50 years, from the 1820s to the 1870s, before starting a gradual rise up to the end of the century, which speeded up in the early decades of the 20th century. But the 50-year halt in increasing life expectancy corresponded with improvements in average real incomes from 1820s onwards, after decades of stagnation. Thus the period of rising incomes did not have a corresponding rise in life expectancy, contrary to McKeown's thesis. However, public health works gathered momentum at a local level from the 1870s onwards, and corresponded to the resumption of improvement in life expectancy. He concludes from this and other evidence on trends in specific diseases that it was not economic growth in itself which had the major influence, but the way that growth was deployed in sanitary reform and improvement of living and working conditions in general. 'Fallible, blundering, but purposive human agency is returned to centre stage in this account of the mortality decline'.[41]

Both have been re-assessed by Guha,[42] who points out defects in both arguments and charts a middle interpretation. What is not in doubt is the overarching role of socio-economic conditions in influencing health. The debate continues about the causes of the trends in the 20th century, including the effects on health of periods of economic depression and the two world wars.[43,44]

Healthy or hungry?

A debate remarkably similar to the Chadwick-Farr controversy of the 1830s ('could you starve to death in England in 1839?')[30] sprang up a hundred years later in the 1930s depression and has been documented in meticulous detail by the medical historian Charles Webster.[45,46] The question was: were there sections of the population suffering severe deprivation to such an extent that it was damaging their nutrition and hence their health, or was this just a myth created by a few agitators?

Just as a century before, this was not purely an academic problem. It brought into question the prevailing social and economic policies and the adequacy of the efforts of the Ministries of Health and Education to build up maternal and child welfare services, to provide free school meals etc. Contrasting statements appeared throughout the 1930s, with the official line from the Ministry of Health and Board of Education typified by this statement from Sir George Newman, who had been Chief Medical Officer (CMO) to both departments in the 1930s:

'English people, on the whole, are today better fed, better clothed, better housed and better educated that at any time of which we have record; and they enjoy a larger life and opportunity than ever before'.[47]

Contrast this with a statement from a 1933 update (deliberately adopting the same title) of Engels' Condition of the Working Class in England:

'The stark reality is that in 1933, for the mass of the population, Britain is a hungry Britain, badly fed, clothed and housed'.[48]

Interpretation of the health statistics played a central role in the arguments on both sides of the question. The case for continued positive improvement in health and welfare despite the depression rested on two main sources. First, averages were quoted in the mortality and morbidity statistics. The overall 'extraordinary decline' in mortality since the beginning of the century, the dramatic decline in infant mortality from 150 per 1,000 in 1900 to below 100 in 1932 were highlighted in the annual reports from the Ministry of Health. Second, reports on the issue of malnutrition were publicised, based on examinations of schoolchildren by local MOHs and their comments on the condition of the adult community. The national statistics showed that, before World War I, dietary deficiency affected between 15 and 20 per cent of schoolchildren. In official reports, the recorded level in schoolchildren fell to five per cent by 1925 and one per cent in the period 1925–32.

This optimistic view on malnutrition was bolstered by positive reports from local MOHs. Webster's analysis of these reports reveals the following:[45,46]

> *London County Council: 'below-average nutrition' stood at about 5 per cent, of which only 1 per cent was definitely ill-nourished. Upon closer inspection, residual poor nutrition emerged as 'an idiosyncrasy of certain children', rather than a problem with clear economic roots.*
>
> *Cumberland: 'really very little malnutrition ... due to actual lack of food – there are a number of poorly-nourished-looking children, but in nearly all of them it is a case of poor general physique, rather than malnutrition'.*
>
> *Neath: 'no real malnutrition' was evident – the children had 'never seemed so healthy and happy'.*
>
> *Sheffield: 'nutrition of the children is not only as good as it was, but even shows some improvement'.*

Individual MOHs, such as McGonigle of Stockton-on-Tees, who drew attention to adverse conditions in their local areas,[49] were censured by the CMO. McGonigle was even threatened with removal from the medical register for ethical misconduct for agreeing to take part in a radio broadcast on malnutrition. However, the exceptionally rosy image started to become tarnished and eventually caused embarrassment, when the returns from some of the MOHs ceased to be credible:

> *'Some 50 authorities, mainly in depressed areas, were sending in returns suggesting that they were experiencing less than half the reported average incidence for the two categories of subnormal nutrition. In depressed areas such as Aberdare or Ebbw Vale not a single child was classified as having 'Bad Nutrition'. The Liverpool returns were thought to be 'frankly incredible'. It was realised by senior officials that 'cheerfulness' was being pursued to a fault'.*
>
> Glover (1940)[50] quoted in Webster[45]

The returns from school medical officers also showed wide discrepancies and bizarre anomalies. For example, the malnutrition rate for Bootle was 12 times that of Liverpool. Welsh mining areas reported negligible malnutrition, whereas rural counties had very high rates. Likewise, while depressed towns had low rates of malnutrition, flourishing cathedral towns appeared to be suffering greatly.[51] This led to a confidential inquiry in which it was confirmed that these data were unreliable and needed more objective measures of nutrient deficiency.

The other side of the argument, that there was a serious problem of ill health caused by depressed economic conditions, rested on disaggregating the data, rather than using national averages. This revealed the extent of the geographic and social class inequalities in mortality, and subsequently in maternal ill health. For example, the infant mortality rate for England in 1931–5 was 62 per 1,000, but in Scotland it was 81 per 1,000. Records for wards in Manchester in 1931 showed infant mortality rates ranging from 44 per 1,000 in the best ward to 143 per 1,000 in the worst. Data such as these for the major towns were assembled and widely disseminated.[45,46]

High levels of maternal mortality were also causing concern. Rates reached a peak in 1933, higher than in 1900. The rate of maternal mortality rose by 22 per cent between 1923 and 1933. There were marked regional and class differentials in maternal disablement – more than 30 per cent of women attending gynaecological departments in big cities were suffering some disablement. The major cause was attributed to the poor state of general health of the women and physical deformities resulting from nutritional defects in early life.

In addition, more scientific nutritional surveys were introduced and calculations of what constituted an adequate diet and how many could afford it were made. For example, Boyd Orr estimated that 50 per cent of children were suffering from undernourishment in 1936,[52] and that 10 million people in the country were underfed.

Titmuss used data for the 1930s Registrar General's reports to calculate the 'human wastage' in the deprived and high unemployment regions of the North and Wales, compared to the standards of health achieved in the South of the country. He calculated that 50,000 excess deaths were occurring each year because of the presence of intense poverty in these areas and made an emotive appeal for action.[53] This is reproduced in Box 2.2, following in the best tradition of the great 19th century public health reformers.

Box 2.2

'... at least 500,000 excess deaths have occurred in the North and Wales during the last ten years (and we) can only point ... to the presence of intense poverty on a scale so considerable and so widespread, but at the same time so veiled and hidden by British stoicism and complacency, that public opinion has hitherto refused to recognise as conceptible the existence of such conditions in the heart of the British Empire in the twentieth century ... Those conditions that can be, and have been, created in the South can likewise be built in the North and Wales ... they would do much to prevent unwanted morbidity and untimely death and eradicate the shadows cast by suffering over the lives of so many English people from conception to the grave'.

Source: Titmuss (1938)[53]

Webster concludes about this period in British history:

'The depression must be regarded as a significant exacerbating factor, tending to worsen still further prevailing low levels of health, and so contributing towards a crisis of subsistence and health different in kind but still similar in gravity to the crises known to students of pre-industrial societies'.[45]

Focusing on occupation and class

Assessment of trends in social class mortality based on occupation has been a prominent feature of analyses in the 20th century. Leete and Fox distinguish two important 19th century developments which led up to the later focus on social classification.[54] First, from the earliest days of the GRO, the DSs had used data from occupation on death certificates and census information on numbers in each occupation to look at mortality rates in different groups of workers. From these analyses, William Farr had been able to draw out some of the effects of particular industrial hazards.[55] Second, he had also started to develop life tables based on the survival chances of different groups in the population, and interest in life tables for other groups increased.[56] However, it was not until 1911 that Stevenson devised a grouping of occupations into five broad classes, plus three industrial classes (see Box 2.3) and used it to study infant mortality.[57] By the 1921 Census, the industrial classes had been dropped and the five group social class scheme was adopted based on 'inferring social position (largely but by no means exclusively a matter of wealth or poverty, culture also having to be taken into account) from occupation'.[58]

It has been suggested that Stevenson's original motive for devising the scheme was prompted by a desire to counter, with facts, the assertions of the Eugenics movement that social inequality and poverty were determined by heredity.[59] Whatever the motive, the first analysis for 1911 revealed wide differentials in infant mortality between the different classes, which he interpreted as an indication that many deaths were preventable, rather than inevitable:

> 'Much may be learnt from this table as to the extent to which infant mortality can be preventable. For instance, the middle-class mortality was only 61 per cent of the total legitimate infant mortality in the country. This at once suggests that at least 40 per cent of the present infant mortality in this country could be avoided if the health conditions of infant life in general could be approximated to those met with in class I ... It may probably be assumed, however, that if health conditions were equally good for all classes of society (and till this is so the inferior conditions must always involve preventable mortality) most of any congenital disadvantage which the labourer's infant suffers would disappear. If this is the case there seems no reason to consider the limit of improvement reached till infant mortality is reduced to the level where that of the professional classes now stands, or, say, to one-third of its present amount'.[57]

Since then, data from successive DSs have been analysed to study trends over the century. Figure 2.4 shows trends in infant mortality by social class from 1911 to 1971, showing a dramatic decline in infant mortality in all social classes, though large differentials between the social classes still existed in the early 1970s.[60] Although the adult mortality trends were more difficult to interpret over such a long period, the evidence suggested that the differentials among adults might be just as large, perhaps larger, in the 1970s as they had been in the 1920s.[60]

Box 2.3 1911 Social class classification[57]

Social Class I	Upper and middle class
Social Class II	Intermediate
Social Class III	Skilled manual
Social Class IV	Intermediate manual
Social Class V	Unskilled manual
Social Class VI	Textile workers
Social Class VII	Miners
Social Class VIII	Agricultural workers

Pamuk re-analysed infant and adult trends from the DSs over the same period, using a complex measure of inequality and came to a similar conclusion. By this measure social class differentials in infant mortality had declined dramatically in absolute terms since 1921, but there had been a relative widening of the differentials since the late 1940s. For adult men, she found that class inequality in mortality declined in the 1920s, but increased again during the 1950s and 1960s, so that by the early 1970s it was greater than it had been in the early part of the century, both in absolute and relative terms. For married women, analysed by their husbands' social class, a similar relative increase in inequality between 1949–53 and 1970–72 was observed.[61]

Towards the Black Report

From 1980 to the present day there have been fresh controversies surrounding the issue of the socio-economic influences on health, at the centre of which has been what has widely become known as the Black Report.[62]

Renewed concern about the level of the social class mortality differentials and awareness of the failure of mortality rates in Britain to improve as far or as fast as in some other rich countries led to the government setting up a research working group in 1977 under the chairmanship of Sir Douglas Black. The task was to assess the national and international evidence on inequalities in health and draw out implications for public policy.[63] The working group drew heavily on analyses from the latest DS[60] which was published in 1978. They concluded that there had been a striking lack of improvement in the health experience of the lower social classes, and even a deterioration over the 1960s and early 1970s. Although the explanation for these patterns was seen to be complex, the differing material conditions of the different sections of the population were judged in the Black Report to play a prominent part:

> 'We do not believe there to be any single and simple explanation of the complex data we have assembled. While there are a number of quite distinct theoretical approaches to explanation we wish to stress the importance of differences in material conditions of life. In our view much of the evidence on social inequalities in health can be adequately understood in terms of specific features of the socio-economic environment: features (such as work accidents, overcrowding, cigarette-smoking) which are strongly class-related in Britain and also have clear causal significance. Other aspects of the evidence indicate the importance of the health services and particularly preventive services'. (p.199)[64]

The Black Report went on to set out 38 recommendations for improvements in health and social policy, with a particular emphasis on tackling poverty in childhood. Since then the report has had a chequered history,[65,66] but its enduring legacy is that the issue of socio-economic influences on health is now receiving as much attention from the research and public health communities, not only in this country but also internationally, as in the 19th century era of major public health reforms. As Macintyre points out, the Black Report should be seen not in isolation, but as part of the long tradition in this country of monitoring, exposing and debating the causes of inequalities in health.[66]

Conclusion

Looking back over the millennium it is the continuity of themes that is striking, rather than the contrasts. Clearly, chances of survival have improved beyond recognition and the nature of the diseases encountered has been transformed too. But health is still greatly influenced by the prevailing social and economic conditions, as outlined in the introductory chapter to this volume. There are still large gaps in health between different groups within the population. The debates about hunger, poverty and diminished life chances and their effects on health have not gone away either, but have surfaced at regular intervals over the centuries. As quoted on page 23,[45] apt parallels can be drawn between the crisis of subsistence and health in the 1930s Depression, and the situation experienced by the population in medieval times.

But this does not mean that the situation is inevitable and that nothing can be done about the problems uncovered. Concern about excess deaths and suffering and the reasons for them have led over the years to purposeful public action – from the Dearth Policy of the 16th century in response to famine, and the 19th century sanitary reforms, to the current renewed concern surfacing at the close of the 20th century, leading to the kinds of action outlined in Chapter 16.

It has been important to study throughout this time what is happening at the population level, to get the 'big picture'. It is noteworthy in this respect that whole branches of the scientific and medical literature in this country have sprung from the study of life and death at the population level. John Graunt's study of the London Bills of Mortality in 1662, mentioned on page 12, has been attributed as the origin of statistics.[67] William Farr's work at the General Register Office in the 19th century has been credited with helping to lay the foundations of epidemiology, medical statistics and the study of occupational mortality. To explain why the subject has inspired such intensive study, perhaps the last words should go to William Farr, from his opening paragraphs to one of the first decennial supplements more than a century ago:

'How the people of England live is one of the most important questions that can be considered; and how – of what causes, and what ages – they die is scarcely of less account; for it is the complement of the primary question teaching men how to live a longer, healthier, and happier life …'

Farr (5 February 1875)[68]

References

1   Chambers, J (1972) *Population, Economy and Society in Pre-industrial Society*. Oxford, Oxford University Press.

2   Wrigley, E and Schofield, R (1989) *The Population of England, 1541–1871: A reconstruction*. Cambridge, Cambridge University Press.

3   Scott, S, Duncan, S and Duncan, C (1995) Infant mortality and famine: a study in historical epidemiology in northern England, *J. Epidemiology and Community* Health, 49: 245–52.

4   Slack, P (1992) Dearth and social policy in early modern England, *Social History of Medicine*, 5: 1–17.

5   Malthus, T (1798) *An Essay on the Principles of Population*. 1970 reprint, London, Penguin.

6   Gray, A (1993) The world transformed: population and the rise of industrial society. In: Gray A. (ed.) *World Health and Disease*. Buckingham, Open University Press.

7   Antonovsky, A (1979) Social class, life expectancy and overall mortality, *Millbank Memorial Fund Quarterly*, XLV (2):31–72.

8   Mackenbach, J (1995) Social inequality and death as illustrated in late-medieval death dances, *American Journal of Public Health*, 85: 1285–92.

9   Hollingsworth, T (1965) A demographic study of the British ducal families. In: Glass, D and Eversley, D (eds) *Population and History*. London, Edward Arnold.

10 Perrenoud, A (1975) L'inégalité sociale devant la mort à Gènève au XVIIème siècle, *Population*, 30: 211–43.

11 Peller, S (1965) Births and deaths among Europe's ruling families since 1500. In: Glass, D and Eversley, D (eds) *Population in History*. London, Edward Arnold.

12 Schultz, H (1991) Social differences in mortality in the 18th century: an analysis of Berlin church registers, *International Review of Social History*, 36: 232–48.

13 Forbes, T (1979) By what disease or casualty: the changing face of death in London. In: Webster, C (ed.) *Health, Medicine and Mortality in the 16th Century*. Cambridge, Cambridge University Press.

14 Graunt, J (1662) *Natural and Political Observations Made Upon the Bills of Mortality*. London.

15 Hall, C (1805) The effects of civilisation on the people in European states. 1965 reprint In: *Reprints of Economic Classics*. New York, Augustus M Kelley.

16 Rosen, G (1993) *A History of Public Health*. Expanded edition. Baltimore, The Johns Hopkins University Press.

17 Wohl, A (1983) *Endangered Lives: Public Health in Victorian Britain*. London, Dent and Sons.

18 Smith, S (1839) On some of the physical causes of sickness and mortality to which the poor are particularly exposed, and which are capable of removal by sanitary regulations, exemplified in the present condition of the Bethnal Green and Whitechapel districts, as ascertained on a personal inspection. Quoted in: Simon, J (1890) *English Sanitary Institutions*. London, Cassell and Company Ltd.

19 Chadwick, E (1842) *Report on the sanitary conditions of the labouring population of Great Britain* London Poor Law Commission.

20 Royal Commission on the Health of Towns (1844) *First Report of Commissioners of Inquiry into the State of Large Towns and Populous Districts*. London.

21 Royal Commission on the Health of Towns (1845) *Second Report of Commissioners of Inquiry into the State of Large Towns and Populous Districts*. London.

22 Engels, F (1844) *The condition of the working class in England*, trans. London, Lawrence and Wishart.

23 Duncan, W (1844). Evidence to the Royal Commission on Health of Towns, Appendix 1. *First Report of Commissioners of Inquiry into the State of Large Towns and Populous Districts*, London.

24 *Lancet* (1843). Editorial, 5 August: 661.

25 Simon, J (1890) *English Sanitary Institutions, Reviewed in their Course of Development, and in some of their Political and Social Relations*. London, Cassell and Company Ltd.

26 *Registrar General's 5th Annual Report*, 1841. London, General Register Office (1843).

27 Lewes, F (1983) William Farr and Cholera, *Population Trends*, 31: 8–12.

28 Farr, W (1864) Letter to the Registrar General on the years 1851-1860. *Supplement to the 25th Report of the Registrar General*. London, General Register Office.

29 *Report of the Poor Law Commission* (1834).

30 Hamlin, C (1995) Could you starve to death in England in 1839? The Chadwick-Farr controversy and the loss of the 'social' in public health, *American Journal of Public Health*, 85: 856–66.

31 Farr, W (1839) Letter to the Registrar General. In: *First Annual Report of the Registrar General*. London, General Register Office.

32 Farr, W (1839) Letter to E Chadwick, 29th November 1839. In: *Poor Law Commission Official Circulars*, 9th March, 1840.

33 Chadwick, E (1840) Letter to the Registrar General. 24th February 1840. In: *Poor Law Commission Official Circulars*, 9th March, 1840.

34 Farr, W (1840) Letter to T Lister, Registrar General, 17th March 1840. In: *Poor Law Commission Official Circulars*, 18th May, 1840.

35 Macfarlane, A and Mugford, M (1984) *Birth Counts: Statistics of Pregnancy and Childbirth*. London, HMSO.

36 Loudon, I (1991) On maternal and infant mortality 1900–1960, *Social History of Medicine*. 4: 29–73.

37 Charlton, J and Murphy, M (1997) Trends in causes of mortality 1841–1994 – an overview. In: Charlton, J and Murphy, M (eds). *The Health of Adult Britain 1841–1994*, DS No.12, Vol. 1. London, The Stationery Office.

38 McCormick, A (1994) The impact of HIV on the population of England and Wales. *Population Trends* 76: 40-45.

39 McKeown, T (1976) *The Modern Rise of Population*. London, Edward Arnold.

40 McKeown, T and Record, R (1962) Reasons for the decline of mortality in England and Wales during the 19th century, *Population Studies,* 26: 94–122.

41 Szreter, S (1988) The importance of social intervention in Britain's mortality decline c. 1850-1914: a re-interpretation of the role of public health, *Social History of Medicine*, 1: 1–370.

42 Guha, S (1994) The importance of social intervention in England's mortality decline: the evidence reviewed, *Social History of Medicine*, 7: 89–113.

43 Winter, J (1979) Infant mortality, maternal mortality, and public health in Britain in the 1930s, *Journal of European Economic History*, 8, 439–462.

44 Winter, J (1982) The decline of mortality in Britain 1870–1950. In: Barker, T and Drake, M (eds) *Population and Society in Britain, 1850–1950*. London, Batsford Academic and Educational.

45 Webster, C (1982) Healthy or hungry thirties?, *History Workshop Journal*, xiii; 110–29.

46 Webster, C (1985) *Health, welfare and unemployment during the depression, Past and Present*, 109: 204–30.

47 Newman, G (1939) *The building of a nation's health*. London.

48 Pollitt, H (1933) Introduction in: Hutt, A. *Condition of the Working Class in England*. London.

49 McGonigle, G and Kirby, J (1936) *Poverty and Public Health*. London, Victor Gollancz.

50 Glover, J (1940) *Critical examination of nutrition returns for 5 years ending August 1939*. Public Records Office, Ministry of Education. Quoted in Webster (1982) ref. 45.

51 Spence, JC (1935) *Lancet*, ii; 268. Quoted in Webster (1982) ref. 45.

52 Boyd Orr, J (1936) *Food, Health and Income, Report on a Survey of Adequacy of Diet in Relation to Income*. London, Macmillan and Company.

53 Titmuss, RM (1938) *Poverty and population: a factual study of contemporary social waste*. London, Macmillan and Company.

54 Leete, R and Fox, J (1976) The Registrar General's social classes: origins and uses, *Population Trends, 8*: 1–7.

55 McDowall, M (1983) William Farr and the study of occupational mortality, *Population Trends*, 31: 12–14.

56 Ansell, C. (1874) *Statistics of Families in the Upper and Professional Classes*. London, National Life Assurance Society and Charles and Edwin Layton.

57 *Registrar General's 74th annual report*, 1911. London, General Register Office (1913).

58 Stevenson, T (1928) The vital statistics of wealth and poverty, *Journal of the Royal Statistical Society*, XCI, part II: 207–230.

59 Szreter, S (1984) The genesis of the Registrar General's social classification of occupations, *British Journal of Sociology*, 35: 522–44.

60 Registrar General (1978) *Occupational mortality. The Registrar General's Decennial Supplement for England and Wales, 1970–72*. Series DS 1. London, HMSO.

61 Pamuk, E (1985) Social class inequality in mortality from 1921 to 1972 in England and Wales, *Population Studies*, 39: 17–31.

62 Black, D Morris, N, Smith, C and Townsend, P (1980) *Inequalities in health: a report of a Research Working Group*. London, DHSS.

63 Townsend, P Whitehead, M and Davidson N (1992) Introduction to inequalities in health. In: *Inequalities in Health: the Black Report and the Health Divide*. New edition. London, Penguin.

64 Townsend, P and Davidson, N (eds) (1992) The Black report. In: Townsend, P, Whitehead, M. and Davidson, N (eds) *Inequalities in Health: the Black Report and the Health Divide*. London, Penguin.

65 Whitehead, M (1992) The health divide. In: Townsend, P Whitehead, M and Davidson, N (eds) *Inequalities in Health: the Black Report and the Health Divide*. London, Penguin.

66 Macintyre, S (1997) The Black report and beyond: what are the issues?, *Social Science and Medicine*, 44: 723–45.

67 Laslett, P (1973) Introduction In: *The earliest classics: Reprints of John Graunt* (1662) and *Gregory King* (1696). London, Gregg International Publishers Ltd.

68 Farr, W (1875) Letter to the Registrar General on the Registration Districts of England during the years 1861–1870. *Supplement to the 35th Report of the Registrar General*. London, General Register Office.

3

A review of recent social and economic trends

Jenny Church and Steve Whyman

Summary

- This chapter reviews the changes that have taken place in the social and economic structure of England and Wales over the last 50 years.

- Demographic changes have included increased longevity, falling fertility, and the resultant ageing of the population. There has been a rise in divorce, in one-person households, and increased diversity in the ethnic composition of the population. The population has grown by 18 per cent between 1951 and 1995, and the number of households by 44 per cent between 1961 and 1995-96.

- The nature and organisation of paid work has undergone major transformations. There has been a shift from full employment to increased proportions of the population outside the labour force, due to unemployment, early retirement and education. Other marked trends include increased participation of women in the labour force, and more part-time and less full-time jobs.

- There has been a growth in the gross domestic product and average household disposable income, although this growing prosperity has not been spread evenly across the population. Incomes have diverged from the average, increasing the gap between those with high and low incomes. There has been a doubling of the proportion of households living on low incomes (defined as half the average income) between 1961 and 1990.

- Housing standards have improved greatly since the 1950s. However there is now a severe shortage of housing for the growing number of households in the country. Homelessness has increased over the 1980s.

- There have been major developments in social welfare and health policy over the past 50 years. A unified social welfare system was implemented in the immediate post-war period, leading to the setting up of a national insurance scheme covering sickness, unemployment and old age pensions, with the associated foundation of the National Health Service. At the same time major reforms to the education system and a programme of house building were set in motion.

Introduction

Many of the social and economic factors which influence health, as outlined in Chapter 1, have undergone profound shifts in recent decades. Major demographic changes have included the ageing of the population, the fall in fertility and the rise in divorce, and the greater diversity in the ethnic and cultural composition of the population.

The nature and organisation of paid work is also undergoing transformation, including the shift from full employment to increased proportions of the population outside the labour force, either through unemployment or through economic inactivity. The economic base of the country has switched from heavy industry and manufacturing to a concentration on service sector employment. There are trends towards increased participation of women in the labour force, more part-time and less full-time working, and more flexible and less permanent contracts of employment.

These employment changes are intimately tied up with the general level of economic development in the country. In particular, increased national prosperity, but its less even distribution, has wide-ranging implications for the ability of different sections of the population to obtain the necessities for good health. The beginning of the 50-year period of this review saw the foundations being laid for a new welfare system, including the setting up of the National Health Service, to ensure wider access to some of these necessities and fundamental changes to provision in social security, education, healthcare and housing.

Physical housing standards have continued to improve and overcrowding has reduced. However, new challenges emerge including the rise in homelessness and the decline in public sector house building.

This chapter maps out the changes which have taken place in each of these areas over the past 50 years, changes that act as the backcloth to the trends in health described in the following chapters.

Population growth and ageing

In 1951 the population of England and Wales numbered 44 million. This had grown to 52 million by 1995. The increase in the size of the population of England and Wales between 1951 and 1995 is a result of the addition of births and immigrants and the subtraction of deaths and emigrants. The number of births minus the number of deaths is termed the natural increase. Figure 3.1 shows the number of births and deaths in England and Wales since 1951. The number of births rose during the late 1950s and early 1960s, peaking in 1964 at nearly 900,000 – the height of the baby boom. The mid-1960s saw the highest annual population growth rates since the beginning of the century, with the number of births exceeding the number of deaths by more than 300,000. In the 1970s, the pendulum swung right back, with the smallest natural increase in population this century – a result of low birth rates. In 1976 and 1977, the number of deaths actually exceeded the number of births for the first time in recent history.

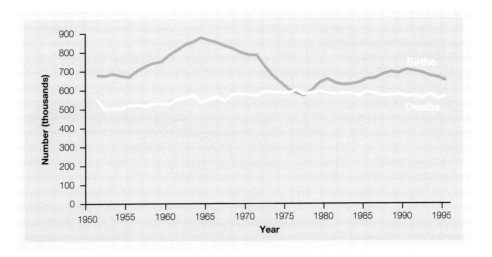

These factors have produced considerable change in the age structure of the population. Figure 3.2 shows a breakdown of the population by age in 1951 and 1991. The peak in the number of young children in 1951 is a consequence of a short baby boom after World War II. This is also reflected in the peak of people in their mid-40s in 1991. A second peak, in 1991, among those in their late 20s is caused by the baby boom of the 1960s. Conversely, the low number of births in the middle to late 1970s is reflected in the small number of teenagers in 1991. The peak in the number of people in their early 70s in 1991 is a result of both the post World War I baby boom and longer life expectancy.

The population over retirement age, 60 years for women and 65 for men, together with the population aged under 16, form what is known as the dependent population. In 1951, the dependent population numbered 17 million, plateaued at nearly 22 million in the mid-1970s, before declining to stand at 21 million in 1995. Figure 3.3 shows the growth in the overall size of the population of England and Wales, and changes in the size of the dependent population.

FIGURE 3.2
Population by age and sex
England and Wales, 1951 and 1991

Source: Office for National Statistics

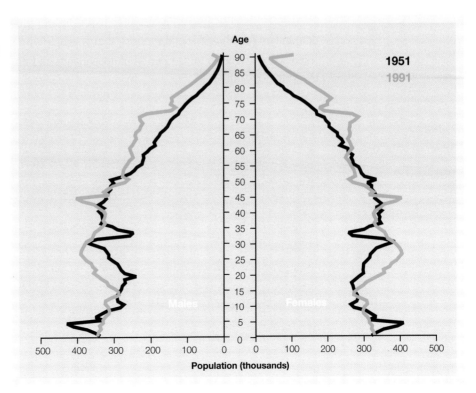

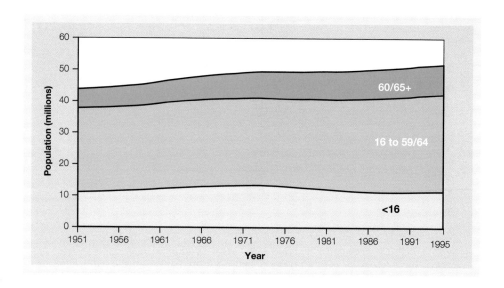

The size of the dependent population can be expressed as a ratio of the population of working age, usually taken to be those aged 16–59/64, and is known as the dependency ratio. Figure 3.4 shows the trend in the overall dependency ratio, along with the young and old-age dependency ratios. The overall dependency ratio increased throughout the 1950s and 60s, before peaking in the mid-1970s. Since then there has been a decline, so that in the mid-1990s the overall dependency ratio is returning to its 1950s level. However, the trend in the overall dependency ratio masks considerable variation between the two age groups that make up the dependent population. The young dependency ratio has dominated the overall pattern, increasing until the mid-1970s before declining to below the 1950s level. In contrast, the old-age dependency ratio has risen continually throughout the second half of the 20th century, increasing by nearly 40 per cent between 1951 and 1995. It is this increase in the proportion of the dependent population made up by the elderly that has the most impact on the provision of healthcare. As more people live to be very old there will be a greater demand on health and social services: that is people who live until their nineties are likely to experience a longer period of dependency and illness than those who live until their seventies.[1,2]

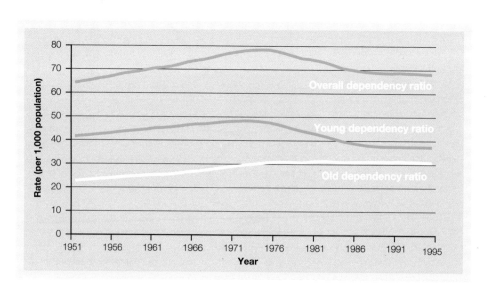

Government figures estimate that annual expenditure on hospital and community health services (HCHS) in 1992–93, cost £750 per head for those aged 65–74 years, £1,300 per head for the 75–84 age group and £2,500 per head for those aged over 85 years.[3] This is in comparison to just £250 per head per year for people aged 16–44. Overall, people aged 65 and over made up only 16 per cent of the population in 1992–93, but accounted for some 42 per cent of total HCHS spending. In 1994–95, out of more than 73 million bed-days in NHS hospitals in England, nearly 53 per cent were used by people over the age of 65. This is in comparison to seven per cent of NHS bed-days in England used by the population under 20 years.[4] Grundy has analysed the effects of demographic ageing from 1971 to 1994.[5]

Within the population over retirement age, the proportion who are aged 80 and over has doubled between 1951 and 1994 – from 11 per cent to 22 per cent. A person's centenary year used to be an occasion of some note, but such events are becoming much more common. By 1991 there were nearly 4,400 centenarians in England and Wales.[6]

Ethnic and cultural diversity

In England and Wales, while the scale of migration has been quite small relative to the size of the population, ethnic and cultural diversity has increased. In the period immediately after World War II, immigrants exceeded emigrants as people from Commonwealth countries, particularly in the Caribbean, were encouraged to come to the UK to work. During the 1960s and 1970s however, the position was reversed as people left the UK to settle in Australia, Canada, the USA and the Middle East. In the 1980s net migration was again inwards. The largest flows in recent years, in both directions, have been between this country and the rest of the European Union.

The 1991 Census marked a milestone in the collection of information about the country's ethnic diversity with a question about ethnic origin. Using more recent data drawn from the Labour Force Survey, Table 3.1 shows the size and age structure of the different ethnic groups. By 1995, it was estimated that 48 million people in England and Wales assessed themselves as white and 3 million reported that they belonged to the other ethnic groups listed. The largest ethnic minority group was Indian, at

TABLE 3.1

Population by age and ethnicity

England and Wales, 1995–96

Thousands

Source: Labour Force Survey, Office for National Statistics

Ethnicity	< 16	16–24	25–34	35–44	45–54	55–64	65 +	all ages
Black Caribbean	116	50	119	79	35	49	33	481
Black African	84	38	86	48	15	10	6	287
Other Black	52	14	29	10	–	–	–	110
Indian	233	128	159	152	93	65	37	867
Pakistani	219	97	84	76	31	29	13	548
Bangladeshi	73	35	30	21	10	10	7	187
Chinese	18	25	22	21	12	10	–	114
Other Asian	43	21	30	34	23	8	–	162
Other ethnic minorities[a]	240	67	76	45	27	15	9	478
White	9,611	5,228	7,563	6,542	6,397	4,858	7,727	47,925
Total[b]	10,695	5,705	8,200	7,030	6,649	5,055	7,840	51,174

[a] Includes all those of mixed origin. [b] Includes ethnic group not stated.

around 27 per cent of the total. The next largest group was Pakistani, followed by Black Caribbeans. The ethnic minority groups show a younger age structure than the white group, in part reflecting past immigration and fertility patterns. In both the Labour Force Survey and the Census people give their own assessment of their ethnic origin. There is evidence that those who described themselves as 'Black British', included in the 'Other Black' group in the table, were likely to be the children of black Caribbean parents.[7]

Changing family and household patterns

There has been considerable variation in fertility patterns in England and Wales over the last 50 years. These changing patterns are largely responsible for the age distribution of the population under 50 years of age, discussed earlier. Figure 3.5 shows the trend in fertility rates in England and Wales from 1951–95 expressed as age-specific rates. The 'all-age' fertility rate, which is the number of live births per 1,000 women aged 15–44, shows that fertility increased between 1951 and 1964, from 72 to 93 per 1,000 women of reproductive age. By 1973, the all-age fertility rate had declined to 1951 levels. From 1980 to 1995, the all-age fertility rate has hovered around 62 births per 1,000 women aged 15–44 years. However, the all-age fertility rate masks considerable changes in the age pattern of fertility. Figure 3.5 and Table 3.2 show that throughout the second half of the 20th century the 25–29 age group has had the highest age-specific fertility rates. Until the early 1970s, the fertility rates of women aged 20–24 and those aged 25–29 were very similar. Since then, the fertility rate for women in the younger age group has been declining more quickly than that for women aged 25–29. Since 1992, women aged 30–34 have had higher fertility rates than those aged 20–24, highlighting the choice of many women to delay childbearing. For each age group, with the exception of the under 20 year olds, fertility rates peaked in 1964 at the height of the baby boom. In contrast, the fertility rate for the youngest women, those aged under 20 years, continued to increase until 1971.

One of the factors underlying the fall in birth rates is the increased control which women can now choose to exercise over their fertility. The oral contraceptive pill became widely available in Britain in the 1960s. It quickly became the most

FIGURE 3.5

Age-specific fertility rates
England and Wales, 1951–95

Source: Birth Statistics, series FM1

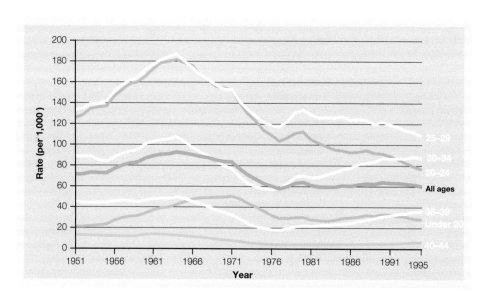

TABLE 3.2

Age-specific fertility rates

England and Wales, 1951–95

Source: Birth Statistics, series FM1

	< 20*	20–24	25–29	30–34	35–39	40–44	45+	all ages*
				(births per 1,000)				
1951	21	126	134	89	46	13	1.0	72
1956	27	147	151	88	46	12	0.8	77
1961	37	173	177	103	48	14	0.9	89
1966	48	176	174	97	45	12	0.9	91
1971	51	153	153	77	33	8	0.5	84
1976	32	109	119	57	19	4	0.3	60
1981	28	105	129	69	22	4	0.5	61
1986	30	93	124	78	25	5	0.4	61
1991	33	89	119	87	32	5	0.3	64
1995	29	77	109	87	36	7	0.3	60

* The rates for women of all ages, under 20 and 45+ are based on the population of women aged 15–44, 15–19 and 45–49 respectively.

commonly used form of contraception. Its popularity has declined somewhat recently while the use of the male condom and of sterilisation have increased.[8]

In 1995–96 there were 44 per cent more households than in 1961 (Table 3.3) as compared with population growth of 12 per cent. This is because households have gradually been getting smaller. The proportion of households containing five or more people halved over this period whereas the number of people living alone rose steeply. Well over a quarter of households consisted of one person in 1995–96. Women over pensionable age formed the largest proportion of people living alone. This proportion has remained relatively stable over the last 25 years, at between 10 and 12 per cent of all households. The recent growth in people living alone has been among those below pension age, particularly men.

Alongside the growth in people living alone has been a fall in the 'traditional' family unit of a couple with children. In 1961 almost half of all households were of this

TABLE 3.3

Composition of house-holds, by type of house hold and family

Great Britain, 1961–96

Source: Census, Department of the Environment, General Household Survey

Composition of households	1961	1971	1981	1991	1995-96
			(percentages)		
One-person households					
Under pensionable age	4	6	8	11	13
Over pensionable age	7	12	14	16	15
Two or more unrelated adults	5	4	5	3	2
One-family households[a]					
Married couple with:					
no children	26	27	26	28	29
1-2 dependent children[b]	30	26	25	20	19
3 or more dependent children[b]	8	9	6	5	4
non-dependent children only	10	8	8	8	6
Lone parent with[a]					
dependent children[b]	2	3	5	6	7
non-dependent children only	4	4	4	4	3
Two or more families	3	1	1	1	1
Total (=100%)(millions)	16.3	18.6	20.2	22.4	23.5

[a] These households may contain some individuals who are not members of the 'nuclear' family
[b] May also include non-dependent children

composition. By 1994 the proportion had fallen to under a third. Compared with just over five per cent of households in 1961, around ten per cent are now headed by a lone parent. Around a fifth of dependent children now live with only one parent, usually their mother. In 1994 nearly two-fifths of lone mothers were single and almost the same proportion were divorced. The remainder were widowed.[9]

Industrial transformation

Although demographic changes over the last 50 years have a strong influence on health, employment factors also have an important impact. There has been a shift in the economy of England and Wales away from manufacturing towards the service industries. Only around 25 per cent of men are now employed in manufacturing compared with 33 per cent in 1981 (Table 3.4). There continue to be considerable gender differences in the pattern of employment. Although the manufacturing sector no longer dominates in the way it did, it is still the major employer of men. However 36 per cent of women are employed in the public administration, education and health sector.

TABLE 3.4

Employees, by industry and gender
England and Wales, 1981–96
(September quarter)
Source: Office for National Statistics

Industry	(percentages)					
	Males			Females		
	1981	1991	1996	1981	1991	1996
Agriculture, hunting, forestry and fishing	2	2	2	1	1	0
Mining, quarrying, electricity, gas and water supply	5	3	1	1	1	0
Manufacturing	33	26	26	18	12	11
Construction	8	7	6	1	1	1
Wholesale and retail trade and repairs	13	15	16	18	18	18
Hotels and restaurants	3	4	4	7	7	7
Transport storage and communication	9	9	9	3	3	3
Financial intermediation	3	4	4	5	6	5
Real estate, renting and business activities	8	11	13	8	11	13
Public administration and defence; compulsory social security	7	7	6	7	6	6
Education	4	5	4	11	11	12
Health and social work	3	4	4	15	18	18
Other services	3	4	4	5	5	5
Total (=100%)(thousands)	11,111	10,139	10,040	8,213	9,432	9,716

Growth in unemployment and economic inactivity

The years immediately following World War II were ones of virtually full employment. Figure 3.6 shows that this is no longer the case. The unemployment rate fluctuates with the economic cycle, but the underlying trend since the mid-1970s has been upwards. Throughout recent years unemployment has been highest among the young, although it is older people who are more likely to be unemployed for long periods. In spring 1996, 28 per cent of unemployed men in their 40s had been unemployed for three years or more. Unemployment rates also vary across the different areas of the country, with inner city and former areas of heavy industry being particularly affected in recent years. The worst unemployment rates in England and Wales were in Inner

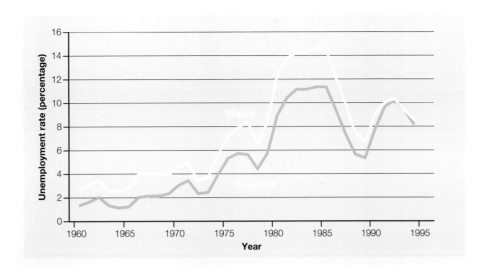

London. In spring 1995, the unemployment rate in Hackney was nearly 30 per cent and in Newham it was just under 25 per cent. The lowest rates are to be found in predominantly rural counties such as Oxfordshire.[10]

An economically active person is defined as someone in paid work, participating in a government training or employment scheme, or without a job but seeking work and available to take a job. There has been a fall in economic activity among the youngest age-groups of both men and women over the last 25 years (see Figure 3.7). This is partly because of the rapid increase in participation rates in further and higher education. Around 40 per cent of all young people aged 19 and 20 were in full or part-time education in 1993–94, compared with 32 per cent of boys and 23 per cent of girls in 1980-81.[11]

The extent to which economic activity rates have been falling among older men as a result of early retirement can also be seen in Figure 3.7. In 1971 over 80 per cent of men aged between 60 and 64 were economically active, compared with only just under 50 per cent in 1996. This means that the size of the truly dependent population is larger than mentioned earlier and is likely to increase still further, if early retirement continues to increase.

The changing nature of work

Figure 3.7 shows clearly the increase in women's participation in the labour force over the last quarter century. In 1971 there was a noticeable dip in economic activity among women in their mid-20s to mid-30s, the main childbearing years, while in 1996 such a dip is no longer evident. Whether or not a woman is economically active depends to a large extent on whether she has children and on their age. Around three quarters of women with no dependent children work either full or part-time or are seeking work. Just over half of those whose youngest child is not yet at school are economically active. The extent to which women work full-time increases with the age of the child, and they become less likely to be out of the labour force altogether.[10]

Over the last ten years, part-time working has become more common for both men and women. Women are nearly six times more likely than men to be in part-time employment. In 1996, 45 per cent of female employees were working part-time

FIGURE 3.7
Economic activity rates,[a]
by age and sex
Great Britain, 1971 and 1996

*Source: Census and Labour Force
Survey, Office for National Statistics*

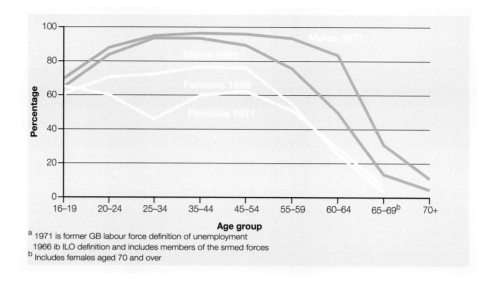

[a] 1971 is former GB labour force definition of unemployment
1966 ib ILO definition and includes members of the srmed forces
[b] Includes females aged 70 and over

compared with 8 per cent of men. Working patterns have become more flexible in a number of other ways during the 1990s. According to the Labour Force Survey in spring 1996, 9 per cent of men and 13 per cent of women in full-time employment worked flexible hours[10]. About 2 per cent of part-time employees are in a job share. Around 10 per cent of women work part-time during school terms only. There has been an increase in temporary and short-term, as opposed to permanent, contracts. In spring 1995, temporary workers represented 7 per cent of all employees. Over 50 per cent of men and 38 per cent of women in temporary jobs reported that they had them because they could not find permanent work.[10]

The average number of hours worked by those in full-time employment was around 44 per week in 1995. However, this average masks a wide range of experiences: 20 per cent of men worked between 49 and 59 hours a week, over 10 per cent worked 60 or more hours, while around 60 per cent worked 40 hours or fewer.[10]

Rising prosperity and income inequality

Between 1951 and 1995, the gross domestic product (GDP) grew at an average rate of 2.4 per cent per year. Figure 3.8 shows GDP at factor cost which excludes taxes on expenditure and subsidies. There have been three significant dips in the trend. The first was brought about by the oil price rises in the mid-1970s. There was then recession in the early 1980s which was accompanied by another sharp oil price rise. There was a further recession in the early 1990s.

This general economic growth has been reflected in the growth of household income. Average real household disposable income is defined as income with the effects of inflation removed and net of taxes on income, national insurance contributions and local taxes. This rose by 72 per cent between 1961 and 1994. However, this growing prosperity has not been spread evenly across the whole population. Figure 3.9 illustrates that incomes have diverged from the average, increasing the gap between those with high and low incomes. There was a three-fold difference between the top decile point (the income above which 10 per cent of individuals fell) and the bottom decile point in 1961. The difference increased to over four-fold in 1990 but has since fallen slightly.

Another indicator of prosperity in the population is the proportion living on low incomes, defined as half the average income. In 1961 around one in ten households

FIGURE 3.8

Gross domestic product (GDP), at factor cost
UK, 1951–95

Source: Office for National Statistics

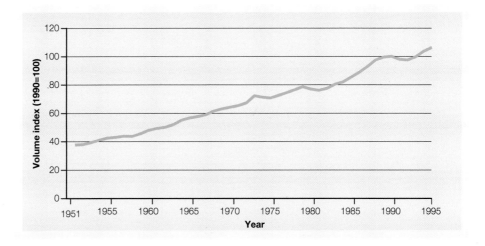

FIGURE 3.9

Real household disposable income, before housing costs
UK, 1961–94

Source: Institute for Fiscal Studies

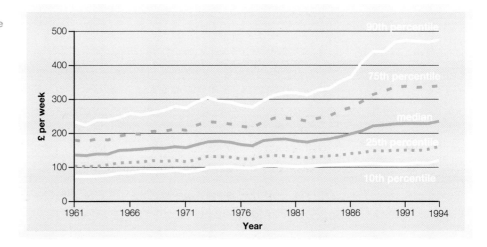

was living on incomes this low. By 1990, this proportion had risen to one in five households, although there has since been a slight improvement.[12]

An important factor underlying these trends has been the widening of the earnings distribution. For men working full time the gap between the ten per cent with highest earnings and the ten per cent with lowest earnings was £203 per week in 1971. By 1995 this gap had increased to £419 per week. Both these figures are adjusted for inflation and based on April 1995 prices. For women, the gap grew from £122 to £290 per week over the same period.[13]

Areas of deprivation and affluence

Census data, together with other variables available for small areas, can be used to produce a measure of the level of deprivation or affluence in local areas. Many such indices have been developed. The Department of the Environment's Index of Local Conditions, for example, combines a number of indicators, chosen to cover a range of economic, social, housing and environmental issues, to produce a single deprivation score for small geographic areas, wards and local authority districts. A measure of concentrated deprivation has then been derived by calculating the percentage of the district population living in the most deprived 10 per cent of wards in England. These particular wards are to be found predominantly in Inner London and other major cities.

TABLE 3.5

Population, by type of
area
England and Wales, 1971 and
1995
Source: Office for National Statistics

Type of area	(thousands)	
	1971	1995
London		
Inner London	3,060	2,677
Outer London	4,470	4,330
Greater London	7,529	7,007
Metropolitan districts		
Principal cities	3,910	3,458
Others	7,952	7,726
Total metropolitan districts	11,862	11,183
Non-metropolitan districts		
Cities	4,715	4,754
Industrial	6,486	6,896
With new towns	1,895	2,415
Resort and retirement	3,184	3,712
Mixed urban-rural	8,821	10,185
Remoter largely rural	4,661	5,668
Total non-metropolitan districts	29,761	33,630
Total	49,152	51,820

The 25 most deprived local authority districts, which together cover about 14 per cent of England's population, have higher proportions of people reporting long-standing illness. Nearly 40 per cent of the ethnic minority population live in these areas and the incidence of lone parent households is 60 per cent higher than the national average.[14] Mixed urban/rural areas such as East Hertfordshire and Mid Sussex have seen considerable population growth while the inner cities have been losing population (see Table 3.5).

Living conditions

There have been major improvements in housing standards since 1951 when 37 per cent of households did not have a fixed bath or shower, whilst 8 per cent possessed neither an internal nor external flush toilet (see Table 3.6). By 1991, these proportions had fallen to well below half of one per cent of households. Although there have been considerable improvements in living conditions since the war, there were still 7.2 per cent of dwellings in 1991 below the statutory minimum standard.[15]

The bedroom standard is a commonly used measure of overcrowding or underoccupation. It compares the number of bedrooms available to a household with

TABLE 3.6

Percentage of households
lacking basic amenities
Great Britain, 1951–91
Source: Census publications

	(percentages)				
	1951	1961	1971	1981	1991
Bath or shower[a]	37.6	22.4	9.1	1.9	0.3
Flush toilet					
Internal or external	7.7	6.5	1.2	—	—
Internal	—	—	11.5	2.7	0.5
Hot water tap	—	21.8	6.4	—	—
Central heating	—	—	—	—	18.9
Total (=100%)(millions)	14.5	16.2	18.1	19.5	21.9

[a] Prior to 1991 data relate to fixed bath only.

FIGURE 3.10

Number of house
completions, by sector
England and Wales*, 1951–95

Source: Department of the
Environment, Welsh Office

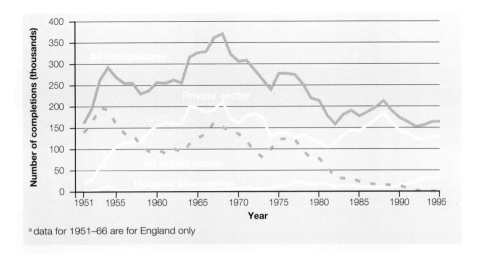

ᵃ data for 1951–66 are for England only

a calculation of its bedroom requirement.[16] The proportion of households living in overcrowded conditions, as measured in this way, has fallen from 7 per cent in 1972 to 3 per cent in 1994–95. However, this masks the fact that some sections of the population are still living in poor housing conditions. For example nearly half of Bangladeshi households were living in overcrowded conditions in 1994–95. Ethnic minority groups are also twice as likely, as households as a whole, to be living in housing requiring high repair costs.[17]

Figure 3.10 shows the pattern of house building over the last 50 years. The 1960s saw the highest number of completions, with the growth of the new towns in particular. Between 1961 and 1976 trends in the number of dwellings built by the private sector roughly mirrored those of the public sector. Since then, local authority building in England and Wales has virtually halted and most new dwellings are provided by the private sector. Within the social sector, housing associations have become more important suppliers in the last few years, accounting for 20 per cent of completions in 1995. Of the current housing stock, over half has been built since 1945.

Homelessness

For the first time ever, the 1991 Census attempted to count the number of people sleeping rough on census day. The count was designed to cover people sleeping in the open air rather than those in shelters, hostels or squats. Overall, more than 2,700 people were found sleeping rough in England and Wales, almost half of whom were in London.[18]

Part III of the Housing Act 1985 requires local authorities to secure accomodation for homeless households in defined categories of 'priority need'. Table 3.7 shows that in 1995, 128,000 homeless households were found accommodation of which only 3 per cent were not in one of the priority need categories. Over half of those in priority need had dependent children. Around a third of households found accommodation by local authorities had become homeless because friends or family were no longer willing or able to accommodate them.[19] A further fifth had become homeless due to a breakup with their partner. From 1980 to 1990 the number of households accepted as homeless more than doubled, from 60,000 to over 150,000. By 1995 the total had fallen to 128,000.

TABLE 3.7

Homeless families found
accommodation by local
authorities

England and Wales, 1986–95

Source: Department of the Environment,
Welsh Office

	(percentages)			
	1986	1989	1991	1995
Homeless households in priority need found accommodation				
Household with dependent children	65	68	65	56
Household member pregnant	14	14	14	11
Household member vulnerable because of:				
mental illness	2	2	3	6
old age	7	6	4	5
physical handicap	3	3	3	6
other reasons	6	5	9	14
Homeless in emergency	3	2	1	1
Total priority need (=100%)	96,634	116,721	144,914	123,301
Homeless households not in priority need found accommodation	9,093	12,121	7,843	4,277
Total	105,727	128,842	152,767	127,578

The development of a unified welfare system

There have been major developments in social welfare and health policy over the 50 year period, in response to the social and economic needs of the population. A unified social welfare system was set out in the Beveridge Plan of 1942 and was implemented in the immediate post-war period. This led to the setting up of a national insurance scheme covering sickness, unemployment and old age pensions, with the associated foundation of the National Health Service in 1948. At the same time, major reforms to the education system and a programme of house building were set in motion. For a more detailed account of the development of these policies and a discussion of the issues they raise, see Bartley and colleagues account in Decennial Supplement No. 12.[20]

Conclusion

So how has the world in which we live changed since World War II? Increased longevity and falling fertility have led to the ageing of the population. We now live in a multicultural society. People are more likely to live on their own, and a significant proportion of children now live with only one parent. There is a higher proportion of women in the labour force than 50 years ago. Economic inactivity has risen due in part to increases in early retirement among older workers and, more recently, to a rapid increase in participation rates in further education among younger people. Over the same period there has been a rise in the underlying level of unemployment in the country, with inner city and areas of heavy industry being particularly affected in recent decades. There has been a growth in the national economy and in average household disposable income. However, this growing prosperity has not been spread evenly across the population, and as a result the gap between the richer and poorer income groups has increased. Housing standards have improved, but homelessness has become a bigger problem over the period. All these factors have contributed to the social picture we see as we approach the millennium.

References

1   Thane, P (1989) Old Age: Burden or Benefit? In: Joshi, H (ed.) *The Changing Population of Britain*. Oxford, Basil Blackwell Ltd.

2   Dunnell, K (1995) Population Review (2): Are we healthier?, *Population Trends*, 82. London, HMSO.

3   Department of Health and Office of Population Censuses and Surveys (1995). *Departmental report 1995*. London, HMSO.

4   Department of Health (1996) *Hospital Episodes Statistics, Volume 2: England Financial Year 1994–95*. London, Department of Health.

5   Grundy, EMD (1996). Population Review (5): The population aged 60 and over. *Population Trends*, 84. London, HMSO.

6   OPCS/GAD (1994) Centenarians: 1991 estimates. *Population Trends*, 75. London, HMSO.

7   Peach, C (1996) Black-caribbeans: class, gender and geography. In: Peach, C (ed.) *Ethnicity in the 1991 Census, Volume two: The Ethnic Minority Population of Great Britain*. London, HMSO.

8   OPCS (annual) *General Household Survey*. London, HMSO.

9   Haskey, J (1996) Population review (6) Families and households in Great Britain. *Population Trends*, 85. London, HMSO.

10 ONS (quarterly) *Labour Force Survey Quarterly Bulletin*. London, HMSO.

11 ONS (1997) *Social Trends*, 27. London, The Stationery Office.

12 Department of Social Security (various years) *Households below average income: a Statistical analysis*. London, HMSO.

13 ONS (annual) *New Earnings Survey*. London, HMSO.

14 Department of the Environment (1995) *1991 Deprivation Index: A Review of Approaches and a Matrix of Results*. London, HMSO.

15 England and Wales fitness standard defined by Section 83 of Schedule 9, 1989 Local Government and Housing Act; Scotland Tolerable Standard Part IV of the Housing (Scotland) Act 1987.

16 ONS (1997) *Social Trends*, 27, Appendix p.240. London, HMSO.

17 ONS (1996) *Social Focus on Ethnic Minorities*. London, HMSO.

18 OPCS (1991). 1991 *Census, Preliminary report for Great Britain - Supplementary monitor on People sleeping rough*. London, OPCS.

19 CSO (1996). *Social Trends*, 26. London, HMSO.

20 Bartley, M, Blane, D and Charlton, J (1997) Socio-economic and demographic trends, 1841–1991. In: Charlton, J and Murphy M *The Health of Adult Britain 1841–1994, volume 1 DS12*. London, The Stationery Office.

4

International evidence on social inequalities in health

Margaret Whitehead and Finn Diderichsen

Summary

This chapter examines the international evidence on social inequalities in health, hence enabling us to view the British situation in an international context.

The international evidence shows that social inequalities in health are persisting and in some cases widening including in countries with overall good health, such as the Netherlands, Sweden and Denmark.

There has been a divergent trend in mortality between the countries of central and eastern Europe and the European Union and Nordic countries. Contributing to this East-West health divide has been the stagnation or decline in life expectancy in many countries of central or eastern Europe.

There is evidence from some countries of western Europe of a deteriorating trend in women's health. Figures from the USA show diverging mortality of the black and white populations.

Variations in methods of data collection, classification, and availability as well as cultural norms and social structure mean that great care is needed in making and interpreting comparisons of international data on social differentials in health.

Bearing these cautions in mind, the overall impression regarding where Britain is placed in the international ranking is that it is not in the worst position, nor in the best, but that it does share with other countries unacceptable levels of social differentials in health within the population.

While giving rise to great concern, the variations in health inequalities over time and place also provide encouragement that the health divide is not inevitable, but may be amenable to reduction by purposeful policy action.

Mounting evidence has led to social differentials in health being recognised as a major public health challenge in many countries.

The aim of this chapter is to give an overview of relevant developments abroad, as a backdrop to the British evidence presented throughout the rest of the volume. There are two key reasons why the British patterns of social differentials in health need to be viewed in an international context. First, Britain can learn from health trends and patterns in countries with similar and divergent socio-economic environments. These might provide clues both to causes of the observed patterns and to policy options for tackling inequalities in health.

Second, much can be learnt from approaches taken in other countries to researching and measuring health inequalities. As Chapter 2 emphasised, Britain has a long tradition of study in this field, but the upsurge in research around Europe, and now in North America, has advanced understanding considerably in recent years.

These two reasons have governed the selection of developments featured in this chapter. Rather than work through a catalogue of countries in turn, the approach we have chosen here is to select common themes which link the growing concern in many countries in relation to social differentials in health.

First of all eight international trends are identified concerned with the changing pattern of health inequalities and the developments these are stimulating in various countries. Then emerging issues concerned with measuring and monitoring health differentials are discussed, including the problems of making cross-country comparisons. We finally address the question of where Britain fits into the international rankings produced by these comparisons.

One of the main messages coming out of the international evidence is that social inequalities in health persist and in some cases are widening across decades marked out by rising unemployment and increasing socio-economic disadvantage. Addressing the issue is one of the major challenges in public health today, both in Britain and abroad.

Significant trends

Unique mortality crisis in the east

No review of what is going on in the wider world on the issue of health inequalities could ignore trends in central and eastern Europe, and in particular Russia, since the current mortality crisis there is absolutely unique in modern times. In no other part of the world are countries experiencing a decline in life expectancy during periods without war, famine or plagues. Everywhere else, life expectancy is increasing, albeit at different rates. In Russia, the more disadvantaged sections of the population appear to be suffering the most, with widening health differentials as a result of the absolute increase in mortality among the underprivileged groups.

The map of Europe has been redrawn in the 1980s, illustrated by the fact that in 1980 the European Region of the WHO consisted of 32 countries – now there are over 50. It is clear that there has been a divergent trend in mortality between the countries in central and eastern Europe, including the newly independent states of the former USSR, on the one hand, and the European Union (EU) and Nordic countries on the other, as illustrated in Figures 4.1–4.4.

FIGURE 4.1

Life expectancy at birth, men

selected European countries, 1970–93

Source: WHO HFA Database, February 1996 version

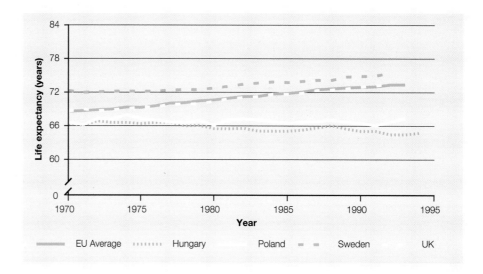

FIGURE 4.2

Life expectancy at birth, women

selected European countries, 1970–93

Source: WHO HFA Database, February 1996 version

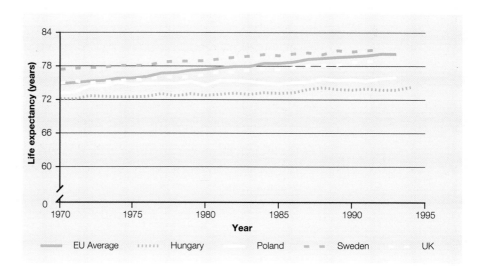

FIGURE 4.3

Life expectancy at birth, men

EU and selected countries of the former USSR, 1970–94

Source: WHO HFA Database, February 1996 version

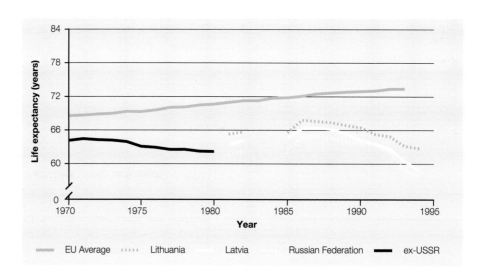

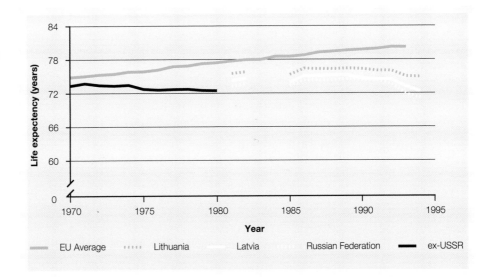

It can be seen that the gap in life expectancy between the best and worst of the selected countries has widened dramatically – from about three years in 1970 to up to 15 in 1995 for men and from about four years to about ten years for women. This gap has developed from a stagnation or decline in life expectancy in some countries, rather than an improvement for all countries at different paces. WHO has estimated the contribution of different causes of death to this East–West health divide. Cardiovascular disease was responsible for over 50 per cent of the life expectancy gap, external causes 29 per cent, respiratory diseases 16 per cent, infectious and parasitic diseases 7 per cent, mainly in the ages 35 –64.[1] As Figure 4.5 shows, for the trends in excess mortality, nearly all causes show a considerable widening, with homicide showing a huge increase. Almost the only cause to show a reduced gap was maternal

FIGURE 4.5

Trends in excess mortality,

Central and eastern Europe compared with WHO European Region

Source: WHO Figure 2.2 (reprinted by kind permission of WHO) [1]

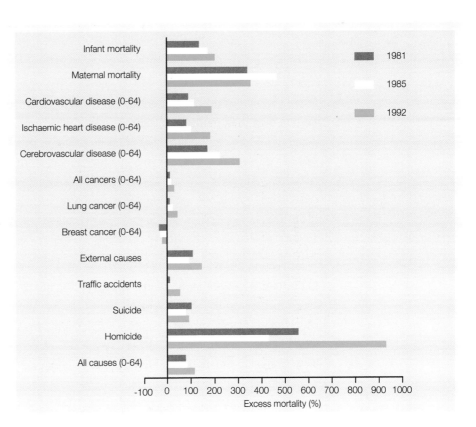

mortality. The main contribution to this improvement comes from Romania, following the legalising of abortion. Previously, high rates of illegal abortions in that country had led to extremely high maternal mortality.

A key indicator of the Russian health crisis is the fact that male life expectancy has now dropped to 59 – below retirement age. What is clear from recent analyses is that the health crisis is centred almost entirely on adult mortality from chronic diseases and external causes, especially violence. After very good progress in the 1940s and 1950s, gradual deterioration in life expectancy occurred from the mid-1960s until the early 1980s, when a brief increase in life expectancy was experienced. This brief improvement was associated with a combination of low winter peaks of respiratory infections in 1981–83, coupled with a sharp rise in alcohol prices, which in turn reduced consumption and alcohol-related harm. A more concerted anti-alcohol campaign was initiated from 1985 to 1988 and death rates immediately started to fall from external causes linked to alcohol abuse.[2] However, the deterioration in life expectancy resumed in 1987, becoming precipitous from 1992 on.

By 1993–94 Russia overtook the USA as the country with the highest homicide rate, with rates two and a half times higher than in the USA, though still below the rate among black Americans. It also overtook Hungary as the country with the highest suicide rates, and rates for accidental poisoning were ten times higher than elsewhere. In absolute terms, however, cardiovascular diseases were still the major contributor to the observed deterioration in mortality.

Many of the causes of death classed as 'avoidable' showed marked increases between 1991 and 1994. These include tuberculosis, dysentery, pneumonia, gastric ulcer, diabetes mellitus and hypertensive disease. This reversed the long-term trend in avoidable mortality from causes which had been declining since 1965.[3] Mortality rates are just the tip of the iceberg. Deterioration in other aspects of health are also reported. Resurgence of communicable diseases, such as the increased incidence of diphtheria and cholera, indicate deterioration in public health infrastructure and living conditions.[1]

Not all sections of the population have suffered to the same degree. Unlike many western countries, mortality has always been higher in rural than in urban populations in men, though there has been less of a differential for women. This gap widened during the 1970s, due to a much greater deterioration in mortality for men in rural areas. However, the rural-urban gap in life expectancy has reduced in the latest crisis from 1992, as the health of urban men was particularly affected: deterioration in life expectancy in Moscow and St Petersburg has been especially great between 1989–1994.[3]

Socio-economic differentials have been assessed using the level of education as an indicator of socio-economic status. The first estimates of life expectancy by educational level showed that in 1989 life expectancy increased with increasing education, with very similar magnitude of differential between educational levels as found in western European countries.[4] In the late 1980s, there was a gap of five years between men in the higher and lower educational groups and two years between women in the respective educational groups at ages 20 to 69, as illustrated in Table 4.1.[4] The improvement in life expectancy seen during the anti-alcohol period in the 1980s was greatest for Russians with higher education.[6]

TABLE 4.1

Life expectancy at age 20
by educational level
Russian Federation 1979 and
1989

Source: Shkolnikov[3] (reprinted by kind
permission of the author).

Educational status	(1) Life expectancy 1979	(2) Life expectancy 1989	(2) - (1)
Men			
Higher and incomplete higher	44.37	45.60	1.23
Secondary special	42.65	44.14	1.49
Secondary	39.14	40.76	1.62
Incomplete secondary, primary and incomplete primary	38.99	39.44	0.45
Women			
Higher and incomplete higher	47.45	48.04	0.59
Secondary special	47.16	47.69	0.53
Secondary	46.02	46.33	0.31
Incomplete secondary, primary and incomplete primary	45.92	45.65	-0.27

Limited evidence is available on what is happening to health differentials in the 1990s, and little at national level. From a longitudinal study of middle-aged men in Moscow and St Petersburg, there is evidence that the renewed deterioration in mortality observed in the 1990s has been more pronounced in the least educated people. In fact, for the men with lower education, survival chances in 1990–94 were poorer than in the 1970s and 1980s.[3] From this study, there are indications that two causes of death have increased faster than others during the 1990s – injuries, including accidents and violence, and (other) alcohol-related deaths. These two causes show major social gradients.[5]

There have been various studies attempting to assess the reasons for the divergent trends.[1,6-8] Central and eastern European countries have faced unprecedented changes over the last few decades, some or all of which could have had a detrimental effect on health status. They have all faced social and political upheaval, some armed conflict or outright war. Economic crises in all the countries have increased material and social stresses. Pollution, dangerous working conditions, interruptions to food supplies, smoking and alcohol abuse, coupled with a breakdown of some of the public health structures and health care services in the turmoil, have all been put forward as possible contributory factors.[6]

Disentangling the different determinants is an on-going and extremely difficult task.[1,7-13] It is striking that the continued deterioration is centred on middle-age men and predominantly involves injuries and cardiovascular diseases. Although alcohol abuse and violence are frequently cited as contributory factors, the focus of attention is shifting to the mechanisms which might underlie these factors. These include the effects on cardiovascular diseases of psychosocial reactions to large and sudden economic shocks.[13]

Widespread and substantial differentials in the west

The most dramatic events may be happening in eastern Europe, but more and more countries in the west are paying attention to socio-economic differentials in health within their boundaries and discovering in many cases that these are substantial, not trivial differences.[14-15]

This is more clearly appreciated in countries where attempts have been made to quantify the size of the differentials and translate them into figures that have some meaning for the lay public and policy-makers. In the Netherlands, for example, data on mortality and self-reported morbidity have been used to calculate both life

TABLE 4.2

Health expectancy in
years, by socioeconomic
status (SES) of men at
birth and at age 65

The Netherlands, 1990

Source: Adapted from van de Water
et al.[16]

Type of life expectancy	at birth			at age 65		
	Low SES	High SES	Difference	Low SES	High SES	Difference
Total life expectancy	72.2	76.7	4.5	13.3	16.4	3.1
Unhealthy life expectancy of which:	20.6	12.6	8.0	6.1	5.8	0.3
in institutions	0.9	1.4	0.5	0.7	1.2	0.5
in poor perceived health	19.7	11.2	8.5	5.4	4.5	0.9
Health expectancy	51.6	64.2	12.6	7.2	10.6	3.4
Healthy life percentage (HLP)	71.5%	83.6%	12.1%	53.8%	64.7%	10.9%

Low SES = primary education
High SES = intermediate/higher vocational training or higher general secondary education or beyond

expectancy and health expectancy – which is calculated as the total life expectancy minus the number of years that will be spent in poor health.[16] Table 4.2 shows the findings for high and low education groups in the population. For men at birth, the high education group has 4.5 extra years of life expectancy and 12.6 extra years of health expectancy than men in the low education group.[16]

These findings are supported by further evidence in the country of large differentials in mortality[17-18] and many indicators of morbidity.[19] From this evidence, it has been estimated that average morbidity and mortality in the Dutch population would be reduced by 25–50 per cent if men with lower education had the morbidity and mortality levels of those with university education.[20]

Likewise in Finland, estimates of the size of gap in disability-free life expectancy between top and bottom educational groups indicate that, after the age of 25, women in the lowest educational group have eight years fewer disability-free life expectancy than the top group. Men in the lowest group have 13 years fewer than their counterparts in the higher educational group.[21]

Calculations at the city level have highlighted stark contrasts for local policy-makers. In the most socio-economically deprived district in Barcelona in 1983–87, life expectancy was 73 years – four years less than for the city as a whole. Infant mortality was 15.6 per 1,000 births compared with nine per 1,000 for the whole of Barcelona.[22] Inequalities in health of a similar magnitude have been found across the neighbourhoods in other Spanish cities such as Valencia[23] and Malaga.[24]

Mounting evidence of this nature has led to the issue of social differentials in health being recognised as a major public health challenge at the national level in countries such as the Netherlands, Sweden, Spain, and the USA.

Concern over widening gap

Having started to monitor health differentials much more closely, several countries are showing signs of heightened concern about widening gaps in health between different sections of the population. This in turn is pushing the subject higher up the political agenda.

In Sweden, for example, there is growing concern that socio-economic health differences have increased among both men and women since the beginning of the 1980s.[25] Figure 4.6 illustrates these trends for men and women in terms of health-weighted years of life. This measure combines illness, disability and general health with remaining life expectancy. For men, for example, the health of salaried

FIGURE 4.6

Trends in health-weighted
years of life, by socio-
economic group

Sweden, 1975–90

Source: Swedish National Board of
Health and Welfare (reprinted by kind
permission of the SNBHW)[26]

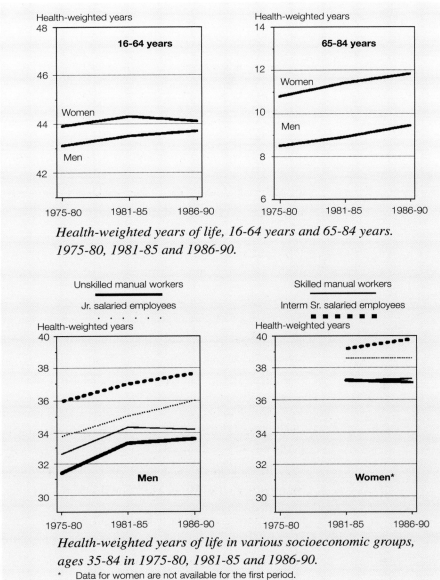

*Health-weighted years of life, 16-64 years and 65-84 years.
1975-80, 1981-85 and 1986-90.*

*Health-weighted years of life in various socioeconomic groups,
ages 35-84 in 1975-80, 1981-85 and 1986-90.*

*   Data for women are not available for the first period.

employees has shown greater improvement than that of manual workers since the
mid-1980s. Among women, positive developments have been confined to senior/
intermediate salaried employees. For women in manual occupations, there has been
no improvement over the 1980s, even a slight decline. Increases in musculoskeletal
problems among women in manual occupations has had a strong impact on the
health-weighted years of life for these groups.

Figure 4.7 shows longer trends in occupational mortality for Swedish men aged 45–
69. Over the whole 30-year period, mortality among professional/managerial workers
decreased strongly. In contrast, there was an absolute increase in mortality among
industrial workers during 1966–80, especially for cardiovascular diseases, followed by
a large decrease in mortality for this group during the 1980s.[26] This finding is of
particular significance because during the period 1961–85 when these inequalities in
health were widening, Sweden experienced narrowing income differentials and low
unemployment. This points to the importance of working conditions for
understanding trends and distribution of male adult mortality in Sweden.[26]

FIGURE 4.7

Occupational mortality,
men aged 45–69

Sweden, 1961–90

*Source: Diderichsen and Hallqvist.
Figure 1 (reprinted by kind permission
from International Journal of
Epidemiology)[26]*

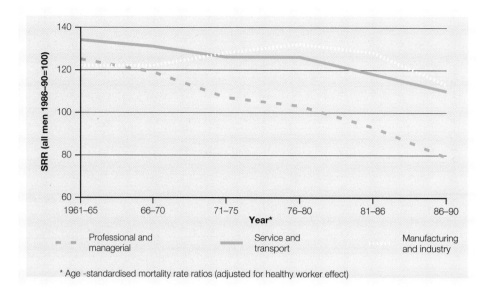

Professional and managerial

Service and transport

Manufacturing and industry

* Age -standardised mortality rate ratios (adjusted for healthy worker effect)

Reports of a widening of social inequalities in mortality have also been noted for older men in Norway. This is happening at the same time as a narrowing of inequalities among younger men.[27] There is also a widening of differentials in long-standing illness in women.[28] Denmark reports increasing social inequalities among men by occupation since 1970.[29]

In Finland, socio-economic differentials in mortality as measured by educational level have been increasing since the 1970s. This pattern is continuing in the 1990s.[30] By 1994, trends in morbidity showed that the gradient for women had remained basically the same as in the mid-1980s. For limiting long-standing illness in men, however, the gradient had flattened off.[31]

From southern Europe, too, come reports of widening inequalities among adults over the 1980s. In Spain, for example, a study of male mortality in eight provinces by occupational group found increasing differentials from 1980–82 to 1988–90. The ratio of all-cause standardised mortality ratios (SMR) for manual labourers to that of professionals and managers was 1.3 in the first period and 1.7 in the second. Over the 1980s the relationship between occupational group and ischaemic heart disease reversed, with higher mortality among the professional group than the manual group in the first period, a trend reversed in the second.[32] A similar reversal of the relationship between social class and male heart disease mortality occurred in Britain in the 1950s.[33]

At the city level, extensive area-based studies in Barcelona have found large differentials between the wealthiest and poorest districts for SMR, life expectancy, and potential years of life lost in 1992, and a widening gap in these differentials from 1983 to 1992[34-35] as illustrated in Figure 4.8. A number of influential studies has also raised concern in the USA.[36] For example, several reports have now documented widening educational and income differentials in mortality in the USA between the 1960s and the 1980s, particularly for men.[37-39] A survival analysis of national data over the years 1973 to 1991 found that the proportion of mortality attributable to poverty in American adults has increased in recent decades and is now comparable to that attributable to cigarette smoking.[40]

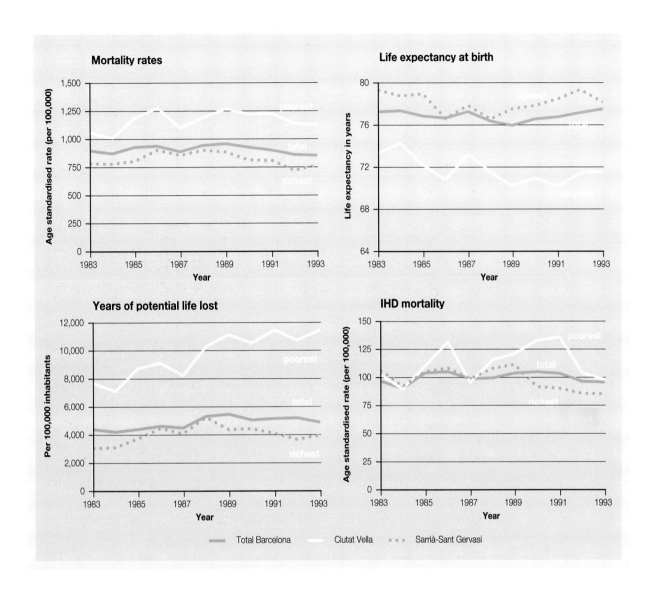

Mortality rates

Age standardised rate (per 100,000)

poorest
total
richest

1,500 / 1,250 / 1,000 / 750 / 500 / 250 / 0

1983 1985 1987 1989 1991 1993
Year

Life expectancy at birth

Life expectancy in years

80 / 76 / 72 / 68 / 64

1983 1985 1987 1989 1991 1993
Year

Years of potential life lost

Per 100,000 inhabitants

poorest
total
richest

12,000 / 10,000 / 8,000 / 6,000 / 4,000 / 2,000 / 0

1983 1985 1987 1989 1991 1993
Year

IHD mortality

Age standardised rate (per 100,000)

poorest
total
richest

150 / 125 / 100 / 75 / 50 / 25 / 0

1983 1985 1987 1989 1991 1993
Year

——— Total Barcelona ——— Ciutat Vella ····· Sarrià-Sant Gervasi

FIGURE 4.8

Wealthiest and poorest districts' mortality

Barcelona, 1983–93

Source: Plasencia et al. (reprinted by kind permission of the authors)[34]

Differentials not inevitable

If inequalities can widen then theoretically they can also narrow. Evidence from different countries and at different times within the same country of changing patterns of inequalities has provided encouragement that the health divide is not inevitable, but may be amenable to reduction by purposeful policy action.

Sweden has been the focus for attention in this respect, in the light of earlier evidence that inequalities in health in childhood in Sweden had all but disappeared by the 1960s.[41-42] It is of particular interest to note what has happened to the pattern for infants and children in more recent years. In contrast to the picture for adults, trends do show a narrowing gap between certain social groups for infant mortality during the 1970s and 1980s.[43] Over the century, for example, differentials in mortality between infants of married and unmarried mothers have reduced to a low level as shown in Table 4.3.[44]

Yet significant inequalities in infant mortality by socio-economic group still remain.[45] Even for older children the mortality rates have been reduced during recent decades, but the socio-economic inequalities seem to persist, albeit on a rather low level.[46]

A narrowing of inequalities in health at younger ages has also been reported from Spain, where studies have mainly been confined to specific regions or cities. A study of

TABLE 4.3

Infant mortality among
children of married and
unmarried mothers
Stockholm, 1901–1981

Source: adapted from Diderichsen.[44]

	Infant mortality per 1,000		Rate difference (B-A)	Rate ratio (B/A)	Proportion of deaths among unmarried mothers (%)	Attributable fraction[b] (%)
	Married mothers (A)	Unmarried mothers (B)				
1901-10	88	182	94	2.1	52	27
1911-20	60	126	66	2.1	50	26
1921-30	46	78	32	1.7	38	16
1931-40	32	62	30	1.9	28	14
1941-50	21	41	20	1.9	18	9
1951-60	16	27	11	1.7	19	8
1966	11	16	5	1.4	26[a]	7
1980-81	6	7	1	1.2	10[a]	1

[a] These figures are rough estimates and for 1980–81 the figures are for mothers living alone independently of their marital status.
[b] The proportion of infant deaths that would be avoided if everyone had the rate of the married mothers.

infant mortality in the 50 Spanish provinces between 1975–8 and 1983–6 showed a steep fall in infant and perinatal mortality overall, with the provinces with the highest mortality experiencing the greatest reduction and vice versa. Mean family income in a province was the main predictor of infant and perinatal mortality in 1975–8, but by 1983–6 health care indicators were the most important factors.[47]

Such evidence is starting to trigger more intensive studies of those circumstances and policies most conducive to improvement.

Monitoring the effect of deteriorating economic conditions

Another important development is the anticipatory approach to the prevention or amelioration of health damage caused by worsening economic conditions. Many countries have been experiencing economic recession in the 1980s and 1990s, and there are signs that some have been sufficiently concerned about the possible health effects to set up a monitoring process.

Finland, for example, has experienced deteriorating economic conditions and rising unemployment in the 1990s, after decades of some of the lowest rates in the world. From an unemployment rate of about 3 per cent, Finland now has a rate of 18 per cent – one of the highest in Europe. This has led to redoubled efforts to identify any damaging effects these developments might have had on health. The effect of unemployment on mortality has been shown for the early 1980s in Finland, with mortality increasing with increasing duration of unemployment.[48]

A series of studies has been initiated to monitor the effects of the worsening economic climate in Finland in the 1990s. A controlled study of the effects of unemployment on the mental health of men and women in 1992 found that unemployment seemed to impair the mental well-being of middle-aged men. This effect was not evident among the women in the study. Insufficient social support and a poor financial situation increased the adverse effects of unemployment.[49]

In studies of self-perceived health and limiting long-standing illness up to 1994, however, detrimental effects of unemployment have not yet been observed.[31] It has been speculated that physical health consequences may take longer to show up in the health statistics than the impact on mental health, or that these may become apparent exclusively within marginalised and vulnerable subgroups not visible when looking at broader population segments.[31] The results have also raised the question of how far the Finnish welfare state may have cushioned the population from the worst effects of recession.[50] National research and development studies are following up these developments.[49,51]

Women's health and social circumstances

Countries vary in the focus of attention in relation to inequalities. In some, particular groups in the population experiencing noticeable deterioration in their position have heightened awareness of the problem in general among policy-makers. For several countries, a stagnating or deteriorating trend in health among women has been the trigger for a wider investigation of the social circumstances underlying these trends.

Social inequalities in women's health have become an issue in Norway and Denmark. In fact in Denmark, initial concerns about why life expectancy there was stagnating in the 1980s, in contrast to its Nordic neighbours, resulted in a national enquiry which identified deteriorating health in women as one of the main contributors to this trend.[29] In particular, Danish middle-aged women have markedly higher mortality than Swedish and Norwegian women. In contrast to the general trend of people with higher education experiencing lower mortality, Danish women with longer education have higher mortality than women with shorter education, unlike their male counterparts.[29]

Similarly, in the Netherlands, although the life expectancy at birth of Dutch women exceeds that of men by more than six years, this advantage is almost entirely cancelled out by the greater number of years which women spend in poor health. Furthermore, trends from 1983 to 1990 suggest that the percentage of life that Dutch men spend in good health is rising, whereas for women it is decreasing.[16]

In Sweden, concern has grown about the slower rate of improvement in women's compared to men's health in the 1990s. For example, average life expectancy of women has not increased as much as that of men. As shown in Figure 4.6, health-weighted years of life have declined for women aged 16–64 since the beginning of the 1980s, and show a widening gap between occupational groups.[25] In relation to the elderly, increasing class differentials with increasing age were observed for women, while for men the differentials decreased with age.[52]

In Britain it has proved difficult to study inequalities in women's health, particularly in relation to mortality, because of the lack of socio-economic measures sensitive to women's social circumstances and capable of being linked to health data. The Nordic countries have been able to carry out much more extensive analyses by linking health data to socio-economic data sources through the personal identification number.

In the past a common finding in the Nordic countries was that socio-economic mortality differentials appeared smaller among women than among men. A Finnish study investigated the possible reasons for this by linking the individual records of all women and men in the 1980 Census to death records for 1981–85 in the 35–64 year-old population.[53] Three questions were addressed:

1   Does the choice of measure determine whether women's socio-economic mortality differences appear smaller than men's? This was investigated by using four

different measures based on educational level, occupation, housing and income. The choice of indicator did not influence the overall result – for all four indicators women's mortality differentials were smaller than those of men.

2   Is there a confounding effect of other socio-demographic factors which either mask women's inequalities or accentuate those among men? There was some evidence for a confounding effect. Women's inequalities were smaller than men's only for the married subpopulation. Among non-married, particularly single women, inequalities were at least as large, or larger than men's.

3   Do the data for women show smaller inequalities because the particular causes of death with wide socio-economic differentials are common among men while those causes of death with little or opposite socio-economic variation contribute more to female mortality? Again, there was some evidence that this was a contributory factor,[53] and emphasises the importance of disaggregating the data in inequalities studies.

Minority status and class

Black and minority ethnic communities have been another important focus for attention, particularly in the USA, where there has been a stronger tradition than in other countries of studying health differentials between the black and white populations. Now these are being supplemented with studies of the relationship between black and minority ethnic disadvantage and socio-economic position.

Since the late 1980s, public health reports for the US Federal Government have highlighted the mortality differentials between whites and blacks. The reduction of the six-year gap in life expectancy between black and white to no more than four years was set as a national health goal in 1989.[54] An influential study showed that the survival chances of black men in Harlem were worse than for men in Bangladesh.[55]

Concern has been heightened by evidence of a major change in the pattern of mortality in the USA between 1984 and 1989. While figures for the total population showed a continued improvement in life expectancy, the mortality patterns diverged for the black and the white populations. Life expectancy increased for white men and women, but decreased for black men and women. This was unprecedented in the USA this century and reversed the narrowing of the gap of the previous decades, when black life expectancy had been increasing more rapidly than white.[56] Analyses of causes showed that, for the white population, improvements in heart disease, stroke, and accident mortality more than compensated for the negative effects of other causes. For the black population, the negative impact on life expectancy of HIV infection, homicide, diabetes and pneumonia overwhelmed improvements in mortality from other causes.

However, many commentators have raised the question of whether 'race' in America is acting as a proxy for underlying socio-economic differentials, such as differences in living and working conditions and position in society. Until the 1990s, a focus exclusively on race may have led to a relative neglect of research into the socio-economic patterning of health in the black population.[57] Table 4.4 illustrates the large differentials in various measures of health status observed by black and minority ethnic groups in 1992, but also gives indicators of socio-economic disadvantage. These differentials raise questions for urgent investigation.

TABLE 4.4

Health status indicators, by black, white and minority ethnic origin
USA, 1992

Source: Centres for Disease Control.[77]

Health status indicators (rates per 100,000 population unless specified)	Total[a]	White	Black	American Indian/ Alaska Native	Asian/ Pacific Islander	Hispanic
1 Infant mortality[b]	8.5	6.9	16.8			
Linked birth and infant death data[b]	8.6	7.1	16.6	11.3	5.8	7.1
2 Total deaths	504.5	477.5	767.5	453.1	285.8	380.6
3 Motor vehicle crash deaths	15.8	15.9	16.3	32	9.9	16.3
4 Work-related injury deaths	3.2	3.1	2.9	3.2	2	3.5
5 Suicides	11.1	11.8	6.9	11	6	7.2
6 Homicides	10.5	6.1	39.4	10.5	5.7	17.6
7 Lung cancer deaths	39.3	38.8	49.8	22.2	17.9	14.5
8 Breast cancer deaths[c]	21.9	21.7	27	11	9.3	13
9 Cardiovascular disease deaths	150.4	172.8	285.3	132.8	107.4	120.5
Heart disease deaths	144.3	139.2	205.4	107.1	77.8	94.8
Stroke deaths	26.2	24.2	45	19.1	23.5	19.3
10 Reported incidence of AIDS	31.2	17.9	104.2	11.9	7.4	52.6
11 Reported incidence of measles	0.1					
12 Reported incidence of tuberculosis	9.8	3.6	29.1	14.6	44.5	20.6
13 Reported incidence of syphilis	10.4	1.2	76.5	1.7	1	6
14 Prevalence of low birth weight[d]	7.1	5.8	13.3	6.2	6.6	6.1
15 % of births to adolescents	4.9	3.9	10.3	8	2	7.1
16 % with lack of prenatal care	22.3	19.2	36.1	37.9	23.4	35.8
17 % living in childhood poverty						
Under 18 years	22.7	17.8	46.1			40.9
Under 15 years	23.4					
5–17 years	20.8					
18 % living in high pollution counties	23.5	23.1	24.8	17.6	37.2	42.3

[a] Includes groups not shown separately [b] Rate per 1,000 live births [c] Rate per 100,000 women
[d] Percentage of live births under 2.5kg

Recent studies have now started to examine the interrelationships between racial disadvantage and class. Long-term trends in infant mortality from 1950 to 1991 have been studied by ethnicity, education, family income and cause of death, followed by forecasts for the year 2010. These show dramatic declines in infant mortality since 1950, but persisting differences by the socio-demographic factors studied. The long-term improvement in US infant mortality did not benefit blacks and whites equally, with a slower decline in the black population. For example, in 1950, infant mortality rates for blacks were 64 per cent higher than for whites. By 1991, the rates for blacks were more than double those for whites. The gap is not expected to diminish in the near future. The study shows that educational inequalities have also widened, and the racial differentials have generally increased across all educational levels.[58]

Using the National Longitudinal Mortality Study, adult deaths from 1979 to 1989 have been analysed against a range of socio-demographic variables. Higher mortality was found in blacks than in whites under 65 years of age, in people not in the labour force, with lower incomes, with less education, and in service and lower level occupations; and in those not married and living alone. These associations were reduced but remained strong and statistically significant when each variable was adjusted for all the other characteristics. However, these relationships were less clear for older people.[59]

Analysis of the effect of known risk factors on excess mortality of black adults in the USA found 31 per cent of the excess mortality could be accounted for statistically by six well-established behavioural risk factors, a further 38 per cent by family income, leaving 31 per cent unexplained.[60]

Secondary analysis of the Multiple Risk Factor Intervention Trial found that socio-economic mortality differentials among black men in the trial were similar in magnitude to those observed among white men. For example, there was a consistent association between lower income and higher mortality, translating into a relative risk of mortality of 1.35 for each $10,000 lower income increment. Adjustment for smoking behaviour, diastolic blood pressure, serum cholesterol, history of heart attack, and medication for diabetes reduced this relative risk somewhat, but only to 1.29. The association between mortality risk and income was not confined to the poorest black men, but could be observed across the full income distribution. It could also be seen for most of the causes of death studied.[61] The complementary study of white men screened in the same trial found that the association between income and all-cause mortality risk was similar in the two population groups, even though there was a higher average level of income among the white men.[62] The study concluded that 'the dependence of mortality risk on socio-economic position among blacks is at least as strong as that among whites in the United States'.[61]

Concentration of heroin and HIV deaths in poor areas

Perhaps the newest trend to emerge from international work in this area is the growing association of HIV and AIDS deaths with poverty. This pattern has been evident in Third World countries for some time, and from Table 4.4 there is an illustration that rates are much higher in poorer parts of the population in the USA, such as among the black and Hispanic communities.

In Europe, evidence is now emerging of a distinctive feature of inequalities in health in Spain, shared by other southern European countries, of high premature death associated with heroin and HIV infection. This has been concentrated in the poorer areas of the major cities in Spain. An analysis of drug-related deaths by area of residence in Barcelona in 1989–93 revealed a nine-fold difference in mean annual death rates between districts in the city, with even larger differences by neighbourhood. All six neighbourhoods with mortality rates above the city average were in areas of poverty and deprivation.[63] Figure 4.9 illustrates the latest evidence of the divergent trends in AIDS premature mortality, from an analysis of wards with the lowest socio-economic level compared to the rest.[64] This emerging pattern is now seen as a serious problem for public health across southern Europe,[65] though it has yet to become evident in Britain (see also Chapter 10).[66]

FIGURE 4.9

Evolution of AIDS premature mortality in the wards with the lowest socio-economic level and the rest of the city,

Barcelona, 1983–94

Source: Borrell et al. (reprinted by kind permission of the Journal of Epidemiology and Community Health and the copyright holders, BMJ, Publishing Group)[64]

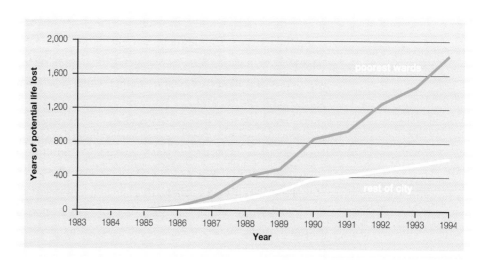

What is immediately striking about international developments, from a methodological perspective, is that researchers in several countries have had to overcome great obstacles just to be able to carry out studies of socio-economic conditions and health. There are examples from the east and the south of Europe where such studies have been strongly discouraged for many years.

For example, health statistics were collected but kept secret in much of central and eastern Europe, and only became available for analysis in the late 1980s.[1] The full extent of the problem was therefore not appreciated until the early 1990s. In the former USSR, in particular, studies of socio-economic differentials were 'almost entirely forbidden'.[3] Much dedicated work has had to go into reconstructing annual series of mortality data so that such studies could be carried out at all.

Spain is another example of a country which has made remarkable progress in the 1990s in measuring and monitoring inequalities in health, after decades when there were severe restrictions on data collection. Under the Franco regime, which ended in 1975, social movements and public health studies in general were discouraged. As a result, the amount of information available about health issues was very limited until the early 1980s. Training in public health research, and the information systems to go with this, have taken time to build up, but are now firmly in place. In 1993, the developments resulted in the setting up of a national Scientific Commission to Study Social Health Inequalities to analyse the evidence on social inequalities in health in Spain and to make policy recommendations.[67] In effect, this represents a Spanish Black Report, published in February 1997 and presenting wide-ranging and up-to-date evidence on the situation in the country.

More systematic approaches to improving routine information systems

In other countries, a major obstacle has been that the routine information systems have not been geared to the collection of appropriate data, and there has been considerable ingenuity employed to make the best use of what is available. The fact that increasing numbers of researchers are now willing to go to such great lengths to carry out these studies is a sign of the growing concern about the issue in many quarters.

In western Europe, the Netherlands has carried out an enormous amount of work since 1989 to document and monitor inequalities in health. It provides a model of how a systematic approach can be applied to improving the information systems in a country, to allow issues of inequalities in health to be given more prominence in policy-making.

In 1989, the first of two national five-year research programmes began and this has had a knock-on effect on the Dutch research community in general. Studies in all the universities in the country have been stimulated either directly or indirectly as a result of this initiative.[20] One of the fruits of the research programme has been the development of standardised procedures for measuring socio-economic status, using education, income or occupation. This allows data on socio-economic factors to be incorporated into all kinds of routine information collection, including patients admission to hospital.[20] As a result, the Central Bureau of Statistics now includes analysis by education and income in most of its health publications. In addition, a large longitudinal study has been set up in the south-eastern part of the Netherlands to look in detail at the causes of inequalities in health. This includes investigating the contribution of lifestyles, living and working conditions and health care.[68]

For two reasons, the Netherlands does not have national mortality statistics by socio-economic status. First, because of privacy concerns, there has been no national population census since 1970. Second, the law does not allow the linkage of national deaths data to socio-economic registers. For mortality studies, therefore, the Netherlands has to rely on sub-national data from a few cities and regions, and special studies set up from time to time.

From a research point of view, the Nordic countries offer opportunities for more detailed and accurate study of health differentials than in many other countries. This is because everyone in these countries has an unique identification number. These can be used to link socio-economic sources such as the census, housing and educational registers on the one hand to death registers and health and treatment records on the other. This means that a high proportion of the population can be included in analyses, including older people over pension age and women not in paid employment. This contrasts with the situation in Britain, for example, where it is difficult to construct a robust social classification for women and older people from routine data sources.

A search for ways of improving the measurement and monitoring of socio-economic health differentials in official statistics is also a feature of American research in recent years. The USA provides an example of a country in which social inequalities in health were high on the agenda in the first third of this century, but interest died away by the 1940s, only very recently experiencing a significant resurgence.[69]

In the 1990s, such interest has led to several significant developments in data collection. In 1994 the National Centre for Health Statistics called a conference in Annapolis to discuss the improvement of measuring and monitoring of social inequalities in health. Participants decided that, in the USA, the task of monitoring had been hampered by absence of centralised data systems and consistent individual identifiers. In addition, health statistics usually only reported on indicators by race, sex and age, though there had been some improvements recently. For example, on death certificates, occupation is recorded in about half the states, and in 1990 educational attainment was added to the death certificate for all states.[36]

The Annapolis conference made a series of recommendations for improving routine data collection,[70] summarised in Box 4.1. At the same time, plans were announced by the US Assistant Secretary of Health, Philip Lee, to follow up the recommendations of the Annapolis conference with a series of studies, resulting in formal documentation of social inequalities in health in the USA. This body of work will now be published as a chartbook and a special issue of the *American Journal of Public Health* in 1997.

> **Box 4.1 1994 Annapolis recommendations for improving US data collection on social differentials in health**
>
> - Collect socio-economic data routinely and routinely present data by socio-economic position, in conjunction with data on sex, race, ethnicity and age.
> - Consider occupation a core socio-economic variable.
> - Three different levels of socio-economic data should be evaluated: individual, household, and neighbourhood.
> - Conduct research to ensure that socio-economic measures are valid for analysing inequalities in health among women, children, older people, and diverse ethnic groups.
> - Use a core set of socio-economic measures in all data bases to permit comparison of results across time etc.
> - Encourage data linkage to combine mortality and morbidity data with socio-economic survey and census data.
> - Make available data on socio-economic gradients in health at the state and local level not just the national level, to improve planning for public health.
>
> *Source: Krieger and Moss[70]*

Refining cross-national comparisons

In recent years there have been increasing efforts to compare the level and nature of social differentials in health in different countries more directly. While valuable information could be gained from such comparisons, there are particular methodological problems which make the task highly complex and fraught with potential pitfalls. Several common sources of bias have been identified in socio-economic mortality studies in particular,[71-72] and these need to be borne in mind when weighing the evidence:

1 Most of the international comparisons are based on large data sets which were designed for other purposes. Routine data collection on which they are based cannot readily be changed and compromises invariably have to be made in trying to match the parameters from different countries.

2 Variations in who is included or not can influence the size of the inequality estimate. For example, if economically inactive people are included in the analysis for some countries, mortality differentials will tend to be greater than in countries where they are excluded, as this section of the population often includes people who are permanently sick. Similarly, the inclusion of older age-groups or institutionalised patients may give an elevated estimate of inequality. In addition, variation across countries in response rates or in the size of the 'unclassified' group can bias the comparison.

3 Variation in the timing of the studies being compared can alter the ranking of countries. As highlighted earlier, several European countries experienced an increase in inequalities in health during the 1980s. Bias could therefore be introduced into a cross-country comparison if data for some countries were from the early 1980s while for others data related to the late 1980s.

4 Finely graded socio-economic classifications containing small percentages of the population may produce larger estimates for the mortality differentials than ones dividing the population into a few large, more heterogeneous groups.

5 The ranking of countries may be very different depending on whether absolute or relative mortality differences are being measured. Relative differences, such as the ratio of the mortality rate of the highest to the lowest social group (rate ratios), do not show whether there are differences between countries in their overall levels of mortality, or in the absolute risk of death for different social groups in society. Yet information on such absolute differences in risk may be the most relevant measures from a policy perspective, particularly when making comparisons across countries and over time. For example, in countries with generally low mortality, the absolute risk of death for lower social groups may be much smaller than for the equivalent group in a high mortality country, and may indicate a protective effect on health of the policy environment in that society.

6 When using complex measures of inequality, the ranking of a country may depend on the particular index used.[73-74]

7 Difficulties are even greater for morbidity comparisons. In addition to the great variation among countries in the definition and questionnaire wording on morbidity indicators, there may be different concepts of health within different societies and attitudes to complaining about ill-health. Blaxter has concluded that 'there is little possibility of comparing morbidity information across the countries of Europe in detail ... comparability by social variables is perhaps intrinsically impossible to achieve'.[75]

Blaxter does concede, however, that it is valid to compare the general patterns emerging in different countries and to look at relative differences. Others suggest that this judgement is too harsh, and some estimates of ranking of countries can be made. It should be clear from all these discussions that great care is needed in matching parameters and in interpreting the results of any international comparison. Refinements continue to be made to try to overcome these problems, and the European Union has most recently been active in funding such studies but as yet no study has solved all the problems completely.

Where is Britain in the international ranking?

Cross-country comparisons have been used to address more directly questions of whether some countries have more pronounced differentials in health than others. If so, where is Britain placed in the international ranking?

All the available evidence shows that the pattern of inequalities is not uniform, but varies greatly between countries. On mortality, Britain is frequently placed somewhere in the middle in comparisons of the relative size of differentials, with larger inequalities in mortality than Sweden and Norway, for instance, but smaller inequalities than France and possibly Finland. Table 4.5 summarises the findings from the major mortality studies.

The findings from morbidity comparisons are less clear cut, reflecting in part the greater variation in the way morbidity is measured and interpreted in different countries. This reinforces the conclusion that it may only be safe to compare the

TABLE 4.5 Cross-country comparisons of health differentials: mortality

Author	Date and age	Socio-economic measure	Measure of inequality	Ranking of country
Vagero and Lundberg[78]	adults early 1980s	RG's social class	ratio manual: non-manual ratio of IV/V : I/II	England and Wales greater than Sweden
Wagstaff et al.[73]	above data reworked	RG's social class	concentration curve	England and Wales greater than Sweden
Leon et al.[79]	infant mortality mid-1980s	RG's social class	manual: non-manual	England and Wales greater than Sweden
Leclerc et al.[80]	middle-aged men 1971-81	RG's social class/ occupational class	Gini coefficient	1. France highest 2. England and Wales, Finland
Wagstaff et al.[73]	above data reworked	occupational class	concentration curve	1. France 2. England and Wales 3. Finland
Kunst and Mackenbach[81]	35-64 men 1971-81	occupational class	inequality index (modified relative index of inequality)	1. France (x6-8) 2. Finland (x 4.5) 3. England and Wales (x2) 4. Sweden (x1.5) 5. Norway, Denmark (x1)
Valkonen[82]	35-54 adults	educational level	inequality coefficient	Similar levels in all countries, ranking varies by sex and age England and Wales, Hungary, Finland, Denmark, Norway, Sweden

relative, not the absolute, differences between countries as far as morbidity is concerned.

Morbidity comparisons including Britain have all used the General Household Survey for various years during the 1980s. The findings of some of the key comparative studies on self-perceived general health are summarised in Table 4.6. Many countries are carrying out regular population surveys in which people are asked to assess their own general state of health. Self-assessed general health has been found to be a good predictor of mortality and correlates reasonably well with several clinical measures of physical and mental health.[76] As indicated, comparisons using this measure generally show a consistent ranking of the USA as having the largest relative inequalities in health and Sweden having smaller. Britain generally has a middle to low ranking, though this varies depending on the socio-economic and inequality indicators used in the studies.

Table 4.7 summarises the findings on long-standing illness, and shows even more variability in ranking of the different countries, depending on the age-group and sex of the population studied, and the measures of socio-economic status and inequality used.

The overall conclusion is that Britain is in neither the worst position, nor the best. It shares with other countries unacceptable levels of social differentials in health within the population.

Author	Date and age	Socio-economic measure	Measure of inequality	Ranking of country
Kunst *et al.*[83]	late 1980s men	educational level	inequality index (modified relative index of inequality)	1. USA – largest 2. Canada 3. Denmark, the Netherlands 4. Sweden, Great Britain
Kunst *et al*[83]	late 1980s women	education level	inequality index (modified relative index of inequality)	1. USA 2. Denmark 3. Sweden, Great Britain, Netherlands, Canada
van Doorslaer *et al.*[84]	early-late 1980s adults (men and women combined)	income	concentration index concentration curve	1. USA 2. Great Britain 3. Spain, Switzerland, Netherlands 4. West Germany, Finland 5. East Germany, Sweden

TABLE 4.7 Cross-country comparisons of health differentials: long-standing illness

Author	Date and age	Socio-economic measure	Measure of inequality	Ranking of country
Vagero and Lundberg[78]	1981 adults men and women	RG's social class	ratio V: I	1. England and Wales 2. Sweden
			ratio manual: non-manual	no difference between 2 countries
Wagstaff *et al.*[73]	above data reworked	RG's social class	concentration index	1. Sweden 2. England and Wales
Arber and Lahelma[85]	1985/86 men	occupational class	odds ratio of class compared with highest class	1. Finland 2. Great Britain
	women	occupational class		differences depending on employed/ housewife status
Lahelma and Arber[86]	mid 1980s men	occupational class	odds ratio of class compared with highest class	1. Finland, Sweden, Norway 2. Great Britain
	women	occupational class	housewives: white collar women	1. Great Britain 2. Norway, Sweden, Finland
Lahelma *et al.*[87]	mid 1980s men and women	educational level	ratio lowest: highest	Men: 1. Norway 2. Sweden, Finland
			concentration index	Women: 1. Sweden 2. Norway, Finland

Conclusions

The international evidence points to significant developments spreading across countries and resulting in raised concern about the issue of social differentials in health. This increasing concern has in part been triggered by greater awareness of the substantial social inequalities in health which exist in all the countries which have set out to assess the scale of the problem. In several countries there is the added concern that these inequalities are widening. The most dramatic developments of this nature come from central and eastern Europe – unparalleled in scale in any industrialised nation this century. In countries such as Russia, where the overall health development has been negative, the increasing inequalities give important additional clues as to why.

But countries with exceptionally good health profiles, such as the Netherlands, Sweden and Denmark, are also signalling persisting or growing inequalities, and these are emerging as prime public health concerns. Differential deterioration in women's health, particularly among women from more disadvantaged social groups, is a development which is becoming the focus of attention by policy-makers and politicians in these countries.

The work going on in other countries has broadened understanding of the issue of inequalities in health in general and in turn has helped to inform the British debate. The evidence shows not only that all countries have social differentials in health, but, crucially, that the magnitude and nature of these inequalities vary from place to place and time to time – indicating that they are not fixed, but in theory could be altered. The best levels achieved by any country should act as a guide to feasible goals for other countries.

In a more general context, the study of inequalities in health at an international level provides new perspectives on the broader task of understanding population health. It raises important issues that can be pursued for a better understanding of the origins of diseases and population health patterns in Britain and abroad.

References

1   World Health Organisation (1994), *Health in Europe*. Copenhagen, WHO Regional Office for Europe.

2   Shkolnikov, V and Vassin, S (1994) Spatial differences in life expectancy in European Russia in the 1980s. In: Lutz, W Volkov, A and Scherbov,S (eds) *Demographic Trends and Patterns in the Soviet Union before 1991*. New York, Routledge-IIASA.

3   Shkolnikov, V (1996) *Russian health crisis of the 1990s in mortality.* Paper presented to the Common Security Forum, September 1996, Stockholm.

4   Andreev, E and Dobrovolskaya, V (1993) *The socio-cultural differences in mortality in Russia.* Zdravoohraneniye Rossiiskoi Federatsii, 12: 18–21. Quoted in Shkolnikov (1996) (in Russian) .

5   Leon, D A *et al.* (1997) *On-going analysis*. personal communication.

6   Makara, P (1994) The effect of social changes on the population's way of life and health: a Hungarian case study. In Levin, L S, McMahon, L and Ziglio, E (eds) . *Economic Change, Social Welfare and Health in Europe*. WHO Regional Publications European series, 54: 77–94, Copenhagen, WHO.

7   Boys, R J, Forster DP and Jozan P (1991) Mortality from causes amenable and non-amenable to medical care: the experience of eastern Europe, *BMJ*, 303: 879–83.

8   Bobak, M and Marmot, M (1996) East-West mortality divide and its potential explanations: proposed research agenda, *BMJ*, 312: 421–5.

9   Gaizauskiené, A and Gurevicius, R (1995) Avoidable mortality in Lithuania, *Journal of Epidemiology and Community Health*, 49: 281–4.

10 Bobak, M and Feachem, R G A (1995) Air pollution and infant mortality in central and eastern Europe: an estimate of the impact, *European Journal of Public Health*, 5: 82–6.

11 Jedrychowski, W, Becher, H, Wahrendorf, J and Basa-Cierpialek Z (1990) A case-control study of

lung cancer with special reference to the effect of air pollution in Poland, *Journal of Epidemiology and Community Health*, 44: 114–20.

12　Spix, C, Heinrich,J, Dockery, D *et al.* (1993) Air pollution and daily mortality in Erfurt, East Germany, 1980–1989, *Environ. Health Perspect*, 101: 518–26.

13　Cornia, A and Paniccià, R (1995) *The demographic impact of sudden impoverishment: Eastern Europe during the 1989-94 transition.*, Innocenti Occasional Papers. Economic Policy Series, 49. Florence, UNICEF, International Child Development Centre.

14　Whitehead, M (1992) The health divide. In: Townsend, P, Whitehead, M and Davidson N (eds) *Inequalities in Health: the Black Report and the Health Divide*. New edition. London, Penguin.

15　Benzeval, M, Judge, K and. Whitehead, M (1995) *Tackling Inequalities in Health: an agenda for action*. London, King's Fund.

16　van de Water, H, Boshuizen, H. and Perenboom, R (1996) Health expectancy in the Netherlands 1983–1990, *European Journal of Public Health*, 6: 21–8.

17　Doornbos, G and Kromhout, D (1990) Educational level and mortality in a 32-year follow-up study of 18-year-old men in the Netherlands, *International Journal of Epidemiology*, 19: 374–9.

18　Duijkers,T J, Kromhout, D, Spruit, I P and Doornbos G (1989) Inter-mediating risk factors in the relation between socioeconomic status and 25-year mortality (the Zutphen Study), *International Journal of Epidemiology,* 18: 658–62.

19　Mackenbach, J P (1993) Inequalities in health in The Netherlands according to age, gender, marital status, level of education, degree of urbanization, and region, *European Journal of Public Health*, 3: 112–18.

20　Mackenbach, J P (1994) Socioeconomic inequalities in health in the Netherlands: impact of a five year research programme, *BMJ*, 309: 1487–91.

21　Valkonen, T, Sihvonen, A-P and Lahelma, E (1994) Disability-free life expectancy by education in Finland. In: Mathers, C McCallum, J and Robine J-M (eds) *Advances in Health Expectancies: Proceedings of the 7th Meeting of the International Network on Health Expectancy(REVES) , Canberra, February 1994*. Canberra: Australian Institute of Health and Welfare.

22　Borrell, C, Plasència, A and Pañella, H (1991) Excess mortality in an inner city area: the case of Ciutat Vella in Barcelona, *Gaceta Sanitaria*, 5: 243–53 (in Spanish) .

23　Arias, A, Rebagliato, M, Palumbo, M *et al.* (1993) Inequalities in health in Barcelona and Valencia,. *Medicina Clinica*, 100: 281–87 (in Spanish) .

24　Santos, F J M and Cerda, J C M (1992) Social inequalities in health in the city of Malaga (Spain), *Gaceta Sanitaria*, 6: 198-203 (in Spanish) .

25　Swedish National Board of Health and Welfare (1995) *Welfare and Public Health in Sweden*. Stockholm, National Board of Health and Welfare / Centre for Epidemiology.

26　Diderichsen, F and Hallqvist, J (1997) Trends in occupational mortality among men in Sweden, 1961–90, *International Journal of Epidemiology,* forthcoming.

27　Dahl, E and Kjaersgaard, P (1993) Trends in socioeconomics mortality differentials in post-war Norway: evidence and interpretations, *Sociology of Health and Illness*, 15: 589–611.

28　Elstad, J I (1996) Inequalities in health related to women's marital, parental, and employment status – a comparison between the early 70s and the late 80s. Norway, *Soc. Sci. Med.* 42: 75–89.

29　Danish Ministry of Health (1994) *Lifetime in Denmark*. Copenhagen, Ministry of Health.

30　Valkonen, T, Martelin, T, Rimpela, A, Notkola, V and Savela, S (1993) *Socio-economic differences in Mortality, 1981-90. Population, 1*. Helsinki, Central Statistical Office of Finland.

31　Lahelma, E, Rahkonen, O and Huuhka M (1997) Changes in the social patterning of health? The case of Finland 1986-94. *Soc. Sci. Med.* 44: 789–99

32　Regidor, E, Gutiérrez-Fisac, J L and Rodriguez, C (1995) Increased socioeconomic differences in mortality in eight Spanish provinces, *Soc. Sci. Med.,* 41: 801–7.

33　Marmot, M *et al* .(1981) Changes in heart disease mortality in England and Wales and other countries, *Health Trends*, 13: 33–8.

34　Plasència, A, Pasarin, M I and Borrell, C (eds) (1995) *Annual Health Report of the City of Barcelona, 1993*. Barcelona: Ajuntament de Barcelona (in Spanish) .

35　Borrell, C and Arias, A (1995) Socio-economic factors and mortality in urban settings: the case of Barcelona (Spain), *Journal of Epidemiology and Community Health*, 49: 460–5.

36　Pappas, G, Hadden, W, Muntaner, C and Moss, N (1997) Understanding social inequality and health: a review of the government's role, *American Journal of Public Health* forthcoming .

37　Feldman, J J, Makuc, D M, Kleinman, J C and Cornoni-Huntley, J (1989) National trends in educational differentials in mortality, *American Journal of Epidemiology,* 129: 919–33.

38　Pappas, G, Queen, S, Hadden, W and Fisher, G (1993) The increasing disparity in mortality between socioeconomic groups in the United States, 1960 and 1986, *The New England Journal of Medicine*, 329: 103–09.

39　Elo, I T and Preston, S H (1996) Educational differentials in mortality: United States, 1979–85. *Soc. Sci. Med*, 42: 47–57.

40   Hahn, R, Eaker, E, Barker, N *et al* .(1995) Poverty and death in the United States – 1973 and 1991, *Epidemiology*, 6: 490–7.

41   Lindgren, G (1976) Height, weight and menarche in Swedish urban school children in relation to socio-economic and regional factors, *Annals of Human Biology*, 3:501–28.

42   Sjolin, S (1975) Infant mortality in Sweden. In: Wallace, H (ed.) *Health Care of Mothers and Children in National Health Services.* Cambridge, Mass., Ballinger.

43   Diderichsen, F (1990) Health and social inequalities in Sweden, *Soc. Sci. Med*, 31: 359–67.

44   Diderichsen, F (1991) Mortality changes as an outcome measure of health policy. I*n: Public Health Changes and Impact of Health Promotion*. Stockholm, Medical Research Council (in Swedish) .

45   Haglund, B, Cnattungius, S and Nordstrom, M L (1993) Social differences in late fetal death and infant mortality in Sweden 1985–86, *Paediatric and Perinatal Epidemiology,* 7: 33–44.

46   Ostberg, V (1992) Social class differences in child mortality, Sweden 1981–86. *Journal of Epidemiology and Community Health*, 46: 480–4.

47   Lardelli, P, Blanco, J I, Delgado, M, Bueno, A, Luna, J de D and Galvez, R. (1993) Influence of socioeconomic and health care development on infant and perinatal mortality in Spain 1975–86, *Journal of Epidemiology and Community Health*, 47: 260–4.

48   Martikainen, P T (1990) Unemployment and mortality among Finnish men, 1981–5, *BMJ,* 301: 407–11.

49   Koskela, K Viinamäki, H Niskanen, L and Kontula, O (1994) Effects of unemployment on mental well-being and health. In: Levin, L, McMahon, L and Ziglio E (eds) *Economic change, social welfare and health in Europe*. WHO Regional Publications European Series, 54. Copenhagen, WHO.

50   Heikkilä, M and Hänninen, S (1994) The social consequences and connections of economic changes: the case of Finland. In: Levin, L, McMahon, L and Ziglio E (eds) *Economic Change, Social Welfare and Health in Europe*. WHO Regional Publications European Series, 54. Copenhagen, WHO.

51   Lahelma, E (1994) The patterning of responses to unemployment: deprivation and adaptation. In: Levin, L, McMahon, L and Ziglio, E (eds) *Economic Change, Social Welfare and Health in Europe*. WHO Regional Publications European Series, 54. Copenhagen, WHO.

52   Olousson, P (1991) Mortality among the elderly in Sweden by social class, *Soc. Sci. Med.*, 32: 437–40.

53   Koskinen, S and Martelin, T (1994) Why are socioeconomic mortality differences smaller among women than among men? *Soc. Sci. Med.*, 38: 1385–96.

54   US Department of Health and Human Services (1989) *Goals for the Nation for the year 2000*. Washington, DC, US Department of Health and Human Services.

55   McCord, C and Freeman, H P (1990) Excess mortality in Harlem, *New England Journal of Medicine*, 322: 173–7.

56. Kochanek, K D, Maurer, J D,and Rosenberg, H M (1994) Why did black life expectancy decline from 1984 through 1989 in the United States? *American Journal of Public Health,* 84: 938–44.

57   Navarro, V (1990) Race or class versus race and class: mortality differentials in the United States. *The Lancet*, 336: 1238–40.

58   Singh, G K, Yu, S M (1995) Infant mortality in the United States: trends, differentials, projections, 1950 through 2010, *American Journal of Public Health*, 85: 957–65.

59   Sorlie, P D, Backlund, E and Keller, J B (1995) US mortality by economic, demographic, and social characteristics: The National Longitudinal Mortality study, *American Journal of Public Health*, 85: 949–55.

60   Otten, M W, Teutsch, S M, Williamson, D F and Marks, J S (1990) The effect of known risk factors on the excess mortality of black adults in the United States. *JAMA,* 263: 845–50.

61   Davey Smith, G, Wentworth, D, Neaton, J D, Stamler, R and Stamler J (1996a) Socioeconomic differentials in mortality risk among men screened for the Multiple Risk Factor Intervention Trial: II. Black Men, *American Journal of Public Health*, 86: 497–504.

62   Davey Smith, G, Neaton, J D, Wentworth, D, Stamler, and R, Stamler J (1996b) Socioeconomic differentials in mortality risk among men screened for the Multiple Risk Factor Intervention Trial: I. White Men, *American Journal of Public Health*, 86: 486–96.

63   Torralba, L, Brugal, M T, Villalbi, J R, Tortosa, M T, Toribio, A and Valverde, J L (1996) Mortality due to acute adverse drug reactions: opiates and cocaine in Barcelona, 1989–93. *Addiction*, 91: 419–26.

64   Borrell, C, Plasencia, A, Pasarin, I and. Ortun, V (1997) Widening social inequalities in mortality: the case of a southern European city, *Journal of Epidemiology and Community Health* , forthcoming.

65   Villalbi, J R (1996) *City initiatives to combat poverty and poor health*. Paper presented to the European Parliament Health Forum Intergroup, 17 April 1996, Strasbourg.

66   McCormick, A (1994) The impact of HIV on the population of England and Wales. *Population Trends*, 76: 40–45.

67   Navarro, V and Benach, J (eds) (1997) *Social health inequalities in Spain: Report of the Scientific Commission to Study Social Health Inequalities in Spain.* Madrid: Ministerio de Sanidad y Consumo (in Spanish) .

68   Mackenbach, J P, van de Mheen, H and Stronks, K (1994) A prospective cohort study investigating the explanation of socio-economic inequalities in health in the Netherlands. *Soc. Sci. Med.*, 38: 299–308.

69   Krieger, N and Fee, E (1996) Measuring social inequalities in health in the United States: An historical review, 1900-1950, *International Journal of Health Services,* forthcoming.

70   Krieger, N and Moss, N (1995) Measuring social inequalities in health: report on the Conference of the National Institutes of Health, *Public Health Reports,* 110: 302–305.

71   Valkonen, T (1993b) Problems in the measurement and international comparisons of socio-economic differences in mortality. *Soc. Sci. Med.*, 36: 409–418.

72   Kunst, A and, Mackenbach, J P (1995) *Measuring socio-economic inequalities in health.* Copenhagen, WHO.

73   Wagstaff, A, Paci, P and van Doorslaer, E (1991) On the measurement of inequalities in health. *Soc. Sci. Med.*, 33: 545–57.

74.   Judge, K, Mulligan, J-M and Benzeval, M (1997) Income inequality and population health. *Soc. Sci. Med* (in press).

75.   Blaxter, M (1989) A comparison of measures of inequality in morbidity. In: Fox. J (ed.) *Health Inequalities in European Countries.* Aldershot, Gower.

76.   Blaxter, M (1990) *Health and Lifestyles.* London, Tavistock/Routledge.

77   Centre for Disease Control (1996) *Health in the United States 1995.* Atlanta, CDC/NCHS.

78   Vagero, D and Lundberg, O (1989) Health inequalities in Britain and Sweden, *The Lancet*, ii: 35–6.

79   Leon, D A, Vagerö D and Otterblad Olausson, P (1992) Social class differences in infant mortality in Sweden: a comparison with England and Wales, *BMJ*, 305: 687–91.

80   Leclerc, A, Lert, F and Fabien, C (1990) Differential mortality: some comparisons between England and Wales, Finland and France, based on inequality measures, *International Journal of Epidemiology*, 19: 1001–1010.

81   Kunst, A E and Mackenbach, J P (1994) International variation in the size of mortality differences associated with occupational status, *International Journal of Epidemiology*, 23: 742–50.

82   Valkonen, T (1989) Adult mortality and level of education: a comparison of six countries. In Fox, J (ed.), *Health Inequalities in European Countries*. Aldershot, Gower.

83   Kunst, A E, Geurts, J J and Van-den-Berg, J (1995) International variation in socioeconomic inequalities in self reported health, *Journal of Epidemiology and Community Health*, 49: 117–23.

84   van Doorslaer, E, *et al.* (1997) Income-related inequalities in health: some international comparisons. *Journal of Health Economics.* (in press).

85   Arber, S and Lahelma, E (1993) Inequalities in women's and men's ill-health: Britain and Finland compared, *Soc. Sci. Med.,* 37: 1055–68.

86   Lahelma, E and Arber, S (1994) Health inequalities among men and women in contrasting welfare states, *European Journal of Public Health*, 4: 213–26.

87   Lahelma, E, Manderbacka, K, Rahkonen, O and Karisto, A (1994) Comparisons of inequalities in health: evidence from national surveys in Finland, Norway and Sweden, *Soc. Sci. Med.*, 38: 517–24.

Part Two

Mortality

A brief introduction to the life expectancy and mortality analyses

Frances Drever and Margaret Whitehead

Introduction

This volume is one of a series of decennial supplements on health-related topics. *Mortality and Geography*[1] was published in 1989 followed by *Occupational Health*[2] and *The Health of Our Children*[3] in 1995. *The Health of Adult Britain*[4] was published in 1997. In this volume, we have concentrated on the relationships between social factors and health. In Part Two, Chapters 6 to 13, new analyses of life expectancy, and mortality of adults and children are presented. There are many technical aspects to these analyses, which are described in Appendices A and B. In this chapter, we highlight the main features of the analyses and explain why the various methods were selected.

Which social classifications have been used?

There is a long tradition in this country of using occupation-based classifications for analyses of deaths data and census populations together. In this volume, we have chosen to continue this tradition and include a number of analyses using the Registrar General's Social Class (based on occupation). From a practical point of view, occupation is collected routinely in the census, at birth and death registration and in many surveys. Conceptually, occupation is of central importance in the study and understanding of the way our society is structured:

> ' ... *the grouping of occupations into classes can be justified on the grounds that employment and paid work remain major sources of variation in authority, function, conditions and reward that are of momentous significance for most people. Moreover, the fact that it has been possible to demonstrate this in many different kinds of society over considerable time periods is an argument in itself'.*[5]

Changes in the classification of occupations at each census could cause problems in interpreting trends in mortality data. A study of the changes in the age structures of the classes and of the major occupations within classes concluded that trends in mortality by social class from 1971 can be interpreted with confidence (see Appendix B). This appendix also looks at the possible effects of underenumeration in the 1991 census. The sensitivity analysis concluded that very large biases in the numbers by social class would have to be present to affect the relative positioning of the mortality rates.

Mortality analyses by social class are discussed both from the full England and Wales deaths database and from the ONS Longitudinal Study (LS) (see Chapters 8 to 11). These are supplemented in Chapters 12 and 13 with analyses of mortality using alternative classifications based on car access, housing tenure and employment status.

Who is covered in these analyses?

We have tried to cover as wide a section of the population as possible in these analyses. The geographical coverage is England and Wales as this was the area covered by the former Office of Population Censuses and Surveys. The life expectancy chapter presents analyses separately for males and females. Life expectancy at birth, age 15 and age 65 are discussed in Chapter 6. Infant and children's mortality are reported in Chapter 7. We have analyses of the mortality of men by RG's Social Class both from the full national deaths database (see Chapters 8, 9 and 10) and from the LS (see Chapters 11 and 12). Mortality of first-generation migrant men is discussed in Chapter 9.

How are analyses for women and children carried out?

One of the major strengths of the LS is its ability to analyse the mortality of women. There are well-known problems when using census and deaths data together for women. In the national deaths data, over half the deaths to women could not be classified to a social class using their own occupation. At Census about 80 per cent could be classified (see Table 9.2).

The problem just described has led us to concentrate our analyses of women's mortality to the LS in which women can be classified at a census point and their subsequent deaths are linked to their records. This is a major reason why the analyses in Chapters 8, 9 and 10 do not include women, while those in 11, 12 and 13 using LS data do.

Infant mortality and the mortality of children up to the age of 16 are discussed in Chapter 7. Again both the LS and the full deaths database have been used. Since 1993 deaths records have been linked to births records. This information will become an increasingly useful source of information on the differences in mortality of children.

Mortality data sources – advantages and disadvantages

Each data source used in the mortality analyses has its advantages and disadvantages. The national deaths database has the advantage of providing a large number of deaths, over 175,000 for the years 1991–93 in England and Wales for men aged 20–64, and so relatively rare causes of death can be examined. The vast majority of these deaths, 92 per cent, could be coded to one of the six classes of the RG's Social Class scheme. This has enabled *Health of the Nation* priority areas to be looked at in detail (Chapter 8), first-generation migrant mortality by social class and major cause of death to be reported on (Chapter 9) and about 50 other causes to be examined in Chapter 10. Even more data are available on the electronic media accompanying this volume.

There are two main disadvantages associated with use of the national deaths database. One has already been discussed, when looking at how the analyses of differences in the mortality experience of women is examined. The other is that the two sources of occupational information used in these calculations come from different sources. It is obvious that the information given at death registration is not given by the deceased, but by whoever is registering the death. Full information on the occupation of the deceased may not be known to the informant. Even if full information is known, it may differ from the information given by the deceased while still alive at the preceding census. This is known as numerator/denominator bias. However, on an international scale, the bias in England and Wales has been assessed as relatively small in comparison with some other countries.[6]

Presentation of results

We have tried to make the results of the analyses reported on in this volume accessible to as wide an audience as possible. Tables printed with the text are presented simply. More detailed tables, for example including confidence intervals or to a high level of accuracy, are available on the electronic media. Where there could have been problems of interpretation because of low numbers of deaths, we have combined groups to ensure the analyses are statistically robust. This happens with causes of deaths or with particular social classes. Technical details of analyses are available in appendices at the end of the volume.

Conclusion

It is important that we continue to monitor the differences in mortality across the different sectors in society. Death rates have fallen throughout the century, but not all parts of society have experienced the same level of decrease in their mortality. Differences do exist. Using any of the measures of socio-economic status discussed here, it is clear that people in different sections of our society have different expectations of life and death rates.

We are very glad to be able to bring together both cross-sectional analyses using census populations and analyses from the ONS Longitudinal Study using the RG's Social Class and a number of proxies of social circumstances including housing tenure and car access. Taken together the analyses in this part of the volume tell of continuing differences in mortality experienced by different sections of society. Whichever way we look at the data, the overwhelming conclusion is that those in professional and non-manual occupations have lower all-cause mortality than those in skilled manual and unskilled occupations.

References

1 Britton, M (ed.) (1990) *Mortality and Geography: A review in the mid-1980s, England and Wales.* DS 9 London, HMSO.

2 Drever, F (ed.) (1995) *Occupational Health - Decennial Supplement.* DS10. London, HMSO

3 Botting, B (ed.) (1995) *The Health of Our Children.* DS 11. London, HMSO.

4 Charlton, J and Murphy, M (eds.) (1997) *The Health of Adult Britain 1841–1994.* DS12 and DS13. London, The Stationery Office.

5 Lee, D and Turner, B (1996) *Conflicts about class: debating inequality in late industrialism.* London, Longman.

6 Kunst, A (1995) *Evaluation of the potential sources of bias in 'unlinked' cross-sectional studies.* Working Document 8 from the Concerted Action 'Socio-economic inequalities in morbidity and mortality in Europe: an international comparison'. Rotterdam, Erasmus University.

6 Expectation of life by social class

Lin Hattersley

Summary

The social class variation in life expectancy of men and women using data from the ONS Longitudinal Study is described in this chapter. A woman's own social class is used wherever possible, making the analysis for women comparable with that for men.

There were clear inequalities in life expectancy by social class, 1987-91. For men there was 5 years difference in the expectation of life at birth between those in Social Classes I and II (75 years) and Social Classes IV and V (70 years); for women the differential was 3 years (80 compared with 77 years).

Male life expectancy at birth, at age 15, and at age 65, increased between 1977-81 and 1987-91, by 2.3, 1.8 and 0.8 years respectively; women also experienced increases but these were slightly smaller, 1.6, 1.2 and 0.5 years respectively.

Although all social classes have increased their life expectancy at birth, age 15, and age 65 since 1977-81 some classes have gained more than others. The smallest increases have occurred in Social Classes IV and V, with the result that the gaps in life expectancy between Classes I and II and Classes IV and V are larger in 1987-91 than in 1977-81.

This chapter presents life expectancy by social class for men and women using the ONS Longitudinal Study (LS). Details of the LS and the methodology used in this analysis are in Appendix A. A collapsed version of the Registrar General's Social Class (based on occupation) has been used combining Social Classes I and II and Social Classes IV and V. Social Classes IIIN and IIIM remain separate. The Registrar General's schema is also described in Appendix A.

Life expectancy is interpreted as follows: at age 15, for example, a life expectancy of 56 means that the average 15 year old can expect to live for about a further 56 years, that is to age 71. This chapter looks at life expectancy at three ages – at birth, at age 15 and at age 65. In order to look at trends, life expectancy has been calculated for the following time periods: 1972–76, 1977–81, 1982–86 and 1987–1991.

The Registrar General's Social Class was first used to examine differences in life expectancy by social class in the Decennial Supplement, *Occupational Mortality 1970–72*.[1] Although overall mortality rates have been falling and life expectancy rising throughout this century in England and Wales[1,2] it has remained unclear whether mortality rates, and the related life expectancies, show the same patterns of decline and rise when examined by social class.[1,3,4,5,6]

Life expectancy by social class shown in the 1970–72 Decennial Supplement was based on population data from the 1971 Census for England and Wales and mortality data for the years 1970–72.[1] As a result, these analyses were subject to numerator/ denominator bias. This has been described in detail elsewhere.[7,8] This earlier study showed that life expectancy at age 15 for men of working ages (15 to 64 years) differed by about four years between Social Classes I and V.

In 1988 Haberman and Bloomfield published a paper on social class differences in Great Britain around 1981 using both the 1981 Census data and LS data in an attempt to avoid some of the problems already mentioned.[9] Life expectancy was calculated for men aged 20 and over. In that analysis the social classes were collapsed into 3 groups, Social Classes I and II, Classes IIIM and IIIN, and Classes IV and V. Thus the class groups were not strictly comparable with previous results. The difference in life expectancy between the first group, Classes I and II, and the last group, Classes IV and V, was just over five years. Subsequent work extended this analysis to include infant and childhood mortality.[10] This enabled an estimate of life expectancy at birth by social class to be made. Between the highest group, Classes I and II, and the lowest group, Classes IV and V, there was a difference of just under five years in life expectancy at birth.

No previous work on differences in mortality by social class has examined life expectancy of women. Defining women's social class is problematic.[1,7,8,11,12] In this analysis, a woman's own social class has been used wherever possible, rather than a proxy. This makes the analysis for women comparable with that for men.

Life expectancy of men

Table 6.1 shows that over the period 1972–91, overall life expectancy at birth for men in England and Wales rose by three years. For 15 year-olds, life expectancy rose by two years and for 65 year-old men it rose by over a year. Table 6.1 and Figure 6.1 show life expectancies of men vary consistently with social class in every time period. The only exception is for life expectancies at birth in 1972–76. It is also clear from Table 6.1 that, although each social class has increased its life expectancy over the whole 20–year period, some social classes have gained more than others. For Social Class I/II, life expectancy at birth rose from just under 72 years in 1972–76 to about 75 years by 1991. By comparison, life expectancy at birth in Social Class IV/V rose from 68 years in 1972–76 to 70 years by the end of the 20–year period.

Rates of increase in life expectancy are not the same across the social classes. Some classes have gained extra years of life faster than others. There are also differential increases in life expectancy at different ages. Overall gains in life expectancy at each of the three ages, birth, 15 and 65, between 1972 and 1991 are shown in Table 6.2. For the full 20–year period, Social Classes I/II and IIIN show the largest absolute increases, of three and four years respectively. This should be compared with a rise for Social Class IV/V of under two years. By age 15, the difference is even more pronounced. Men in Social Class IIIN still had the greatest increase at just over three years. For Social Class I/II, the rise was two and a half years. For Social Class IV/V, however, the rise was less than one year.

When the first five years of follow-up are excluded, because of possible health selection effects, these differences still remain at birth and at age 15. At age 65 the differential gains between Social Class IV/V and the other social classes become smaller. The increase in life expectancy remains smallest for Social Class IV/V, at about five months.

Table 6.3 shows the percentage change in life expectancy for each social class between 1977–81 and the later periods. Life expectancy at birth in Social Classes I/II rose by about 2 per cent by 1986. By 1991 it had risen by just under three per cent from its value in 1977–81. Social Class IIIN showed continued gain in life expectancy over the

FIGURE 6.1

Life expectancy, by social class, men, selected ages

England and Wales, selected years

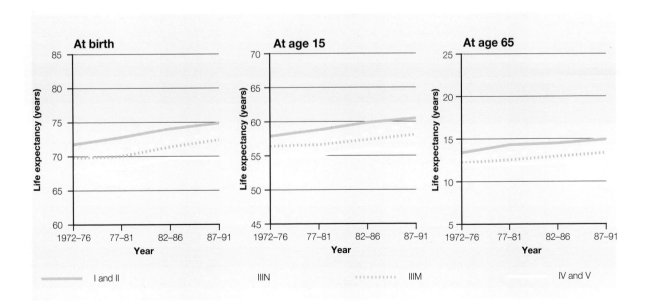

TABLE 6.1

Life expectancy by social class, men, selected ages

England and Wales, selected years

Social class	1972–76	1977–81	1982–86	1987–91
Life expectancy at birth (years)				
I and II	71.7	72.8	74.1	74.9
IIIN	69.5	70.8	72.2	73.5
IIIM	69.8	70.0	71.4	72.4
IV and V	67.8	68.3	69.8	69.7
Total	69.2	70.0	71.4	72.3
Life expectancy at age 15 (years)				
I and II	57.9	58.8	59.9	60.5
IIIN	56.5	56.9	58.2	59.8
IIIM	56.4	56.6	57.3	58.1
IV and V	54.9	55.1	55.9	55.8
Total	56.0	56.4	57.4	58.2
Life expectancy at age 65 (years)				
I and II	13.4	14.3	14.5	15.0
IIIN	12.6	13.3	13.6	14.1
IIIM	12.2	12.6	13.0	13.4
IV and V	12.0	12.0	12.3	12.4
Total	12.3	12.7	13.1	13.5

TABLE 6.2

Change in life expectancy by social class, men, selected ages

England and Wales, selected years

Social class	1972–1991			1977–1991		
	At birth	At age 15	At age 65	At birth	At age 15	At age 65
I and II	3.1 *	2.6 *	1.5 *	2.1 *	1.7 *	0.6 *
IIIN	4.0 *	3.3 *	1.5 *	2.8 *	2.9 *	0.7 *
IIIM	2.6 *	1.7 *	1.2 *	2.4 *	1.5 *	0.8 *
IV and V	1.9 *	0.9 *	0.4 *	1.4 *	0.8 *	0.4 *
Total	3.0	2.2	1.2	2.3	1.7	0.9

Note: differences between tables due to rounding

* statistically significant at 1% level

TABLE 6.3

Percentage change in life expectancy by social class, males

England and Wales

Social class	Between 1977–81 and	
	1982–86	1987–91
at birth	% change	% change
I and II	1.8	2.9
IIIN	2.0	3.9
IIIM	2.0	3.4
IV and V	2.1	2.0
at age 15	% change	% change
I and II	1.8	2.9
IIIN	2.3	5.2
IIIM	1.3	2.7
IV and V	1.6	1.4
at age 65	% change	% change
I and II	1.3	4.4
IIIN	2.1	5.5
IIIM	3.3	6.6
IV and V	2.2	3.0

TABLE 6.4

Differences in life
expectancy by social
class, men, selected ages
England and Wales, selected
years

*(using Social Class I/II as the
standard)*

	1977–81	1982–86	1987–91
Life expectancy at birth			
Social class:			
Life expectancy I/II	72.8	74.1	74.9
Difference between I/II and:			
IIIN	-2.0*	-1.9*	-1.3
IIIM	-2.8*	-2.7*	-2.5
IV and V	-4.5*	-4.3*	-5.2
Life expectancy at age 15			
Social class:			
Life expectancy I/II	58.8	59.9	60.5
Difference between I/II and:			
IIIN	-1.9*	-1.7*	-0.7
IIIM	-2.2*	-2.5*	-2.4
IV and V	-3.7*	-4.0*	-4.7
Life expectancy at age 65			
Social class:			
Life expectancy I/II	14.3	14.5	15.0
Difference between I/II and:			
IIIN	-1.0*	-0.9*	-0.9
IIIM	-1.8*	-1.5*	-1.6
IV and V	-2.3*	-2.2*	-2.6

Note: differences between tables due to rounding
* statistically significant at 1% level

two periods. In contrast, life expectancy increased by about 2 per cent for Social Class IV/V by the end of 1986 but then no further gains were made.

At age 15, Social Classes IIIN and IIIM showed fairly constant gains in life expectancy. For Class I/II the percentage increase was larger in 1982–86 than in 1987–91. For Class IV/V, however, no further gains were made in 1987–91. At age 65, larger gains were made for Social Classes I/II and IIIN in 1987–91 than in 1982–86. For Social Class IV/V however, the rate of increase was considerably less for 1987–91 than for 1982–86.

Table 6.4 shows the differences in life expectancy across the social classes using the most advantaged Class I/II as the standard. For example, in 1977-81, Class IIIN had a life expectancy at birth two years fewer than Class I/II. By 1987–91 this difference narrowed to about one year. In contrast, the difference widened between Class I/II and Class IV/V from 4.5 years to 5.2 years.

At age 15, a similar trend can be seen; that is a narrowing of the differences between Class I/II and Class IIIN over time but a widening with respect to Class IV/V. At age 65, however, differences remained fairly constant between Class I/II and the other classes.

Life expectancy of women

Table 6.5 shows life expectancy in the different classes for women at birth, at age 15 and at age 65. Over the period 1972–91, overall life expectancy for women rose by about three years at birth, by two years at age 15 and by one year at age 65. At birth the relationship between life expectancy and social class is evident for most of the time

TABLE 6.5

Life expectancy by social
class, women, selected
ages
England and Wales, selected
years

Social class	1972–76	1977–81	1982–86	1987–91
Life expectancy at birth (years)				
I and II	77.1	78.2	78.7	80.2
IIIN	78.0	78.1	78.6	79.4
IIIM	75.1	76.1	77.1	77.6
IV and V	74.7	75.7	76.8	76.8
Total	75.1	76.3	77.1	77.9
Life expectancy at age 15 (years)				
I and II	63.0	64.1	64.3	65.8
IIIN	63.8	64.1	64.3	65.3
IIIM	61.6	62.2	62.9	63.2
IV and V	61.9	62.0	62.7	62.5
Total	61.6	62.4	62.9	63.6
Life expectancy at age 65 (years)				
I and II	17.3	17.9	18.0	18.7
IIIN	17.8	17.6	18.0	18.3
IIIM	16.3	16.9	16.8	16.8
IV and V	16.7	16.6	17.0	16.7
Total	16.2	16.7	16.9	17.2

periods. At ages 15 and 65 the relationship between social class and life expectancy for women is not always consistent in earlier periods, but by 1987–91 systematic variations are evident.

Women in each social class showed increases in life expectancy at birth and at age 15 over the 20–year period of this analysis. As can be seen from Figure 6.2, life expectancy at birth for women in Class I/II rose by about three years from 77 years in 1972-76 to 80 years in 1987-91. By comparison, women in Class IV/V had a life expectancy at birth of about 75 years in 1972-76 rising to 77 years by the end of the 20–year period. Over this whole time period, changes in life expectancy for women were not as marked as those for men.

FIGURE 6.2

Life expectancy by social
class, women, selected
ages
England and Wales, selected
years

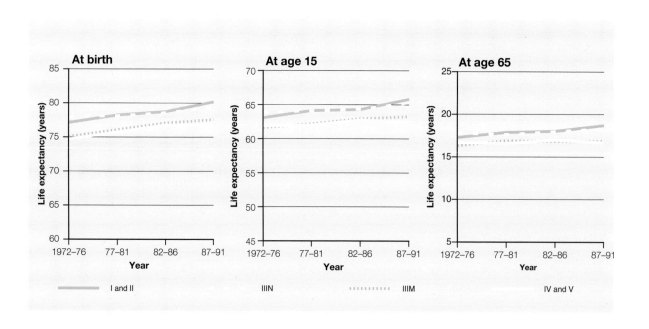

Overall changes in life expectancy at birth, at age 15 and at age 65 are shown in Table 6.6. Like men, women in some classes gained more than others. The amount of gain varies considerably when considering both the size of gain and when it occurred. Over the 20–year period life expectancy at birth increased by three years for Class I/II, whereas, for Class IV/V the increase was only two years. At age 15 the increase in Class I/II was nearly three years and in Class IV/V the increase was 0.6 years, or about eight months. At age 65 the differential is even more marked. For women in Class I/II, the increase was one and a half years whereas there was no change in life expectancy for women in Class IV/V.

Overall changes in life expectancy with the first five years excluded to eliminate possible health selection effects are also shown in Table 6.6. Although the magnitude of these differences reduce, the pattern of larger gains in Class I/II compared with IV/V remains the same for the period 1977–91.

As was shown previously for men, there are differences in the rates of increase in life expectancy for women across the social classes. Percentage gains in life expectancy are shown in Table 6.7. Earlier it was noted that at ages 15 and 65, class differences for women became consistent by the last period, 1987–91. The trends in differential gains between the classes over the full 20-year period help to explain the emerging class gradient in 1987–91.

TABLE 6.6
Change in life expectancy by social class, women at selected ages
England and Wales, in years

Social class	1972–1991			1977–1991		
	At birth	At age 15	At age 65	At birth	At age 15	At age 65
I and II	3.0*	2.8*	1.4*	1.9*	1.7*	0.8*
IIIN	1.3*	1.5*	0.6*	1.3	1.2	0.7*
IIIM	2.5*	1.6*	0.5*	1.5*	1.1*	0.0
IV and V	2.1*	0.6*	0.0	1.0	0.5*	0.1
Total	2.8	2.0	1.0	1.6	1.2	0.5

* statistically significant at 1% level

TABLE 6.7
Percentage change in life expectancy, by social class, females
England and Wales

Social class	Between 1977–81 and	
	1982–86	1987–91
at birth	% change	% change
I and II	0.6	2.5
IIIN	0.6	1.6
IIIM	1.3	1.9
IV and V	1.3	1.4
at age 15	% change	% change
I and II	0.3	2.7
IIIN	0.3	1.9
IIIM	1.2	1.7
IV and V	1.2	0.8
at age 65	% change	% change
I and II	0.8	4.7
IIIN	2.0	4.0
IIIM	-0.4	-0.3
IV and V	2.5	0.6

TABLE 6.8

Differences in life
expectancy by social
class, women, selected
ages
England and Wales, selected
years
(using Social Class I/II as the
standard)

	1977–81	1982–86	1987–91
Life expectancy at birth			
Social class:			
Life expectancy I/II	78.2	78.7	80.2
Difference between I/II			
IIIN	-0.1	-0.1	-0.8
IIIM	-2.2*	-1.7*	-2.6*
IV and V	-2.5*	-2.0*	-3.4*
Life expectancy at age 15			
Social class:			
Life expectancy I/II	64.1	64.3	65.8
Difference between I/II			
IIIN	0.0	0.0	-0.5*
IIIM	-1.9*	-1.4*	-2.6*
IV and V	-2.1*	-1.5*	-3.4*
Life expectancy at age 65			
Social class:			
Life expectancy I/II	17.9	18.0	18.7
Difference between I/II			
IIIN	-0.2	0.0	-0.4*
IIIM	-1.0*	-1.2*	-1.9*
IV and V	-1.3*	-1.0*	-2.0*

Note: differences between tables due to rounding
* statistically significant at 1% level

At birth, the gains in life expectancy were larger after 1986 for Classes I/II and IIIN. In contrast, for Classes IIIM and IV/V the gains were larger in 1982–86 than in 1987–91. At age 15, a similar trend is seen accounting for the clearer class differences in 1987–91. At age 65, Classes I/II and IIIN show large gains in life expectancy in 1987–91 while Class IIIM and IV/V show virtually no change.

The pattern of changes in life expectancy of women, using Class I/II as the standard, is shown in Table 6.8. At each age the differences between Class I/II and the other classes have shown a widening in 1987–91. Apart from Class IIIN, the difference in life expectancy at birth between Class I/II and other classes increased. This increase was particularly noticeable for Class IV/V where the difference in life expectancy at birth rose by a year between 1977 and 1991. The pattern of differences in life expectancy at age 15 and at age 65 for women are similar. The difference in life expectancy at age 15 between Class I/II and Class IIIM and Class IV/V increased by about one year. At age 65, the difference between Class I/II and IIIM was one year in 1977–81 and by 1991 this had risen to a difference of nearly two years. When comparing Class IV/V with Class I/II, the difference in life expectancy increased from one to two years.

Comparisons between life expectancy of men and women

At each age, men and women show different patterns in life expectancy by social class. Although men have been showing increases in life expectancy at a relatively higher

TABLE 6.9
Differences in life expectancy by social class, for
men and women selected
ages
England and Wales, selected
years

Social class:	1972–76	1977–81	1982–86	1987–91
At birth (years)				
I and II	5.4	5.5	4.7	5.3
IIIN	8.5	7.3	6.4	5.8
IIIM	5.3	6.1	5.7	5.2
IV and V	6.9	7.4	7.0	7.1
Total	5.9	6.3	5.7	5.6
At age 15 (years)				
I and II	5.2	5.3	4.4	5.3
IIIN	7.3	7.2	6.1	5.5
IIIM	5.2	5.6	5.6	5.1
IV and V	7.0	6.9	6.8	6.6
Total	5.6	6.0	5.5	5.4
At age 65 (years)				
I and II	3.8	3.5	3.5	3.7
IIIN	5.1	4.3	4.4	4.3
IIIM	4.1	4.3	3.8	3.4
IV and V	4.6	4.5	4.7	4.3
Total	3.9	4.0	3.8	3.7

growth rate than women, they still have lower life expectancies in each social class. Table 6.9 shows that, overall, the differences in life expectancy of men and women at birth have remained fairly constant over time. For some social classes the difference in life expectancies of men and women of the same social class is narrowing. For example, the difference in life expectancy at birth for men and women in Class IIIN has fallen by about three years from a difference of eight and a half years in 1972–76 to under six years in 1987–91. Interpreting the differences in life expectancies between men and women is complicated by differences in their class distributions at different ages. At working ages, the largest class for men is IIIM whereas for women it is Class IIIN.

Conclusion

This analysis of life expectancy by social class has tried to answer two questions. First, are there inequalities in life expectancy across the classes, and second, if there are, are these inequalities widening.

For men and women, there were clear inequalities in life expectancy by social class in 1987–91. For men, life expectancy at birth for Class I/II was 75 years and for IV/V was 70 years. At age 15, the corresponding figures were 61 years for Class I/II and about 56 years for IV/V; at age 65 it was 15 and 12 years respectively. In 1987–91, life expectancy at birth for women was 80 years in Class I/II and 77 years in Class IV/V; at age 15 it was 66 years in Class I/II and 63 years in Class IV/V; at age 65 it was 19 and 17 years respectively.

Although life expectancy has been rising for most social classes since 1972, the rate of this rise varied by sex and class.

Over the 1977–91 period, life expectancy at birth for men in Classes I/II and IIIN rose more than for other classes. Men in Class IV/V made the least gain. The difference between I/II and IV/V rose from four and a half years in 1977–81 to just over five years in 1987–91. At age 15, the difference between these classes rose from about four years to five years. If they survived to age 65, the difference between Class I/II and IV/V increased by only about four months.

Life expectancy for women showed patterns different from those of men over time. At birth, there was a consistent class gradient which widened across the time periods. The difference in life expectancy between I/II and IV/V increased by about one year between the 1970s and late 1980s. By age 15, and age 65 clear class gradients only became evident in the late 1980s. Non-manual classes made progressive increases in life expectancy over the entire period whereas for manual classes very little gains were made in 1987–91. At age 15, the difference between Class I/II and IV/V rose from two years in 1977–81 to three and a half years in 1987–91. At age 65 the corresponding rise was from just over one year to two years.

References

1   Office of Population Censuses and Surveys (1978) *Occupational mortality: decennial supplement 1970–72*. Series DS, 1. London, HMSO.

2   Office of Population Censuses and Surveys (1987) *English Life Tables no.14. 1980–82*. Series DS, 7. London, HMSO.

3   Fox, J, Goldblatt, P and Jones, D (1990) Social class mortality differentials: artefact, selection or life circumstances? In: Goldblatt, P (ed) *Mortality and Social Organisation: Longitudinal Study 1971–81*. Series LS, 6. London, HMSO.

4   Moser, K, Pugh, H and Goldblatt, P (1990) Mortality and social classification of women. In: Goldblatt, P (ed.) *Mortality and Social Organisation: Longitudinal Study 1971–81*. Series LS, 6. London, HMSO.

5   Harding, S (1995) Social class differences in mortality of men: recent evidence from the OPCS Longitudinal Study. *Population Trends*, 80: 31–37.

6   Bethune, A, Harding, S, Scott, A and Filakti, H (1995) Mortality of Longitudinal Study 1971 and 1981 Census cohorts. In: Drever, F (ed.) *Occupational Health – Decennial Supplement*. Series DS, 10. London, HMSO.

7   Fox, J and Goldblatt, P (1982) *Socio-demographic mortality differentials: Longitudinal Study 1971–75*. Series LS,1. London, HMSO.

8   Goldblatt, P (1990) Mortality and alternative social classifications. In: Goldblatt, P (ed.) *Mortality and Social Organisation: Longitudinal Study 1971–81*. Series LS, 6. London, HMSO.

9   Haberman, S and Bloomfield, DSF (1988) Social class differences in mortality in Great Britain around 1981. *The Journal of the Institute of Actuaries*, 115, Part III (461): 495–517.

10   Bloomfield, DSF and Haberman, S (1992) Male social class mortality differences around 1981: an extension to include childhood ages. *The Journal of the Institute of Actuaries*, 119, Part III (474): 545–559.

11   Moser, K, Goldblatt, P and Pugh, H (1990) Occupational mortality of women in employment. In: Goldblatt, P (ed.) *Mortality and Social Organisation: Longitudinal Study 1971–81*. Series LS, 6. London, HMSO.

12   Filakti, H and Fox, J (1995) Differences in mortality by housing tenure and by car access from the OPCS Longitudinal Study. *Population Trends*, 81: 27–30.

7 Mortality in childhood

Beverley Botting

Summary

This chapter describes the social class differentials in infant and childhood mortality at ages 0-15, classifying children by their parents' (usually fathers') social class. Data are drawn from the national mortality statistics, and the ONS Longitudinal Study.

During the 1980s and early 1990s infant and childhood mortality rates have fallen for all social classes, but the social class differentials have persisted. Infant mortality differentials have narrowed, but childhood mortality differentials have widened slightly.

In 1993-95 the infant mortality rate for Social Class V births was 70 per cent higher than that of Social Class I births.

Infant mortality rates 1990-95 from congenital anomalies, immaturity, infections and sudden infant death syndrome are higher in Social Classes IV and V than in Social Classes I and II.

Children whose mothers were born in the New Commonwealth or Pakistan had higher infant mortality rates 1990-95 than those with mothers born in the UK; this difference was apparent within most social classes.

Throughout childhood, mortality rates for children in Social Class V were noticeably higher than those for other classes both in the early 1980s and early 1990s. Within each social class boys were at a higher risk than girls.

Childhood death rates from injury and poisoning fell between the early 1980s and early 1990s for all social classes. However the differential between the classes increased due to the smaller declines occuring in Social Classes IV and V as compared to Social Classes I and II.

Significant differentials exist in the health and survival of children in different sections of the population. In particular, these differences can be seen when children are grouped according to their parents' social class, usually the father's. The focus of this chapter is on social class differentials in infant and childhood mortality up to the age of 15. Current patterns and trends are covered between the 1981 Census and 1995. This period has almost complete birthweight information and no changes in cause of death classification. Chapter 14 discusses differences in children's health and behaviour.

Infant mortality

Traditionally, infant mortality has been seen as a major indicator of the health of a nation. Additionally, as children are among the most vulnerable in society, their survival has been used as a measure of the social development of a country, indicating the degree to which it protects its weakest members. In developed countries, infant mortality levels are at an all time low. Despite this, differentials still exist across different groups within countries. In England and Wales, these differentials are clearly illustrated by the gradient in infant death rates across the social classes.

Infant mortality covers all deaths under the age of one year. It is further sub-divided into the different perinatal, neonatal, and postneonatal mortality, as defined in Box 7.1. For the analyses in this chapter, social class is derived from the information on parents' occupations collected at the registration of births and deaths as described in Appendix A. Since 1975, all infant death computer records have been linked to their birth record. Anyone born in 1993 or subsequent years will have their death information linked to their birth record. Most deaths in childhood occur in the first year of life.

Analysis by social class, based on the father's occupation, for infant deaths and stillbirths are published every year in the ONS series DH3.[1] Until recently these have been presented just for births within marriage. If the parents are not married, but the father attends the registration, his details are recorded on the birth certificate and a social class can be derived. In 1993 in England and Wales 93 per cent of births took place either inside marriage or outside marriage jointly registered by both parents. Data on births both inside marriage and jointly registered have been published

BOX 7.1 Definitions

Stillbirth rate: the number of stillbirths per 1,000 total births (stillbirth and live births).

Perinatal mortality rate: the number of stillbirths plus the number of deaths to babies aged under 7 days per 1,000 total births.

Neonatal mortality rate: number of deaths to babies aged under 28 days per 1,000 live births

Postneonatal mortality rate: number of deaths to babies aged 28 days and over but under 1 year per 1,000 live births

Infant mortality rate: number of death of children under 1 year per 1,000 live births.

Father's social class	Numbers		Percentages	
	Inside marriage	Outside marriage/ joint registration	Inside marriage	Outside marriage/ joint registration
I	12,366	1,381	90%	10%
II	37,078	7,548	83%	17%
IIIN	14,964	3,704	80%	20%
IIIM	39,905	19,878	67%	33%
IV	16,987	9,548	64%	36%
V	5,608	5,046	53%	47%
England & Wales [a]	133,621	50,042	73%	27%

Notes:
Figures for live births are a 10 per cent sample coded for father's occupation
This table excludes sole registrations.
[a] Includes categories: Other; Not stated

routinely, in the DH3 series, since 1993. Table 7.1 shows the proportions of births by social class within marriage or jointly registered outside marriage. These data are based on a 10 per cent sample of births. Where the father is Social Class I, 90 per cent of the births are within marriage. This pattern is different for Class V fathers where roughly half the births are inside marriage and half jointly registered outside marriage. It is therefore important to include analyses of births both inside and outside marriage whenever possible, to gain a more accurate assessment of the social class pattern of mortality.

Current patterns in social class differentials

Based on data for 1993–95 combined, Table 7.2 shows stillbirth rates and perinatal mortality rates by father's social class for births both inside marriage and those outside marriage where the father was present at the child's birth registration. The stillbirth rate is the number of stillbirths per 1,000 births, whether stillbirths or live births. The perinatal mortality rate is the number of stillbirths plus the number of babies who die aged under 7 days per 1,000 births, whether stillbirths or live births. Sixty three per cent of the perinatal deaths are stillbirths.

Both the stillbirth rate and the perinatal mortality rate show social class gradients for births inside marriage and those outside marriage registered by both parents. In all but one case the mortality of babies born outside marriage in each social class is higher than that of babies born inside marriage.

TABLE 7.2

Stillbirth and perinatal
mortality rates, by father's
social class
England and Wales, 1993-95

Father's social class	Stillbirth rate			Perinatal rate		
	Inside marriage	Outside marriage [a]	Combined [b]	Inside marriage	Outside marriage [a]	Combined [b]
I	4.4	5.5	4.5	6.9	8.0	7.0
II	4.5	4.8	4.5	7.1	8.0	7.3
IIIN	5.3	5.8	5.4	8.2	9.5	8.4
IIIM	5.0	6.1	5.4	7.9	9.7	8.5
IV	6.2	6.3	6.2	9.7	10.1	9.9
V	8.3	7.2	7.8	11.4	11.5	11.5
England & Wales	5.2	6.2	5.5	8.2	10.0	8.7

Notes:
Rates are estimates per 1,000 live and stillbirths
This table excludes sole registrations.
[a] Joint registrations only
[b] Inside marriage and outside marriage/joint registrations

Table 7.3 and Figure 7.1 show infant mortality rates and their constituent parts, neonatal and postneonatal mortality rates by social class. The infant mortality rate is the numbers of deaths of children under 1 year per 1,000 live births. The neonatal rate compares deaths of babies aged under 28 days with the number of live births and the postneonatal rate looks at deaths to children aged 28 days and over but under 1 year. Neonatal deaths tend to be a result of factors related to the birth, such as prematurity, whereas postneonatal deaths are more likely to be affected by external influences.

In 1993–95, for both births inside marriage and those outside marriage registered by both parents, the ratio of the infant mortality rate for Social Class V to that for Social Class I was 1.6. However, there was a widening of the differential with increasing age in infancy. For births inside marriage the ratio was 1.4 for deaths in the first 28 days of life and 1.9 for later infant deaths. For joint registrations outside marriage, the differences were less marked, but still substantial, at 1.6 and 1.7.

TABLE 7.3

Infant mortality rates, by father's social class

England and Wales, 1993–95

Father's social class	Neonatal rate			Postneonatal rate			Infant rate		
	Inside marriage	Outside marriage [a]	Combined [b]	Inside marriage	Outside marriage [a]	Combined [b]	Inside marriage	Outside marriage [a]	Combined [b]
I	3.1	3.5	3.1	1.3	1.8	1.3	4.4	5.4	4.5
II	3.4	4.4	3.5	1.2	1.6	1.3	4.6	5.9	4.8
IIIN	3.7	4.8	3.9	1.4	2.1	1.6	5.1	6.9	5.5
IIIM	3.8	4.7	4.1	1.6	2.3	1.8	5.4	7.0	5.9
IV	4.4	4.9	4.6	1.8	2.3	2.0	6.2	7.2	6.6
V	4.3	5.5	4.9	2.5	3.0	2.8	6.9	8.5	7.7
England & Wales	3.8	4.9	4.1	1.6	2.4	1.8	5.3	7.4	5.9

Notes:
Rates are estimates per 1,000 live births
This table excludes sole registrations.
[a] Joint registrations only
[b] Inside marriage and outside marriage/joint registrations

FIGURE 7.1

Infant mortality rates, by social class of father

England and Wales, 1993–95

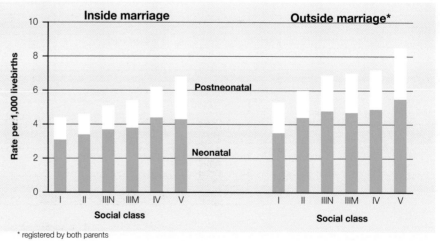

* registered by both parents

Low birthweight risk

Low birthweight is the strongest risk factor for infant mortality. In England and Wales in 1994 only 1 per cent of babies weighed less than 1.5 kg at birth, but these babies had a risk of dying in infancy 90 times higher than babies weighing 3 to 3.5 kg. The mean birthweight for babies in England and Wales in 1994 was 3.3 kg.

Birthweights vary by social class. As shown in Table 7.4, in 1994 in England and Wales, the average birthweight in Social Class V was 115 grams lighter than in Social Class I for births inside marriage and 130 grams lighter for births outside marriage registered by both parents. Within the same birthweight group, there are social class differences in infant mortality rates. Figure 7.2 shows the patterns for different birthweights above 1.5 kg based on data for 1990–95. For each of the weights shown there is very little difference between the rates for the non-manual classes (I, II and IIIN) with increasing rates for the manual classes (IIIM, IV and V). Social Class II had the lowest rates. In contrast, there is little difference across the social classes for the smallest babies, weighing under 1.5 kg except that the rate for Social Class V is higher than for the other classes, see Figure 7.3. These small babies are the most likely to die soon after birth and so are the ones less likely to be affected by external influences after birth.

Father's social class	Mean birthweight (grams)		
	Inside marriage	Outside marriage [a]	Sole registration
I	3,420	3,360	..
II	3,400	3,360	..
IIIN	3,380	3,280	..
IIIM	3,350	3,280	..
IV	3,320	3,280	..
V	3,310	3,230	..
England and Wales [b]	3,370	3,280	3,140

Note:
Social class (based on father's occupation) is derived for only a 10 per cent sample of live births.
[a] Joint registrations only
[b] Includes categories: Other; Not stated
.. Not available

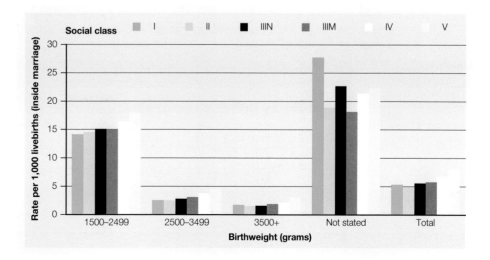

FIGURE 7.3

Infant mortality by
birthweight and social
class of father (inside
marriage)

England and Wales, 1990–1995

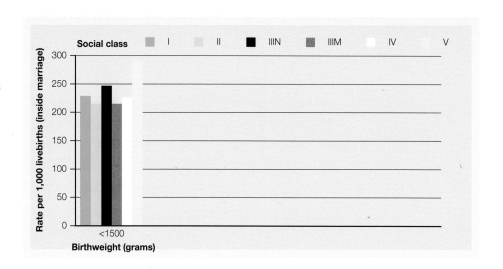

Causes of infant death

Figure 7.4 shows infant mortality rates inside marriage for selected causes of death by
social class derived from father's occupation. These show clear social class gradients
with death rates highest for Social Class V and lowest for Social Classes I and II.
Different causes of death are more important at different ages of infancy. For example,
immaturity is a major cause of death in the neonatal period whereas Sudden Infant
Death Syndrome, cot deaths, is an important cause of postneonatal death. Combining
the deaths for several years in Figure 7.4 conceals a dramatic fall in the number of cot
deaths between 1989 and 1994. For cot deaths, babies in Class V have an infant
mortality rate of 1.3 per 1,000 live births. This is nearly 3 times the infant mortality
rate in Class I which is less than 0.5 deaths per 1,000 live births.

FIGURE 7.4

Infant mortality by social
class of father (inside
marriage), selected
causes of death

England and Wales, 1990–1995

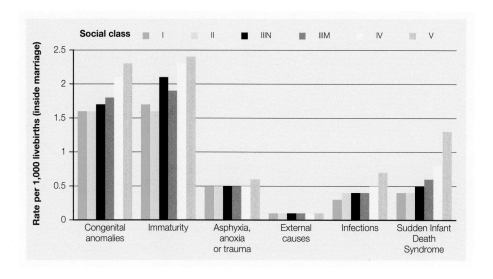

Trends by father's social class

Figure 7.5 shows trends in infant mortality by social class of father for births inside
marriage, from 1980 to 1995. These death rates are shown as three-year moving
averages. Overall, mortality rates have fallen in each of the social classes over this
period. However, in Social Class I, infant mortality went up slightly in the mid-1980s
and has since come down. Rates for Social Classes I and II fluctuated around similar
levels from the mid-1980s onwards. Social Class IIIM showed a steady fall in rate over
the period, whereas Social Classes IV and V plateaued in the mid to late 1980s before
falling more sharply in the early 1990s.

FIGURE 7.5

Infant mortality by social
class (for births inside
marriage only), 3 year
moving average

England and Wales, 1981–1994

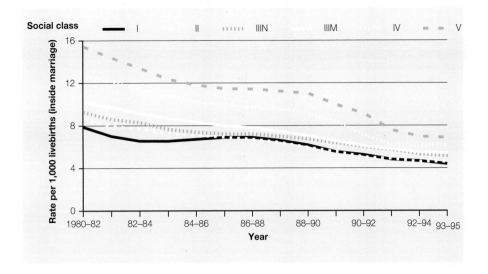

Over the 1980s, the ratio between the infant mortality rates for Social Class V and Social Class I fell from 2.0 to 1.7. The ratio subsequently fell to 1.6 for the most recent data. A large reduction in these differentials was observed between 1991 and 1992. Part of this change may be associated with the dramatic fall in cot deaths, mentioned above, over those two years.

Trends by mother's social class

Since the mother carries the child during pregnancy and is usually the main carer in early life, it has often been suggested that her social class should provide a better evaluation of any risk factor compared with that of the child's father. It has not been possible to analyse such data until recently because mother's occupation has only been collected at birth registration since 1986, and then only on a voluntary basis. There are problems in using and interpreting these data because many women choose not to give an occupation at birth registration.

The proportion of women who gave an occupation which could be classified to one of the social classes rose from 31 per cent in 1986 to 57 per cent in 1995. Over this decade, for each social class, the increase in the proportion of women giving an occupation at birth of their child was similar to that given at the death of the children. Therefore, the effect of any changes in the infant mortality rates due to increases in the proportion of women giving their occupation is likely to be similar across the social classes. It is therefore valid to compare changes in infant mortality rates by social class over time. An earlier analysis presented results for 1986–90.[2]

Analyses by mother's social class show similar, but smaller, differentials in infant mortality compared to the analysis by father's social class. There is no clear pattern for Classes I, and IIIM with increasing rates for the remaining classes. Table 7.5 shows trends in infant mortality rates by mother's social class for England and Wales. Between 1986–90 and 1991–95, the overall infant mortality rate fell by 26 per cent, from 8.8 to 6.5 deaths per 1,000 live births. Between the two periods, the largest fall in infant mortality rates was for Social Class I, from 6.6 deaths per 1,000 live births to 4.7, a fall of 29 per cent. The rate for the other social classes fell by between 17 and 20 per cent. As a result of this differential decline in rates, the gap in infant mortality between Social Classes I and V increased from 1.5 in 1986–90 to 1.7 in 1991–95, when measured by mother's social class.

TABLE 7.5

Infant mortality rates, by
mother's social class
England and Wales

Source: Office for National Statistics

Mother's social class	1986-90	1991-95
I	6.6	4.7
II	5.9	4.9
IIIN	5.7	4.7
IIIM	6.5	5.2
IV	7.1	5.9
V	9.7	7.8
England and Wales	8.8	6.5

Mother's country of birth

In 1994, 82 thousand births in England and Wales were to women born outside the
United Kingdom. Of these, the majority, 59 per cent, were to women born in the New
Commonwealth, which includes Bangladesh, India, Pakistan, East Africa and the
Caribbean. Although there has recently been increasing flows of population from the
EU, they currently comprise less than 10 per cent of births to women born outside the
UK.

Country of birth of the parents is recorded at both birth and death registration. It is
used here as a proxy for ethnic origin. It has to be borne in mind that this method will
not identify second generation immigrants who were born in England and Wales.
People in different ethnic groups have different social and demographic
characteristics, such as housing, smoking patterns and diet. These are likely to affect
their children's mortality patterns.

At the 1991 Census, it was estimated that there were 3 million people of ethnic
minority origin residing in England and Wales, making up almost 6 per cent of the
total population.[3] There is a higher proportion of ethnic minority children in the
England and Wales population than the overall figure of 6 per cent, reflecting that
many of the ethnic minority groups moved to Britain in recent decades as young
adults. In fact, in 1991, 10 per cent of all children aged under 15 were in ethnic
minority groups.

As shown in Figure 7.6 infant mortality rates in England and Wales in 1990–95 varied
with the mother's country of birth and social class based on the father's occupation.
The overall infant mortality rates for children with mothers born in the New
Commonwealth was 50 per cent higher than those born in the UK. In addition, the

FIGURE 7.6

Infant mortality by
mother's country of birth
and social class of father
(inside marriage)
England and Wales, 1990–1995

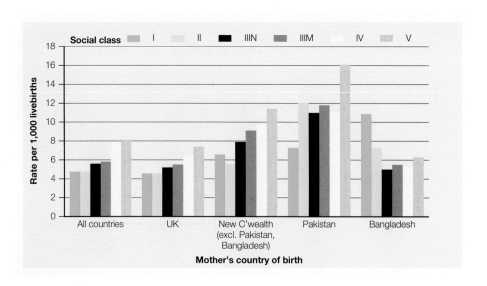

rates for different social classes within each country of birth group varied. The infant mortality rate for mothers born in Pakistan was particularly high, twice the rate as for UK-born mothers. This pattern was seen in all social classes. Live births to women born in Pakistan comprised 54 per cent of the live births to women born in the New Commonwealth, but 82 per cent of the infant deaths.

For infants whose mothers had been born in Bangladesh, there was little difference between social classes, except for a high death rate in Social Class I. However, these rates were based on very few deaths during the period – only 5 infant deaths in Social Class I – and so may be less reliable.

Mortality of children

Mortality rates for children aged 1–15 have dropped substantially over the period 1979 to 1995. In 1979, boys aged 1–15 had a mortality rate of 37 per 100,000 and girls of these ages had a rate of 26 per 100,000. By 1995, the mortality rate of boys had fallen to 21 per 100,000 and that of girls to 17 per 100,000. There are different mortality rates within the age range 1–15. Figure 7.7 shows the age-specific death rates for boys and girls for the period 1991–95. In general, rates decrease dramatically from age 1 to age 4. They then remain fairly stable until about age 11 when they start to rise again. At each age, boys have higher mortality rates than girls.

It is not possible to repeat the types of analysis carried out for infant mortality for all children. This is because population denominators by social class are not available each year. At census, children are categorised by the social class of the head of their household. Thus for the years around a census, population denominators can be used to analyse social class differences in childhood mortality. Each year there are only small numbers of deaths to children, so data for several years are combined to reduce random variation in the numbers. The age groups have been chosen to be consistent with those used in previous analyses of children's mortality by social class.[4] Table 7.6 shows social class differences for the years around the 1981 and 1991 Censuses.

Around the 1981 Census, in each age-group, mortality increased from Social Classes I and II through to Class V. This gradient was most marked at ages 1–4, when children in Social Class V had death rates three times higher than in Social Class I. This reduced to a less than two-fold difference in adolescence. Moreover, boys were consistently at a higher risk than girls.

FIGURE 7.7
Age-specific mortality rates, children
England and Wales, 1991–95

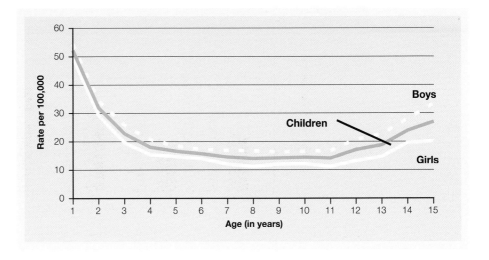

TABLE 7.6

Childhood mortality rates,
rate per 100,000, by age
England and Wales

	Children		Boys		Girls	
	1979-80, 82-83	1991-93	1979-80, 82-83	1991-93	1979-80, 82-83	1991-93
Age 1-4						
I	34	27	34	34	34	21
II	34	23	35	24	32	22
IIIN	41	23	44	24	37	22
IIIM	47	37	53	40	42	33
IV	57	30	63	33	51	28
V	98	71	111	75	84	67
England & Wales	48	34	53	37	44	30
Age 5-9						
I	21	14	25	16	18	12
II	19	12	21	13	16	11
IIIN	22	11	25	13	19	7
IIIM	23	19	26	21	19	16
IV	28	14	32	16	23	13
V	42	30	51	34	31	26
England & Wales	25	16	29	18	20	14
Age 10-14						
I	19	14	21	15	16	13
II	19	13	23	14	16	12
IIIN	18	15	21	17	14	12
IIIM	23	22	26	25	19	18
IV	24	20	30	26	17	15
V	30	29	36	41	24	17
England & Wales	23	18	28	22	19	15
Age 1-15						
I	24	18	26	21	21	15
II	22	16	25	17	19	15
IIIN	25	16	28	19	21	14
IIIM	28	26	32	29	24	22
IV	33	22	38	26	27	19
V	49	42	57	49	40	35
England & Wales	30	23	35	26	25	19

These trends persisted in the period around the 1991 Census. In each age-group, the mortality rates for children in Social Class V were noticeably higher than those for the other classes. Apart from adolescent girls, both boys and girls in Class V had substantially higher mortality rates than those in other social classes. Between 1981 and 1991 mortality rates fell for the majority of the social classes within the different age-groups. The exception was for boys in Social Class V in the 10–14 age-group, which had a slightly higher rate around 1991 than in 1981. Over the ten-year period between the censuses, the gap in mortality between Social Classes V and I widened slightly, from 2.1 to 2.3 for children aged 1–15, 2.2 to 2.3 for boys aged 1–15 and 1.9 to 2.3 for girls aged 1–15.

These analyses give snapshots of two periods almost a decade apart. The ONS Longitudinal Study (LS), can be used to analyse trends over the decade 1981–91. Table 7.7 shows childhood mortality rates for 1982–86 and 1987–91. This confirms that, with the exception of Social Class IIIN, death rates for children aged under five years fell between the two periods. However, the social class gradients, seen in the earlier analyses, persisted. Although this table is based on a small number of deaths,

TABLE 7.7

Mortality rates (ages 0-14, 0-4) per 100,000 population

England and Wales

Source: ONS Longitudinal Study

Social class	1982-86	1987-91
Ages 0-14		
I	57	37
II	74	68
IIIN	86	122
IIIM	75	67
IV	86	88
V	161	122
England and Wales	87	81
Ages 0-4		
I	162	88
II	169	164
IIIN	240	291
IIIM	216	162
IV	208	205
V	399	268
England and Wales	219	188

the data suggest that over the period the differentials between Social Classes V and I widened — from 2.8 to 3.3 for children aged 0–14 and from 2.5 to 3.0 for those aged 0–4. These compare with 2.1 to 3.3 for children aged 1–15 in the 1979–83, 1989–93 mortality analyses presented earlier.

Children's accidental deaths

An important cause of childhood mortality is accidental death. This was recognised by its inclusion as a *Health of the Nation* target for England. The target to achieve a reduction in accidental deaths among children aged under 15 by at least 33 per cent between 1990 and 2005 has already been met. This, however, does not take account of the differences in death rates between social classes.

Childhood injury death rates by social class have been compared for the years around the 1981 and 1991 Censuses.[5] Death rates from injury and poisoning fell between the two periods for children in each social class, although the differential between the social classes had increased. The decline in rates for children in Social Classes IV and V (21 per cent and 2 per cent respectively), was smaller than those for children in Social Classes I and II (32 per cent and 37 per cent). Motor vehicle accidents accounted for half of all childhood injury deaths and showed a similar social class gradient to that for all accidental deaths in childhood.

A previous analysis of social class specific mortality for children had noted that death rates from fire and flames showed one of the steepest socio-economic gradients.[4] Between 1981 and 1991, the death rate due to fire and flames decreased for children in Social Classes I and II but increased for children in Social Classes IV and V. Most of the deaths in this category are from residential fires.

Conclusion

During the 1980s and the first half of the 1990s infant and childhood mortality rates have fallen for all social classes. This is not a reason for complacency, however, since social class differentials have persisted over the period. Indeed, for childhood mortality there is some evidence that differentials have widened. While differentials exist for different ethnic groups and different causes of death this suggests that there is the potential to improve further rates for the lower social classes.

References

1   OPCS (annual) *Perinatal and Infant Mortality: social and biological factors*. Series DH3. London, HMSO.

2   Botting, B and Cooper, J, (1993) Mother's occupation: Part II, *Population Trends* 74, London, HMSO.

3   OPCS (1993) *1991 Census. Ethnic group and country of birth, Great Britain* Vol 2, London, HMSO.

4   OPCS (1988) *Occupational mortality 1979-80, 1982-83; childhood supplement*, London, HMSO.

5   Roberts, I and Power, C (1996) Does the decline in child injury mortality vary by social class? A comparison of class specific mortality in 1981 and 1991. *British Medical Journal*; 313: 784-6.

8 Patterns and trends in male mortality

Frances Drever and Julia Bunting

Summary

This chapter examines patterns and trends in all-cause male mortality at ages 20-64; mortality data 1991-93 for England and Wales is used, and comparisons are made with data for the 1970s and 1980s. Cause-specific mortality for the main areas highlighted in the Department of Health's *Health of the Nation*[1] strategy are examined.

The social class gradient in all-cause mortality observed in earlier decades is still seen in 1991-93. As compared to Social Class I Social Class V has almost three times the mortality and Social Class IIIM and IV have nearly double the mortality.

In 1991-93 men in Social Class V aged 20-24 at death experience the same mortality rates as men in Social Class I twenty years older. Men in Social Class V aged 35-39 and 40-44 at death have higher mortality than those in Social Classes I and II ten years their senior.

As compared with all-cause mortality the social class differentials for stroke, lung cancer, accidents and suicide mortality are even greater. Men in Social Class I have higher mortality from skin cancer than other men.

In absolute terms there has been a fall in mortality rates over the period 1970-72 to 1991-93 for each of Social Classes I to IV. The mortality rate of Social Class V was higher in the early 1980s than 10 years earlier, but has since fallen but only to slightly below its 1970-72 level.

Mortality from suicide and undetermined injury increased during the 1970s and 1980s in all social classes except Social Class I where it decreased.

There has been a relative widening of the differential in all-cause mortality over the 1970s and 1980s. The differential between Social Class V and Social Class I widened from an almost two-fold difference in 1970-72 to almost a three-fold difference in 1991-93.

The differentials between Social Class V and Social Class I for mortality from lung cancer, ischaemic heart disease, strokes, accidents, and suicide have all widened considerably over the 20 year period.

As noted in Chapter 2, since 1911 the Registrar General has included analyses of mortality by social class in the decennial supplements.[2] These analyses take advantage of the up-dated information from each census on the socio-economic characteristics of the population together with the information on occupation from death registration data. This chapter looks at mortality of men by social class. Appendices A and B discuss the different methods used and possible sources of bias.

The last decennial supplement on adult mortality and occupation was published in 1986, based on four years of deaths data around the 1981 Census.[3] The fiche tables accompanying the volume contained information on mortality and social class.[4] The analysis showed substantial differentials in mortality by social class for both men and women – more than double between the top and the bottom of the social scale. These differentials translated into a five-year gap in expectation of life at age 20 between professional and managerial men (Classes I and II) and partly skilled and unskilled manual men (Classes IV and V).[5] In addition, analysis of trends showed a widening gap in the mortality of manual compared to non-manual classes between 1970–72 and 1979–83 for all-cause mortality, lung cancer, coronary heart disease and stroke. These trends occurred for both men and women.[6]

Using decennial supplement data, Blane and colleagues[7] found a widening in social class differentials in 'years of potential life lost' in men in the 1970s. Wagstaff and colleagues[8] confirmed Blane's findings, reworking the data using a different measure of social inequality.

This chapter provides an update of the analysis at the national level for the years around the 1991 Census. The priority areas of the Department of Health's *Health of the Nation*[1] strategy are discussed. Trends in mortality are also analysed for the 20-year period from 1971 to the 1991 Census. These analyses are further to those published previously.[9] The mortality rates have been recalculated using five-year age-groups and comparable causes of death. Previously published data for 1970–72 used ages 15–64 and those for the other time periods ages 20–64. Mortality rates for each period now use ages 20–64. The availability of more data has made it possible to include accidents in the discussion. This has also enabled the suicide information presented previously to be updated to include undetermined injury and make the results more comparable with the data presented for later years. Chapter 10 contains detailed analyses for the major causes of death in 1991–93.

Current patterns of mortality

Background information

Standardised mortality ratios (SMRs) are used to compare death rates in different segments of the population, taking into account differences in their composition. The SMR for males aged 20–64 in England and Wales is 100. SMRs below 100 indicate lower mortality than expected. SMRs greater than 100 indicate higher than average mortality. See Appendix A for more detailed information.

In the figures, SMRs have been plotted on a log scale to ease interpretation. On a linear scale, an SMR of 200 would be twice as far from 100 as one of 50. However, an

TABLE 8.1

Proportion of men aged
20–64 in each social
class, pro rata grossed
1991 Census data

England and Wales, 1991–93

Social class	(percentage) Deaths	Population
I – Professional	4	7
II – Managerial and Technical	19	26
IIIN – Skilled (non–manual)	9	10
IIIM – Skilled (manual)	34	29
IV – Partly skilled	17	14
V – Unskilled	9	5
Number	175,847	15,062,200

SMR value of 200 means that there were twice as many observed deaths as expected deaths. An SMR value of 50 means that there were half as many observed deaths as expected deaths. On a log scale, SMRs of 50 and 200 are equidistant from 100, the reference point, to show that they are equally far from the reference SMR.

A very crude comparison of the differences in death rates across social classes can be gained by looking at the proportions of people in each social class in the 1991 Census and in the death registrations for the years 1991–93. Much more sophisticated methods of analysis are needed to draw considered conclusions. These methods are discussed in Appendices A and B. Roughly, five per cent of men aged 20–64 in England and Wales at the 1991 Census were classified as Social Class V – unskilled. Of the men aged 20–64 who died during the period 1991–93, roughly 10 per cent were Social Class V. If the death rates of England and Wales as a whole applied across the social classes, then roughly five per cent of deaths should have been of men in Social Class V. Table 8.1 gives the proportions of men in each social class at the 1991 Census and in the deaths registration data. As noted in Appendix B, not all people can be given a class. However, about 92 per cent of the deaths and about 91 per cent of men aged 20–64 at the 1991 Census were allocated to a social class.

All-cause mortality

Table 8.2 and Figure 8.1 show, for each social class, the SMR for all-cause mortality for men aged 20–64 in England and Wales for the years 1991–93. There is a progressive increase in mortality from Social Class I with the lowest SMR of 66 through to Social Class V with an SMR of 189. The differences across the social classes are substantial. Mortality is almost three times higher in Social Class V (SMR 189) than in Social Class I (SMR 66). Classes IIIM and IV (SMRs 117, 116 respectively) have nearly double the mortality of Class I. For Class IIIN, mortality is more than 50 per cent higher than Class I. Class II has 9 per cent higher mortality than Class I. However, the mortality gradient is not smooth. There are steep steps in the gradient between Social Classes II and IIIN, and again between Social Classes IV and V, with a shallower gradient in the middle.

The SMRs discussed so far look at overall differences for the ages 20–64. It is useful to look at age-specific mortality rates which help to see at which ages differences occur (Table 8.3). Mortality rates rise as we look at older age-groups. At ages below 30, the England and Wales age-specific mortality rates are about one death per 400 men in the age-group. The rates rise steeply so that by age 50–54, the England and Wales rate is about one death per 60 men. By age 60–64, the rate is about one death per 20 men in England and Wales in this age group.

Social class	SMR
I – Professional	66
II – Managerial and Technical	72
IIIN – Skilled (non–manual)	100
IIIM – Skilled (manual)	117
IV – Partly skilled	116
V – Unskilled	189
England and Wales	100
Number of deaths	*175,847*

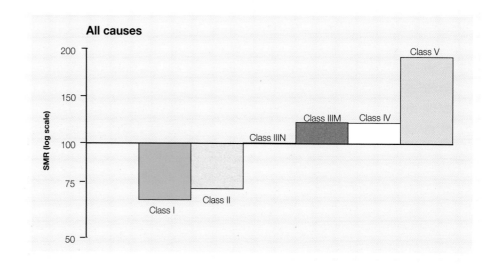

Social class	(rate per 100,000)								
	20-24	25-29	30-34	35-39	40-44	45-49	50-54	55-59	60-64
I – Professional	98	91	142	228	373	704	1,186	2,057	3,735
II – Managerial and Technical	139	146	197	279	380	722	1,230	2,148	3,992
IIIN – Skilled (non–manual)	158	181	319	448	600	1,125	1,773	2,975	5,414
IIIM – Skilled (manual)	219	221	279	429	619	1,141	1,989	3,521	6,736
IV – Partly skilled	195	260	325	485	681	1,244	2,020	3,491	6,227
V – Unskilled	368	489	660	950	1,334	2,047	3,430	5,534	9,341
England and Wales	246	250	307	425	579	1,035	1,745	2,966	5,181
Percentage classified	*67*	*77*	*83*	*87*	*90*	*92*	*94*	*95*	*96*

Figure 8.2 shows age-specific mortality rates by social class for men in England and Wales during the years 1991–93. Class V has a higher mortality rate than any of the other classes at each age-group. Classes I and II have similar mortality rates which are lower than the other groups. Between ages 45 and 64, Class V rates are about three times those in Class I. At ages 60–64, the mortality rate in men in Class V is one death per 11 men. In Class I in the same age-group, the mortality rate is one death per 27 men. However, the higher mortality rates at older ages in this figure mask the patterns at younger ages. To help see what is happening, Figure 8.3 shows the age-specific mortality rates for the ages 20–44. From this, we can see that Class I has the lowest mortality rate at each age. Class II and Class I have similar rates from age 40 and over. The differences across the classes are even more marked at these younger ages than at older ages. At ages 30–34, the death rate in Class V is one death per 150 men.

FIGURE 8.2

Age-specific mortality
rates by social class, all
causes, men aged 20–64

England and Wales, 1991–93

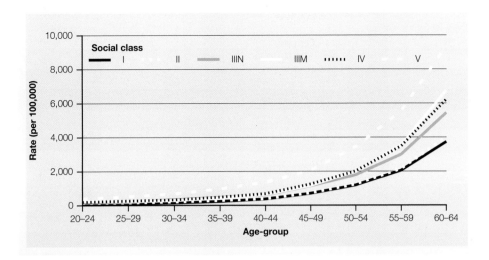

FIGURE 8.3

Age-specific mortality
rates by social class, all
causes, men aged 20-44

England and Wales, 1991–93

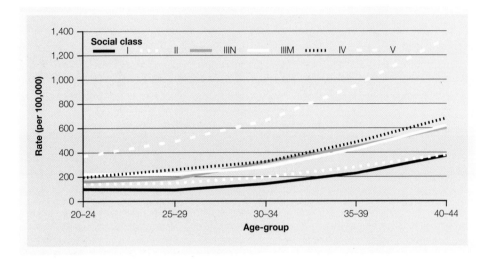

In Class I, however, the death rate is about one death per 700 men. Thus Class V has
four and a half times the mortality of Class I in this age-group. At ages 35–39, Class V
has a mortality rate over four times that in Class I. At younger ages, it is more difficult
to interpret the differences. As can be seen in Table 8.3, at ages 20–24, two thirds of
deaths were allocated to a social class. This rose to over four fifths by ages 30–34 and
nearly nine tenths at ages 35–39. At older ages, even higher proportions of deaths were
allocated to a social class.

Health of the Nation mortality

Mortality from priority areas covered in the *Health of the Nation* strategy[1] are shown
in Table 8.4 and Figure 8.4. A similar pattern of increasing mortality with declining
social class is clearly demonstrated for stroke, ischaemic heart disease, lung cancer,
accidents and suicide. However, the size and nature of the differences varies for the different
causes. There is a four-fold difference in mortality from accidents and from suicide and
undetermined injury between the top and the bottom of the social class scale. For lung
cancer, the differential is even greater, nearly five-fold. For stroke and ischaemic heart
disease, Class V has three times the mortality of Class I. For accidents and suicide, there is a
very sharp step in the gradient between Class V and the other classes, Class V having twice

TABLE 8.4

SMRs, by social class,
men aged 20–64 selected
causes
England and Wales, 1991–93

Social class	Stroke	IHD	Lung cancer	Skin cancer	Accidents	Suicide
I – Professional	70	63	45	136	54	55
II – Managerial and Technical	67	73	61	106	57	63
IIIN – Skilled (non–manual)	96	107	87	106	74	87
IIIM – Skilled (manual)	118	125	138	107	107	96
IV – Partly skilled	125	121	132	91	106	107
V – Unskilled	219	182	206	100	226	215
England and Wales	100	100	100	100	100	100
Number of deaths	8,350	52,219	16,082	992	10,275	9,725

Notes:
Stroke: cerebrovascular disease (ICD 430–438)
IHD: ischaemic heart disease (ICD 410–414)
Lung cancer: malignant neoplasm of bronchus, trachea and lung (ICD 162)
Skin cancer: malignant melanoma of the skin (ICD 172)
Accidents: accidents and adverse effects (ICD E800–E949)
Suicide: suicide and injury undetermined as to whether accidently or purposely inflicted
(ICD E950–E959, E980–E989 excluding E988.8)

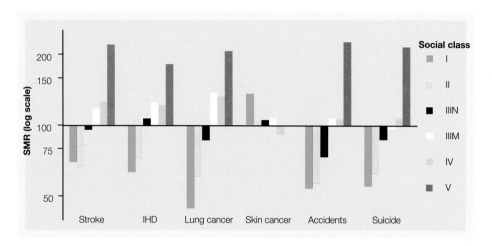

the SMR of Class IV for these causes of death. For stroke, ischaemic heart disease and lung cancer, the gap between Class V and the other classes is still considerable. For these causes, Class V has about one and a half times the SMR of the nearest classes. There is a pronounced gap in mortality between manual and non-manual classes for stroke, ischaemic heart disease, lung cancer and accidents, but not for suicide. Skin cancer has a different pattern altogether. There are fewer than 1,000 deaths over the three years, and so confidence intervals are large. However, it can be seen that Social Class I has significantly high mortality from this cause. The other social classes have SMRs around 100, the England and Wales value.

As with all-cause mortality, it is useful to look at age-specific mortality rates. The number of deaths from skin cancer to men aged 20–64 is under 1,000 over the three years. It has been excluded from the following discussion because of this. Figure 8.5 shows the age-specific mortality rates for a number of causes selected as priority areas. Lung cancer, cerebrovascular disease and ischaemic heart disease have similar patterns of mortality with increasing mortality rates with increasing age. These diseases can be considered as diseases which give rise to death in older age groups. Class V has the highest age-specific rates for all the causes shown and Classes IIIM and IV have similar age-specific rates. Accidents and suicide and undetermined injury have different patterns in that the age-specific mortality rates do not rise substantially at older ages. For lung cancer and cerebrovascular disease, there are fewer than 250 deaths over the three years 1991–93 in any of the age groups for men under 40. Ischaemic heart disease has fewer than 300 deaths over this period for age groups under 35. However, there are nearly 1,000 deaths in the age group 35–39 and more deaths in the older age groups. Accidents have more than 800 deaths in each of the age groups 20–64 and suicide and undetermined injury has over 600 deaths in each age group.

FIGURE 8.5

Age-specific mortality
rates, by social class,
selected causes of death,
men aged 20–64

England and Wales, 1991–93

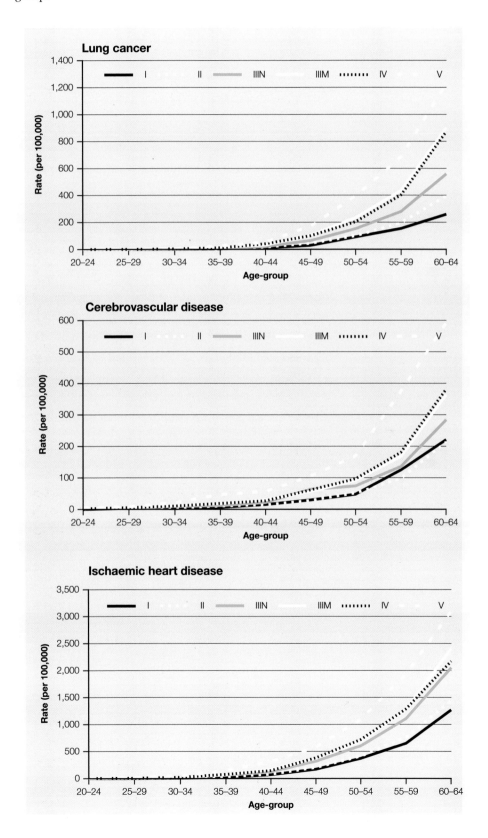

Lung cancer shows large differentials in the age-specific mortality rates. At ages 50–59, the mortality rates in Class V are more than four times those in Class I. In the age group 60–64, the rate in Class V is over four and a half times that in Class I. However, the highest differential for lung cancer is in the 45–49 age group where Class V has almost six times the mortality rate of Class I with a rate of 170 deaths per 100,000 men compared to the Class I rate of 30 deaths per 100,000.

The differentials in age-specific mortality rates between Classes I and V for cerebrovascular disease are about three or three and a half at each of the age groups from 40 to 64. At ages 40 to 54, Class V has about three and a half times the mortality rate of Class I. For ages 55–59, the mortality rate in Class V is 374 per 100,000 men which is three times that in Class I where the rate is 124 per 100,000 men.

Ischaemic heart disease is the major cause of death in men aged 45–64. In each of the five-year age groups from 45, it accounts for 30 per cent or more of all deaths. For men aged 45–49, the differential between mortality rates in Class V compared to Class I is about four and a half. The rate in Class V is about one death per 300 men whereas the rate is only one death per 1,400 men in Class I. By age 60–64, this differential has fallen to about two and a half. The mortality rate at these ages is about one death per 30 men in Class V, and one death per 80 men in Class I.

Figure 8.6 shows the age-specific mortality rates for lung cancer, cerebrovascular disease and ischaemic heart disease on the same scale as those for accidents and suicide and undetermined injury shown in Figure 8.5. This shows clearly that accidents and suicide and undetermined injury are more important causes of death in ages below 40 than other causes discussed earlier. The patterns of age-specific mortality rates for accidents and for suicide and undetermined injury are not as obvious as those at older ages for lung cancer, cerebrovascular disease and ischaemic heart disease. At each age, Class V still has higher mortality rates than any other class.

The age-specific rates for accidents for Class V vary from 137 per 100,000 in the age group 50–54 to 175 per 100,000 in the age group 25–29. At ages 25–34, Class V has a five-fold differential over Class I where the age-specific mortality rates are about 30 per 100,000. The differential is even higher in the 40–44 age group where Class V has a mortality rate of 166 per 100,000 compared to a rate in Class I of only 23 per 100,000. This is a seven-fold differential. In each class, the age-specific mortality rates are fairly stable. Class I, however, shows a declining rate at ages 25–44 and then a doubling in the rate at age 45–49, 23 per 100,000 compared to 45 per 100,000. The age-specific rate then remains in this region until age 64.

Suicide and undetermined injury show a different pattern in age-specific mortality rates. The general pattern is of increasing age-specific rates at younger ages and then decreasing rates or rates levelling off at older ages. However, the ages at which the change from increasing to decreasing rates occurs differs across the social classes. Class V shows the youngest change in rates with decreasing rates from age 35. In contrast, Class I does not have much evidence of decreasing rates and the rates do not level off until about age 50.

At younger age groups, the differentials in mortality rates from suicide and undetermined injury are of the order of between seven and eight-fold. Because of the change in age-specific mortality rates in Class V, the differential between Class V and Class I at

FIGURE 8.6

Age-specific mortality
rates, by social class,
selected causes of death,
men aged 20–64

England and Wales, 1991–93

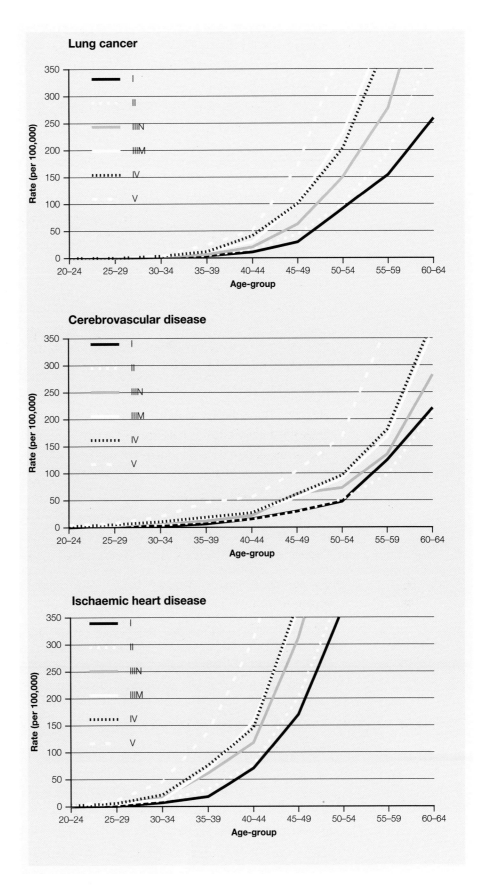

Lung cancer

Cerebrovascular disease

Ischaemic heart disease

FIGURE 8.6 - *continued*

Age-specific mortality
rates by social class,
selected causes of death,
men aged 20–64,
England and Wales, 1991–93

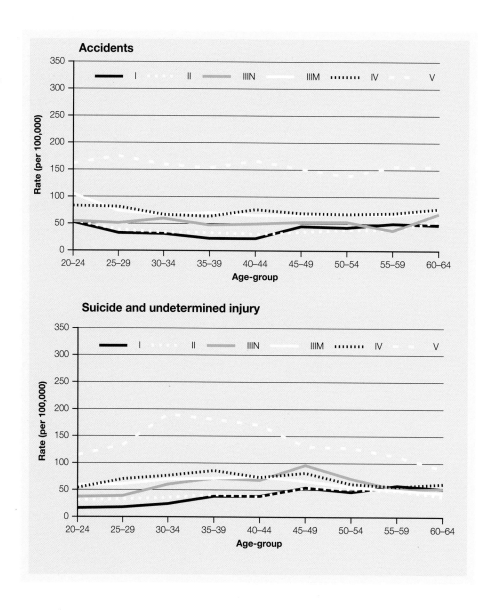

ages 35–39 is less than five-fold, with Class V having a mortality rate of one death per 550 men and Class I with a rate of one death per 2,600 men. By age 55, the differential has dropped to Class V having twice the mortality rate of Class I. Class V has a mortality rate for suicide in the age 55–59 of one death per 900 men and Class I has a rate of one death per 1,700 men.

Trends from 1970–72 to 1991–93

Table 8.5 shows the trends in all-cause mortality expressed as European standardised rates (ESRs) per 100,000 men aged 20–64. For each of the three periods, rates have been calculated using the same European standard population.[8] ESRs make it possible to compare absolute as well as relative changes in mortality over time. Information on the method is in Appendix A.

In each social class, there has been a decline in all-cause mortality over the two decades. In England and Wales as a whole, there has been a 33 per cent drop in the ESR from 1970–72 to 1991–93. Classes I and II have experienced falls of about 44 per cent over the same period. Classes IIIM and IV had similar all-cause ESRs in 1970–72 at 683 and 721 deaths per 100,000 respectively. The rates for both have declined to about 490 deaths per 100,000 in 1991–93. This represents a fall of 28 per cent for Class IIIM and one of 32 per cent for Class IV. Social Class V has not experienced as favourable a trend. Twenty years ago, the all-cause ESR for Social Class V was 897 per 100,000. In the early 1980s, this rose to 910 per 100,000. The current all-cause ESR of 806 deaths per 100,000 is just 10 per cent below the level of 20 years ago.

There has been very little differential in all-cause ESRs between Classes I and II over the 20-year period, but the gap between these and the other social classes has become larger over the same period. The difference in all-cause mortality between Classes V and I has widened from an almost two-fold differential in 1970–72 to an almost three-fold gap in 1991–93. The ratio of the all-cause ESR in Class IV to that in Class I has increased from 1.4 to 1.8 over the same period, with a similar increase for Class IIIM compared to Class I. Class IIIN has experienced a slightly smaller increase in the differential between it and Class I, from 1.3 to 1.5.

Table 8.6 shows changes over time for some of the major causes of death mentioned in the Department of Health's *Health of the Nation* strategy.[1] There have been considerable declines in mortality from ischaemic heart disease, lung cancer, stroke and accidents over the last 20 years. Skin cancer is still a relatively rare cause of death and so data are not presented here. Mortality rates from suicide and undetermined injury have increased over the 20 years.

The trend in ischaemic heart disease ESRs is similar to that for all-cause mortality in that there have been decreases in these rates for England and Wales and for each social class. However, the change in the ESR for Class V for ischaemic heart disease has been very small, just 3 per cent. Accident rates in England and Wales dropped by a third, from an ESR of 34 per 100,000 men aged 20–64 in 1970–72 to an ESR of 22 per 100,000 in 1991–93. However, Class V had a much smaller decrease of 22 per cent, from 67 to 52 per 100,000 men aged 20–64. For both stroke and lung cancer, ESRs in Class V decreased by about 25 per cent. However, this decrease was about half that in the England and Wales ESRs for these diseases. The England and Wales ESR for stroke halved from 40 to 20 per 100,000. The equivalent drop in lung cancer was 47 per cent from 73 to 39 per 100,000.

The pattern in differentials in ESR for stroke is very similar to that of all-cause mortality. However, the pattern varies for other conditions. For ischaemic heart disease,

Social class	(rates per100,000)		
	1970–72	1979–83	1991–93
I – Professional	500	373	280
II – Managerial and Technical	526	425	300
IIIN – Skilled (non–manual)	637	522	426
IIIM – Skilled (manual)	683	580	493
IV – Partly skilled	721	639	492
V – Unskilled	897	910	806
England and Wales	624	549	419

Notes:
1979-1983 includes only deaths in the years 1979, 1980, 1982 and 1983 as the industrial dispute in 1981 involving Registrars of Births, Deaths and Marriages in England and Wales produced occupational details of uncertain quality.

TABLE 8.6
European standardised
mortality rate, by social
class, men aged 20–64,
selected causes

England and Wales, selected
years

Social class	1970–72	1979–83	1991–93		1970–72	1979–83	1991–93
			rates per 100,000				
	Lung cancer			IHD			
I – Professional	41	26	17		195	144	81
II – Managerial and Technical	52	39	24		197	168	92
IIIN – Skilled (non–manual)	63	47	34		245	208	136
IIIM – Skilled (manual)	90	72	54		232	218	159
IV – Partly skilled	93	76	52		232	227	156
V – Unskilled	109	108	82		243	287	235
England and Wales	73	60	39		209	201	127
	Stroke			Accidents			
I – Professional	35	20	14		23	17	13
II – Managerial and Technical	37	23	13		25	20	13
IIIN – Skilled (non–manual)	41	28	19		25	21	17
IIIM – Skilled (manual)	45	34	24		34	27	24
IV – Partly skilled	46	37	25		39	35	24
V – Unskilled	59	55	45		67	63	52
England and Wales	40	30	20		34	28	22
	Suicide						
I – Professional	16	16	13				
II – Managerial and Technical	13	15	14				
IIIN – Skilled (non–manual)	17	18	20				
IIIM – Skilled (manual)	12	16	21				
IV – Partly skilled	18	23	23				
V – Unskilled	32	44	47				
England and Wales	15	20	22				

Notes:
1979-1983 includes only deaths in the years 1979, 1980, 1982 and 1983 as the industrial dispute in 1981 involving
Registrars of Births, Deaths and Marriages in England and Wales produced occupational details of uncertain quality.

there was a slight gradient in mortality in 1970–72, but a distinct gradient had developed by the early 1980s. This confirms the pattern found for the same period using Longitudinal Study (LS) data.[10] This gradient has become more pronounced in the early 1990s. For lung cancer, very pronounced differentials between the ESRs for manual and non-manual classes have been apparent at each of the three periods. These differentials have continued to widen. By 1991–93, there was a five-fold difference in mortality between the top and the bottom of the social scale, compared to just under a three-fold differential in 1970–72.

By 1991–93, Class V had a four-fold differential with Class I for suicide and undetermined injury. This had risen from a two-fold difference in 1970–72. Accidents also show widening differentials. In 1970–72, Class V had an ESR nearly three times that of Class I. By 1991–93, Class V had over four times the mortality rate from accidents of Class I.

Conclusion

The social gradient in all-cause mortality observed in the earlier decades has been maintained up to 1991–93. Since the previous Census of 1981, there has been a decline in ESRs in all social classes as well as in England and Wales, continuing the downward trend observed in similar analyses at the time of the 1971 and 1981 Censuses. The mortality rate for Social Class V in 1991–93, at 806 deaths per 100,000 is only 10 per cent lower than it was 20 years ago when it stood at 897 deaths per 100,000. In 1979–83 the death rate was slightly higher, at 910 deaths per 100,000.

Progressively higher mortality is observed with decreasing social class, such that all-cause mortality in Social Class V is almost three times that of Social Class I. For some specific causes of death, the differentials in mortality are even greater. For example, there is a four-fold difference in mortality from accidents and from suicide and undetermined injury and a nearly five-fold difference in lung cancer mortality between Social Classes I and V. The large numbers of deaths in these analyses, and the narrow confidence intervals, make the findings of distinct differentials in mortality statistically robust.

Trends in mortality since 1970–72 show more pronounced social class differentials developing over the 20-year period up to 1991–93 for all-cause mortality and for specific major causes investigated here. For ischaemic heart disease, which showed only a slight gradient in 1970–72, a marked gradient has developed.

References

1   Department of Health (1992) *The Health of the Nation - a strategy for Health in England* . London, HMSO.

2   General Register Office (1919) Registrar General's 75th Annual Report - 1911 Supplement. London, HMSO.

3   OPCS (1986) *Occupational mortality decennial supplement 1979–80, 82–83*. Series DS, 6. London, HMSO.

4   OPCS (1986) *Occupational mortality decennial supplement 1979-80, 82-83, part II microfiche tables*. Series DS, 6. London, HMSO.

5   Haberman, M and Bloomfield, D (1988) Social class differentials in mortality in Great Britain around 1981, *Journal of the Institute of Actuaries*, 115: 495–517.

6   Marmot, M and McDowall, M (1986) Mortality decline and widening social inequalities, *The Lancet*, ii: 274–6.

7   Blane, D, Davey Smith, G and Bartley, M (1990) Social class differences in years of potential life lost: size, trends and principal causes, *British Medical Journal*, 301: 429–32.

8   Waterhouse, J *et al*. (eds) (1976) *Cancer incidence in five continents*. IARC 1991 World Health Annual of Statistics.

9   Drever, F, Whitehead, M and Roden, M (1996) Current patterns and trends in male mortality by social class (based on occupation), *Population Trends*, 86: 15–20.

10 Devis, T (1993) Measuring mortality differences by cause of death and social class defined by occupation, *Population Trends*, 73: 32–5.

9 Differences in mortality of migrants

Seeromanie Harding and Roy Maxwell

Summary

This chapter uses data for 1991-93 to examine social class differences in mortality at ages 20-64 of men in the largest migrant groups living in England and Wales. The extent to which the increased mortality from main causes of deaths reflect poorer socio-economic circumstances is investigated.

Migrant groups included in this analysis are those born in the Caribbean Commonwealth, West and South Africa, East African Commonwealth, Indian subcontinent, Scotland and Ireland (Northern Ireland and the Republic of Ireland). Since groups are identified here using country of birth information second generation migrant populations born in England and Wales are not included.

Higher proportions of men from the Caribbean and Ireland were in manual classes than in the male population of England and Wales as a whole; East African, West/South African and Scottish men were more concentrated in non-manual classes.

Relative to all men 20-64 in England and Wales all-cause mortality is low among Caribbean men, but high for all other migrant groups. There are particularly strong social class gradients in mortality for men born in Scotland and Ireland, and a smaller, but still marked, gradient for men born on the Indian subcontinent. Among men born on the Indian subcontinent mortality was highest for Bangladeshis who also had larger class differences in mortality than those born in India.

Mortality is high from ischaemic heart disease and respiratory diseases among East Africans, and from stroke among West/South Africans and Caribbeans. Men from the Indian subcontinent show high mortality from heart disease and strokes, and Scots and Irish from all main causes of death. Although social class makes an important contribution, particularly for the Irish, it does not explain these patterns of excess mortality.

For the Irish, relative differences in mortality between classes are wider in the 1990s than 1970s. Earlier work did not find evidence of class differences for Indians and among Caribbeans mortality was generally higher in non-manual classes. In the 1990s class gradients have become apparent for both these groups.

Introduction

Differences in the patterns of mortality among migrants living in England and Wales have been observed for the last two decades.[1,2,3] It is uncertain to what extent the patterns of excess mortality such as that of hypertensive diseases among those of Black African origin [4,5] and coronary heart disease among migrants from the Indian subcontinent [6,7] reflect underlying differences in socio-economic positions. The only national study to address these issues was that of Marmot and colleagues[1] which examined mortality in the early 1970s by social class based on occupation. They concluded that this measure could not explain the overall mortality differences between migrants and the host population. In the USA, the relationship between ethnicity, class and health has been the focus of more recent studies and the evidence suggests that black/white differentials in mortality for some diseases may be partly attributable to social disadvantage.[8,9]

In this analysis, we use the most recently available data in the 1990s to update the earlier work of the 1970s on social class differences in mortality of the largest migrant groups living in England and Wales. We also examine the contribution of social class to the cause-specific pattern of mortality.

Country of birth groupings

Although ethnic origin was recorded at the 1991 Census, it is not recorded at death registration. By using country of birth as a proxy for ethnic origin, this analysis excludes second-generation migrant populations born in England and Wales. A further problem with using country of birth is that it includes foreign-born people of European extraction, but since they tend to be older than the age-range covered here we expect their effect on mortality in this study to be small. Detailed discussion about the limitations of this measure for non-white groups can be found elsewhere.[1,2]

Country of birth groupings used in this analysis are those born in the Caribbean Commonwealth, West and South Africa, East African Commonwealth, Indian subcontinent (India, Pakistan, Bangladesh, Sri Lanka), Scotland and Ireland – both Northern Ireland and the Republic of Ireland. The African grouping is disaggregated as the majority of East Africans are of Indian origin and those from West/South Africa of 'Black African' origin.[10] Some findings are given separately for those born in India, Pakistan and Bangladesh. The earlier analysis[1] on the 1970s highlighted the problem of country of birth being recorded differently on census forms compared to death certificates for those born in India, Pakistan and Bangladesh and also for those born in Northern Ireland and the Republic of Ireland. Special tabulations from the Longitudinal Study suggest the continuation of this problem so caution should be exercised when interpreting differences among those born on the Indian subcontinent.

Because of small numbers of deaths in some of the groups, Social Classes I and II and Social Classes IV and V are combined after adjusting for differences in mortality between the individual classes. Social class variations in the main underlying causes of death – ischaemic heart disease, cerebrovascular diseases, lung cancer, respiratory diseases, and accidents and injuries including suicide are examined. Detailed tables with numbers of deaths, standardised mortality ratios and 95% confidence intervals are available on the electronic media accompanying this volume.

Table 9.1 shows that the proportions of men in England and Wales excluded from Classes I to V in the 1991 Census and at death registration, years 1991–93, varied. Those who were not required to state an occupation at the 1991 Census include people who had not been in paid work in the ten years prior to the census, those in government training schemes, students, and anyone whose occupation was inadequately described or not stated. The proportions not classified to a social class were generally higher among migrants than among all men in England and Wales. At death registration the last main occupation is recorded so that higher proportions are expected to be classified from details at death than at census. The impact of this could be an overestimation of mortality in some classes. Among all men and all migrant groups, except East Africans, higher proportions were classified from their details at death registration than from those at census.

As can be seen from Table 9.2, 20 per cent of all single women and 21 per cent of all married women could not be classified to a social class from details on occupation at the 1991 Census. At death, the comparable proportions were 49 per cent and 56 per cent. With the exception of Scottish women and married Caribbean women, higher proportions of migrant women could not be classified at census and at death registration. Because of these large proportions of unclassified women, this chapter presents mortality by social class for men only.

Underenumeration at census is also an issue of incomplete data for young black men.[11] The adjustment factors used in this analysis corrects for underenumeration by social class at a national level but not for differences in underenumeration of ethnic groups.

TABLE 9.1

Proportions of migrants not classified to Social Classes I–V at the 1991 Census and at death registration, men aged 20–64

England and Wales

	Country of birth						
	All countries	Caribbean	West/ South Africa	East Africa	Indian sub- continent	Scotland	Ireland (all parts)
Total at Census = 100%	15,018,619	102,182	43,275	103,715	309,430	293,614	283,159
Not classified (%)	9	15	23	12	16	10	12
Total deaths = 100%	175,847	1,680	399	853	4,114	4,596	5,994
Not classified (%)	8	9	16	16	10	9	8

TABLE 9.2

Proportions of migrants not classified to Social Classes I–V at the 1991 Census and at death registration, women aged 20–64

England and Wales

	Country of birth						
	All countries	Caribbean	West/ South Africa	East Africa	Indian sub- continent	Scotland	Ireland (all parts)
Not married [a]							
Total at Census = 100%	4,962,480	54,879	19,012	28,883	46,205	86,571	104,477
Not classified (%)	20	22	31	27	49	23	22
Total deaths = 100%	37,117	532	98	206	545	858	1,127
Not classified (%)	49	30	32	60	72	46	50
Married							
Total at Census = 100%	9,990,461	62,470	24,729	65,969	254,239	176,643	194,361
Not classified (%)	21	19	26	25	55	17	24
Total deaths = 100%	67,564	546	107	255	1,319	1,496	2,019
Not classified (%)	56	39	45	67	79	53	53

Note: Table covers persons inadequately described, occupation not stated, not in paid employment in the 10 years prior to census, students, in government training schemes
[a] single, widowed, divorced

Social class distributions of men

Table 9.3 shows the social class distributions of males by ethnic group. Higher proportions of East African (67 per cent), West/South African (61 per cent), and Scottish men (55 per cent) were classified to a non-manual class compared with all men in England and Wales (47 per cent). Caribbean men were largely concentrated in manual occupations (74 per cent). More of the Irish (62 per cent), were also in a manual class compared with all men (54 per cent).

All-cause mortality of men by social class

Relative to the rate for all men aged 20–64 in England and Wales, overall mortality is low among Caribbean men (SMR 89), but high for men in all other migrant groups (see Table 9.4 and Figure 9.1). Irish men showed the highest mortality with 35 per cent excess deaths. Scottish, West/South African and East African men also showed higher mortality, the excess being between 20 and 30 per cent.

There is a clear association between social class and mortality of all men in England and Wales. Systematic differences by social class can also be seen for those born in the Indian sub-continent, Scotland and Ireland. However, in each social class, mortality of these migrants is higher than that of all men in England and Wales in the same class. The class gradients were steeper for Scottish and Irish men because of the substantially higher mortality for Class IV/V in these migrant groups. Whereas all men in Class IV/V showed an excess of 35 per cent, Scottish men showed an excess of 86 per cent, and Irish men 73 per cent. Although a higher proportion of the Irish were in a manual social class compared with all men, adjusting for these differences explained very little of their overall higher mortality.

The pattern of class mortality among Caribbeans and East Africans is not as consistent as for the other groups, but mortality was generally higher in manual classes than in non-manual classes. The gradient was least clear for West/South Africans.

FIGURE 9.1

SMRs, by social class and country of birth, all causes, men aged 20–64

England and Wales, 1991–93

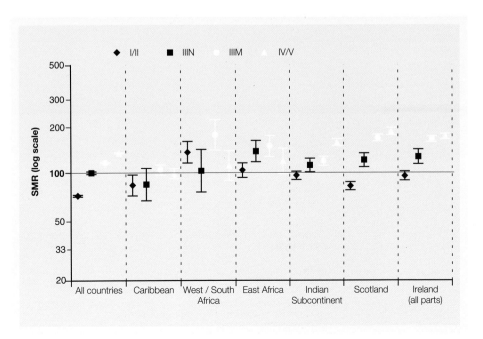

Social class:	Country of birth						
	All countries	Caribbean	West/ South Africa	East Africa	Indian sub-continent	Scotland	Ireland (all parts)
	%	%	%	%	%	%	%
I/II	36	19	46	50	33	45	31
IIIN	11	7	15	17	12	10	7
IIIM	33	42	16	19	28	26	34
IV/V	21	32	22	14	28	19	28
Total (100%)	13,725,593	86,818	33,350	91,070	259,431	263,697	247,818

Social class:		Country of birth						
		All countries	Caribbean	West/ South Africa	East Africa	Indian sub-continent	Scotland	Ireland (all parts)
I/II	SMR	71*	83*	136*	104	96	82*	95
	Deaths	39,944	155	145	302	1,004	1,091	824
IIIN	SMR	100	84*	103	138*	112*	121*	127*
	Deaths	15,220	66	38	150	384	355	306
IIIM	SMR	117*	105	177*	150*	120*	169*	166*
	Deaths	60,443	676	75	158	921	1,464	2,137
IV/V	SMR	135*	99	112	120*	158*	186*	173*
	Deaths	46,824	640	76	108	1,387	1,251	2,271
Non-manual	SMR	77*	83*	128*	113*	100	89*	102
Manual	SMR	124*	102	137*	136*	140*	176*	169*
All[a]	SMR	100	89*	126*	123*	107*	129*	135*
	Deaths	175,847	1,680	399	853	4,114	4,596	5,994
Adjusted for classes I-V	SMR	100	82*	135*	137*	117*	132*	129*
	Deaths	162,431	1,537	334	718	3,696	4,161	5,538

[a] includes unclassified
* SMR significantly different from 100

Social class:	Country of birth				
	All countries	Indian subcontinent	India	Pakistan	Bangladesh
I/II	71*	96	94	101	132*
IIIN	100	112*	105	120	159*
IIIM	117*	120*	124 *	104	148*
IV/V	135*	158*	146 *	147*	233*
Non-manual	77*	100	96	106	144*
Manual	124*	140*	135 *	128*	201*
All[a]	100	107*	106 *	102	137*
Deaths	175,847	4,114	2,387	1,010	578
Adjusted for classes I-V	100	117*	114 *	110*	159*
Deaths	162,431	3,696	2,172	877	528

[a] includes unclassified
* SMR significantly different from 100

Men born on the Indian subcontinent

Table 9.5 shows that the overall SMR for those born on the Indian subcontinent obscures differences within this group. Mortality of Bangladeshi men (SMR 137) was significantly different from that of Indians (SMR 106) and Pakistanis (SMR 102). Differences by social class are evident for both Indians and Bangladeshis but the disadvantage among Bangladeshis appears greater in both the non-manual and manual classes. Bangladeshi men in non-manual classes showed 44 per cent excess deaths whereas Indian men in non-manual classes showed average mortality. Among those in a manual class, mortality of Bangladeshis was twice the national rate whereas it was 35 per cent higher for Indians. Further adjustment for differences in class distributions did not explain the higher overall mortality of Bangladeshi men.

Age differences in male mortality by social class

Tables 9.6 and 9.7 and Figures 9.2 and 9.3 show mortality by class for men aged 20–44 and 45–64. Excess mortality was greater at ages 20–44 than at ages 45–64 for Scottish and Irish men because of the substantially higher mortality of those in Class IV/V at younger ages. Although class differences were larger than for all men, class was not an important factor in explaining the overall excess for the Irish. After adjusting for class, the excess among the Irish at ages 20–44 was reduced from 45 to 40 per cent, and at ages 45–64 from 33 to 27 per cent .

In contrast, it can be seen that the pattern of class mortality at ages 20–64 among those born on the Indian subcontinent was mainly determined by those aged 45–64. In Class IV/V mortality at ages 20–44 (SMR 93) is not significantly different from the national rate, but at ages 45–64, the magnitude of excess mortality (SMR 172) is similar to that of the Scots and Irish (SMR 176 and 170 respectively). At ages 20–44, both East and West/South Africans show excess mortality in the manual class grouping.

TABLE 9.6

SMRs by social class and country of birth, men aged 20–44, all causes

England and Wales, 1991–93

Social class:	Country of birth						
	All countries	Caribbean	West/ South Africa	East Africa	Indian sub- continent	Scotland	Ireland (all parts)
I/II	61*	81	89	87	85*	72*	81*
IIIN	90*	163*	44*	122	96	123	123
IIIM	98	96	205*	137*	106	168*	146*
IV/V	130*	143*	123	115	93	243*	208*
Non-manual	68*	101	78	95	88	81*	88
Manual	110*	111	159*	128*	100	199*	171*
All[a]	100	113	119*	126*	99	142*	145*
Deaths	34,124	174	141	386	680	931	751
Adjusted for classes I-V	100	112	124*	131*	101	151*	140*
Deaths	28,224	142	98	293	567	774	625

[a] includes unclassified
* SMR significantly different from 100

TABLE 9.7

**SMRs by social class
and country of birth, men
aged 45–64, all causes**

England and Wales, 1991–93

Social class:		Country of birth					
	All countries	Caribbean	West/ South Africa	East Africa	Indian sub- continent	Scotland	Ireland (all parts)
I/II	73*	84	171*	120*	98	85*	99
IIIN	103*	70*	138	148*	116*	120*	127*
IIIM	122*	106	162*	164*	124*	169*	168*
IV/V	136*	97	107	123	172*	176*	170*
Non-manual	79*	79*	162*	129*	103	91*	105
Manual	127*	101	127*	144*	151*	172*	169*
All[a]	100	87*	131*	121*	109*	126*	133*
deaths	141,723	1,506	258	467	3,434	3,665	5,243
Adjusted for classes I-V	100	79*	140*	141*	121*	128*	127*
deaths	134,207	1,395	236	425	3,129	3,387	4,913

[a] includes unclassified
* SMR significantly different from 100

FIGURE 9.2

**SMRs by social class and
country of birth, all
causes, men aged 20-44**

England and Wales, 1991–93

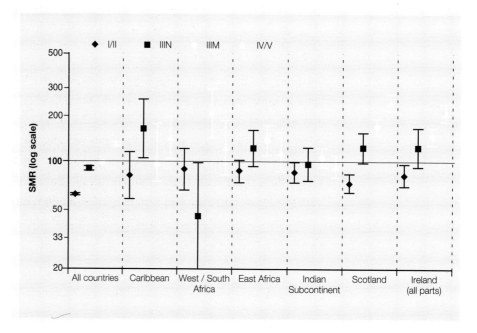

FIGURE 9.3

**SMRs by social class and
country of birth, all
causes, men aged 45-64**

England and Wales, 1991–93

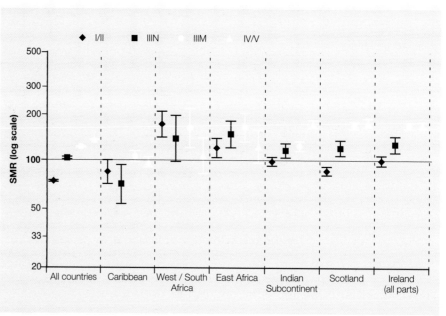

Ischaemic heart disease accounted for the largest proportion of deaths among men regardless of country of birth. Men born in East Africa, the Indian subcontinent and Scotland show higher mortality, and those from the Caribbean lower mortality, compared with all men (see Table 9.8 and Figure 9.4). Mortality was significantly higher among manual classes than among non-manual classes for men from the Indian subcontinent, Scotland and Ireland, and was also consistently higher than for all men in the corresponding non-manual and manual classes. This relative disadvantage was greatest for men from the Indian sub-continent. Whereas mortality of all men in a non-manual class was 22 per cent lower than average, that of men born on the Indian subcontinent in the same class was 43 per cent higher. Mortality of all men in a manual class was 30 per cent higher than average, but men from the Indian subcontinent experienced twice the national rate. The wide range of mortality levels among Scottish men results in a steeper gradient than that of all men. Standardising for social class reduced some of the overall excess among the Irish but not among the Scots or Indians. East Africans generally showed higher mortality among the manual classes but as with those from the Indian subcontinent, even men in Class I/II showed large excess mortality.

Cerebrovascular disease was the next major cause of death for men from the Caribbean, West/South Africa and Indian subcontinent. As can be seen in Table 9.9 and Figure 9.5, mortality from this cause was also substantially higher among these men than in all men in England and Wales. Excess mortality was greatest among West/South Africans (SMR 315). Irish-born men also showed significantly higher mortality. Across all groups there is generally higher mortality in the manual classes than in the non-manual classes. Differences in social class distributions explain some, but not all, of the overall excess among Caribbean (SMR reduced from 169 to 146) and Irish men (SMR reduced from 131 to 124).

FIGURE 9.4

SMRs by social class and country of birth, ischaemic heart disease, men aged 20-64

England and Wales, 1991–93

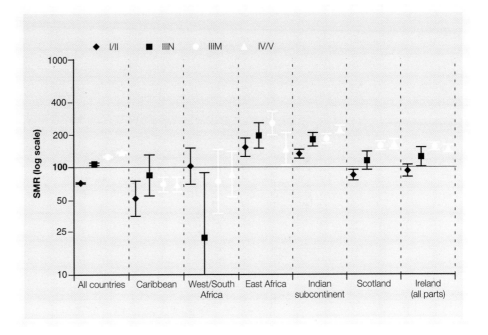

TABLE 9.8

SMRs by social class and country of birth, men aged 20–64, ischaemic heart disease

England and Wales, 1991–93

Social class:	Country of birth						
	All countries	Caribbean	West/ South Africa	East Africa	Indian sub-continent	Scotland	Ireland (all parts)
I/II	71*	51*	102	152*	132*	84*	92
IIIN	107*	84	22*	195*	179*	114	124*
IIIM	125*	69*	73	255*	183*	157*	155*
IV/V	137*	69*	86	147*	223*	163*	148*
Non-manual	78*	61*	81	165*	143*	89*	99
Manual	130*	69*	81	203*	205*	159*	151*
All[a]	100	60*	83	160*	150*	117*	121*
Deaths	52,219	369	65	260	1,736	1,253	1,706
Adjusted for classes I-V	100	55*	79	188*	165*	121*	115*
Deaths	49,845	343	52	243	1,595	1,176	1,597

[a] includes unclassified
* SMR significantly different from 100

TABLE 9.9

SMRs by social class and country of birth, men aged 20–64, cerebrovascular disease

England and Wales, 1991–93

Social class:	Country of birth						
	All countries	Caribbean	West/ South Africa	East Africa	Indian sub-continent	Scotland	Ireland (all parts)
II/II	68*	103	362*	60	138*	54*	93
IIIN	96	133	395*	199*	93	79	111
IIIM	118*	205*	602*	144	135*	190*	172*
IV/V	149*	193*	263*	159	326*	141*	174*
Non-manual	73*	112	371*	99	127*	59*	97
Manual	130*	199*	390*	151	238*	169*	173*
All[a]	100	169*	315*	113	163*	111	130*
Deaths	8,350	160	42	32	299	189	288
Adjusted for classes I-V	100	146*	372*	128	175*	112	124*
Deaths	7,835	144	41	28	267	170	276

[a] includes unclassified
* SMR significantly different from 100

FIGURE 9.5

SMRs by social class and country of birth, cerebrovascular disease, men aged 20-64

England and Wales, 1991–93

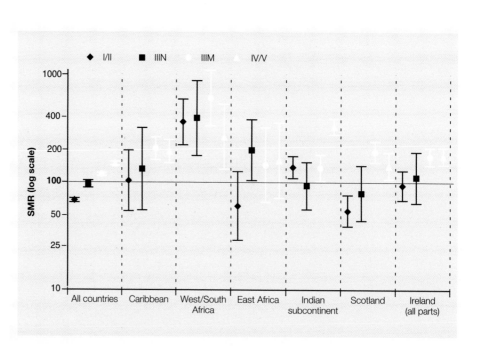

Lung cancer was the next main cause of death for all men and also for Scottish and Irish men, among whom mortality was 46 per cent and 57 per cent higher than for all men respectively (see Table 9.10 and Figure 9.6). Class differences in these groups were larger than for all men because of the very high mortality of those in manual classes. A similar pattern of steeper class gradients is also seen for respiratory diseases among these men (see Table 9.11). Even after adjusting for class, excess mortality among the Irish remained high at 43 per cent above the mortality of all men in England and Wales. Although the overall SMR for respiratory diseases is below 100 for men born on the Indian subcontinent, there was significantly higher mortality in Class IV/V (SMR 166) which resulted in a non-manual/manual gradient.

Irish and Scottish men showed higher mortality from accidents and injuries, and suicides (see Tables 9.12 and 9.13, Figure 9.7). The class gradients for these causes were much steeper than for all men because of the substantially higher mortality in the manual classes. For both of these causes, mortality of Scottish and Irish men in Class IV/V was more than twice the national rate. Among Irish men, although adjusting for class explained 20 per cent of the overall excess deaths from accident and injuries, mortality remained 69 per cent higher than for all men.

FIGURE 9.6

SMRs by social class and country of birth, lung cancer, men aged 20-64

England and Wales, 1991–93

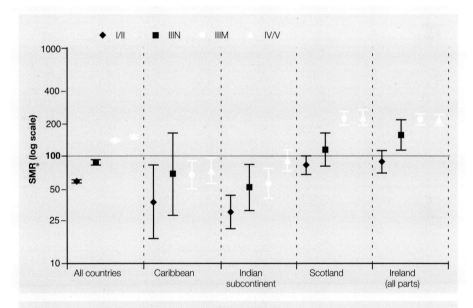

FIGURE 9.7

SMRs by social class and country of birth, accidents and injuries (minus suicides), men aged 20-64

England and Wales, 1991–93

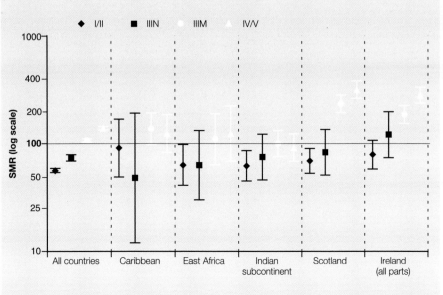

TABLE 9.10

SMRs by social class and country of birth, men aged 20–64, lung cancer

England and Wales, 1991–93

Social class	Country of birth				
	All countries	Caribbean	Indian subcontinent	Scotland	Ireland (all parts)
I/II	58*	37*	30*	82	88
IIIN	87*	68	51*	114	156*
IIIM	138*	66*	55*	221*	216*
IV/V	151*	72*	90	225*	214*
Non-manual	64*	46*	35*	88	103
Manual	143*	69*	74*	223*	215*
All[a]	100	59*	48*	146*	157*
Deaths	16,082	114	171	479	693
Adjusted for classes I-V	100	49*	52*	151*	145*
Deaths	15,463	104	154	448	667

[a] includes unclassified
* SMR significantly different from 100

TABLE 9.11

SMRs, by social class and country of birth, men aged 20–64, respiratory diseases

England and Wales, 1991–93

Social class	Country of birth					
	All countries	Caribbean	East Africa	Indian sub-continent	Scotland	Ireland (all parts)
I/II	53*	122	113	68*	73*	94
IIIN	92*	47	165	64	118	147
IIIM	115*	91	178	85	179*	166*
IV/V	159*	93	132	166*	212*	246*
Non-manual	61*	99	127	67*	81	106
Manual	133*	92	156	129*	194*	207*
All[a]	100	80*	154*	90	138*	162*
Deaths	9,704	86	53 *	190	270	410
Adjusted for classes I-V	100	70*	162*	98	142*	143*
Deaths	8,730	82	40	165	235	371

[a] includes unclassified
* SMR significantly different from 100

TABLE 9.12

SMRs by social class and country of birth, men aged 20–64, accidents and injuries (minus suicides)

England and Wales, 1991–93

Social class	Country of birth					
	All countries	Caribbean	East Africa	Indian sub-continent	Scotland	Ireland (all parts)
I/II	56*	91	63*	62*	69*	79
IIIN	74*	48	63	75	83	121
IIIM	106*	136	109	99	233*	185*
IV/V	138*	123	123	91	315*	280*
Non-manual	60*	79	63	66*	71*	88
Manual	119*	131*	115	95	268*	228*
All[a]	100	121	86	80*	177*	189*
Deaths	10,769	83	63	172	363	371
Adjusted for classes I-V	100	109	104	87	184*	169*
Deaths	8,983	68	511	46	293	299

[a] Includes unclassified
* SMR significantly different from 100

TABLE 9.13

SMRs by social class and
country of birth, men
aged 20–64, suicides

England and Wales, 1991–93

Social class	Country of birth					
	All countries	Caribbean	East Africa	Indian sub-continent	Scotland	Ireland (all parts)
I/II	61*	37*	45*	81	86	77
IIIN	87*	50	59	88	81	111
IIIM	96	48*	85	65*	159*	122
IV/V	134*	89	70	60*	275*	216*
Non-manual	67*	41*	49*	83	85	83
Manual	111*	65*	79	63*	208*	164*
All[a]	100	59*	75*	73*	149*	135*
deaths	9,725	38	52	146	284	244
Adjusted for classes I-V	100	57*	75	76*	160*	134*
Deaths	8,069	32	36	122	240	210

[a] includes unclassified
* SMR significantly different from 100

Social class:	Country of birth							
	All countries		Caribbean		Indian sub-continent		Ireland (all parts)	
	1970-72	1991-93	1970-72	1991-93	1970-72	1991-93	1970-72	1991-93
I/II	80*	71*	145*	83*	97	96	98	95
IIIN	99	100	133*	84*	114*	112*	108	127*
IIIM	106*	117*	87*	105	105	120*	122*	166*
IV/V	121*	135*	95	99	108*	158*	142*	173*
Non-manual	86*	77*	140*	83*	103	100	102	102
Manual	112*	124*	91*	102	107*	140*	134*	169*
All	100	100	90*	89*	101	107*	122*	135*
Adjusted[c]	100	100	84*	82*	98	117*	115*	129*

[a] Recalculated from data in Table 3.4 in *Immigrant Mortality in England and Wales 1970-78* by Marmot MG et al (1984); refers to men aged 15-64.
[b] men aged 20-64
[c] 1970-72 adjustment included unclassified, 1991-93 adjustment for classes I-V
* SMR significantly different from 100

Conclusion

Irish men showed higher mortality from all major causes of death which varied consistently with social class. More of the Irish were in a manual social class compared with all men in England and Wales, but even after adjusting for these differences the mortality of the Irish remained significantly higher. This is the first time that the pattern of social class mortality of Scottish migrants living in England and Wales has been presented. In spite of their higher social class positions, similar patterns to those of the Irish were observed. In contrast to the previous report on men from the Indian subcontinent,[1] their overall mortality was consistently associated with social class. The class gradients were not as consistent for East Africans and Caribbeans, but mortality of men in manual classes was generally higher than that of those in non-manual classes.

All-cause mortality of East African men was higher than that of men born on the Indian subcontinent. Given the similarity in the origin of East Africans to Indians[10] (the largest subgroup), and also their largely non-manual class profile, this is surprising. Further investigation is under way which involves examining names on the death certificates to assess the proportions of 'Indian' as opposed to 'African' or 'European' at death. East Africans and those from the Indian subcontinent showed the highest mortality from ischaemic heart disease and West/South Africans, Caribbeans, and those born on the Indian subcontinent showed the highest mortality from cerebrovascular disease. The similarity between the West/South Africans and Caribbeans, in their higher risks of cerebrovascular disease, may reflect influences associated with their exposure to common risk factors. Among the groups who have settled here longer, men from the Indian subcontinent and the Caribbean, it was clear that social class was an important factor but it was not an adequate explanation for the pattern of excess deaths.

The relative contribution of genetic and environmental factors to mortality patterns among migrants is complicated by various issues. The previous analysis by social class, based on data from the early 1970s, paid considerable attention to selective migration, comparing death rates with those in the countries of origin.[1,12] With the peaks of migration for those from the Indian subcontinent and the Caribbean now more than two decades ago, some adaptation to the current environment could be expected. Table 9.14 shows that, whereas in this earlier analysis by Marmot and colleagues[1] social class differences were not discernible for men from the Indian subcontinent and almost reversed for Caribbeans, by the 1990s a pattern has become apparent. There is evidence that those of Indian origin have been more socially mobile than Caribbeans[13] which may have contributed to the relative changes in patterns of mortality. For Irish migrants the pattern of mortality has always been consistent, but it would appear that relative differences by social class have increased in the 1990s. From the data available we are unable to examine whether this is due to a rise in the death rates of men in manual classes. Recent work has shown that their overall death rates have fallen but that they still remain higher than those seen in Ireland, suggesting the continuation of some selection effects.[14] Factors in the current environment such as health-related behaviour, social support, etc., are, however, clearly important to the health of the Irish since even the children of Irish migrants[15,16] show higher mortality. Recent studies in the USA have begun to explore the complex mechanisms, such as failed job improvement and work-related stress, through which social disadvantage may contribute to the differences in overall survival between blacks and whites.[17,18,19, 20]

The findings reported here for the period 1991–93 show important continuities and discontinuities with the previous work on the 1970s.[1] Social class differences in mortality are larger among Irish and Scottish men than among all men in England and Wales. Among the non-white ethnic groups, the relationship between social class and mortality is becoming apparent in the 1990s for groups who have settled here for some time. Our overall conclusion, however, supports the earlier ones that social class is not an adequate explanation for the patterns of excess mortality observed.

References

1   Marmot, M, Adelstein A and Bulusu, L (1984)
    *Immigrant mortality in England and Wales
    1970-78*. London; HMSO.

2   Balarajan, R and Bulusu, L (1990) Mortality
    among immigrants in England and Wales, 1979-
    83. In: Britton, M (ed.) *Mortality and Geography -
    a review in the mid-1980s England and Wales*,
    London; HMSO.

3   Balarajan R and Raleigh, V (1993) *The Health of
    the Nation: Ethnicity and Health*. London;
    Department of Health.

4   Chaturvedi, N and McKeigue, P (1994) Methods for
    epidemiological surveys of ethnic minority groups,
    Epidemiology and Community Health, 48: 107–
    111.

5   Cruikshank, J (1989) Cardiovascular disease in
    black and Indian origin populations outside the
    USA. In: Cruikshank, J and Beevers, D (eds.) *Ethnic
    Factors in Health and Disease*. London;
    Butterworth and Co.

6   Balarajan, R (1995) Ethnicity and variations in the
    nation's health, *Health Trends*, 27: 114–119.

7   McKeigue, P, Miller, G and Marmot, M (1989)
    Coronary heart disease in South Asians overseas: a
    review, *J. Clin. Epidemiol*, 42 (7): 597–609.

8   Pappas, G, Queen, S, Hayden, W and Fisher, G
    (1993) The increasing disparity in mortality
    between socio-economic groups in the United
    States, 1960 and 1986, *The New England Journal
    of Medicine*, 329: 103–109.

9   Pappas, G (1994) Elucidating the relationships
    between race, socioeconomic status, and health,
    American Journal of Public Health, 84 (6): 892–
    893.

10 OPCS (1993) *Ethnic group and country of birth*.
    London; HMSO.

11 Simpson, S (1996) Non-response to the 1991
    Census: the effect on ethnic group enumeration. In:
    *Demographic characteristics of the ethnic
    minority populations*, London; HMSO.

12 Adelstein, A, Marmot, M, Dean, G and Bradshaw, J
    (1986) Comparison of mortality of Irish immi-
    grants in England and Wales with Irish and British
    nationals, *Irish Medical Journal* 79: 185–189.

13 Robinson V (1990) Roots to mobility: the social
    mobility of Britain's black population, 1971-87,
    Ethnic and Racial Studies 13 (2)

14 Wild, and McKeigue, P (1997) Cross-sectional
    analysis of mortality by country of birth in England
    and Wales, 1970-92, *BMJ,* 311: 705–710.

15 Raftery, J, Jones, D and Rosato, M (1990) The
    mortality of first and second generation Irish
    immigrants in the UK, *Social Science and
    Medicine* 31: 577–584.

16 Harding, S and Balarajan, R (1996) Patterns of
    mortality among second generation Irish in
    England and Wales, *BMJ* 312: 1389–1392.

17 Navarro, V (1990) Race or class versus race and
    class: mortality differentials in the United States,
    Lancet, 1238–1240.

18 Kochanek, K, Maurer, J and Rosenberg, H (1994)
    Why did black life expectancy decline from 1984
    through 1989 in the United States?, *American
    Journal of Public Health,* 84 (6): 938–944.

19 Waitaman, N and Smith, K (1994) The effects of
    occupational class transitions on hypertension:
    racial disparities among working age men,
    American Journal of Public Health, 84 (6): 945–
    950.

20 Perez-Stable, E, Marin, G and Vanoss Marin, B
    (1994) Behavioural risk factors. A comparison of
    Latinos and non-Latino Whites in San Francisco,
    American Journal of Public Health, 84 (6): 971–
    976.

10 | Male mortality from major causes of death

Frances Drever, Julia Bunting and Douglas Harding

Summary

- Here we examine patterns in cause-specific male mortality at ages 20-64 for each International Classification of Diseases chapter, and the major causes of death within chapters; mortality data 1991-93 for England and Wales are used.

- One-third of deaths to men aged 20-64 were from neoplasms, almost two-fifths from diseases of the circulatory system, and 12% from external causes of injury and poisonings. The major causes of death are those picked out in the Department of Health's *Health of the Nation* strategy and are discussed further in Chapter 8; they are ischaemic heart disease (30% of all deaths), lung cancer (9%), accidents (6%), suicide (6%), and stroke (5%).

- All of the main ICD chapters show a strong social class gradient with men in Social Classes I and II experiencing lower mortality than men in Social Classes IV and V.

- Lung cancer accounts for 29% of the deaths from neoplasms. Of the next four largest causes in this group, stomach and oesophageal cancers show increasing mortality with lower class. Cancer of the colon shows no clear pattern, and brain cancer has the opposite gradient to most cancers with high mortality in Social Classes I, IIIN and IIIM.

- Eighty-seven per cent of deaths from circulatory diseases are due to ischaemic heart disease and stroke; in Social Class V mortality from each of these causes is twice that of England and Wales as a whole, and three times that of Social Class I.

- Mortality from accidents, and from suicide in Social Class V is twice that for England and Wales as a whole, and four times that of Social Class I; mortality from motor vehicle accidents is three times higher in Social Class V than Social Class I.

- Mortality from HIV infection is high in Social Classes II and IIIN, and low for manual classes.

- For certain causes of death a large proportion of the total deaths cannot be coded to a social class with the result that the social class gradient may be distorted.

Introduction

The International Classification of Diseases – 9th revision (ICD)[1] was introduced in England and Wales for coding deaths in 1979. More information on the classification is contained in Appendix A. This analysis looks at mortality from each of the chapters of the ICD and for major causes of death within chapters. The causes of death discussed in detail in the analysis of *Health of the Nation* priority areas are included within their ICD chapters for completeness.

Table 10.1 shows the standardised mortality ratios (SMRs) by social class for each of the chapters of the ICD. Two chapters are missing from this table, namely Chapter XI – Complications of pregnancy and Chapter XV – Certain conditions originating in the perinatal period. Not surprisingly, there were no deaths to men in Chapter XI and only 16 deaths to men aged 20–64 in Chapter XV. The final category used for grouping causes of deaths is the supplementary classification of external causes of injury and poisoning. For the purposes of this analysis, this can be considered to be a chapter of the ICD.

Although Table 10.1 gives some overall impression of differences in social class gradients in different parts of the ICD, each chapter covers a wide variety of individual diseases. The rest of this analysis looks at diseases within chapters of the ICD both trying to explain which diseases contribute greatly to the differences in a chapter of the ICD as a whole and looking at social class differences in individual diseases.

Information is presented in the form of tables and figures for each chapter of the ICD. Each table shows the SMRs by social class for an ICD chapter as a whole, and for major causes of death within that chapter. The numbers of deaths in England and Wales in 1991–93 for men aged 20–64 from each cause of death are given in the tables. The SMRs which are statistically different from 100 are marked in the tables.

The figures show the SMRs by social class for the diseases discussed in the text together with their 95 per cent confidence intervals. Whenever possible, the diagrams within each chapter are to the same scale. If the confidence interval does not contain 100, then the SMR is statistically significant, i.e. statistically different from the England and Wales value. A log scale is used to ease interpretation of relative differences. An SMR of 200 means there are twice as many deaths for that cause in that social class as may be expected if the age-specific death rates in the class were the same as for that

TABLE 10.1

SMRs by social class and chapter of the ICD, men aged 20–64

England and Wales, 1991–93

							Chapters of the 9th revision of the International Classification of Diseases										
Social class:	I	II	III	IV	V	VI	VII	VIII	IX	X	XII	XIII	XIV	XVI	External	All cause
I – Professional	75	78	72	64	27	62	65	42	68	39	40	52	44	51	53	66
II – Managerial and Technical	90	79	98	83	41	57	72	56	68	58	52	62	44	40	59	72
IIIN – Skilled (non–manual)	126	101	141	119	67	103	106	92	105	111	71	103	109	107	79	100
IIIM – Skilled (manual)	82	126	89	91	81	85	123	115	100	100	96	115	66	75	101	117
IV – Partly skilled	106	116	94	112	98	96	121	128	118	119	186	113	71	100	107	116
V – Unskilled	156	165	152	105	323	181	186	248	246	208	174	159	91	254	224	189
England and Wales	100	100	100	100	100	100	100	100	100	100	100	100	100	100	100	100
Number of deaths	*1,387*	*55,827*	*3,946*	*457*	*1,396*	*3,578*	*69,384*	*9,704*	*6,453*	*715*	*81*	*445*	*823*	*592*	*21,043*	*175,847*

Note:
Two chapters of the ICD are not included in the SMR breakdown. These are chapter XI: Complications of pregnancy, childbirth, and the puerperium (0 deaths) and Chapter XV: Certain conditions originating in the perinatal period (16 deaths).

cause of death in England and Wales as a whole. An SMR of 50 means there were half the number of deaths expected. Each of these is equally far away from the reference point, England and Wales at 100. On a linear scale, an SMR of 200 would be twice as far from 100 as 50 would be. On a log scale, SMRs of 200 and 50 are equidistant from the reference of 100.

More complete data on the numbers of deaths, the populations and SMRs are available on the electronic media accompanying this volume. A number of diseases not mentioned in the commentary are also included in the data files.

ICD Chapter I: Infectious and parasitic diseases excluding HIV infection (001–139 excluding 042–044)

In 1993 a set of new ICD codes for HIV infection, 042–044, was included in the England and Wales death registration system. In order to have the same diseases included in this ICD chapter for the whole of the three year period 1991–93, the analyses excluded the 1993 deaths in the codes 042–044 and moved them to be with code 279, disorders involving the immune mechanism. This moved about 500 deaths for men aged 20–64 from this chapter of the ICD to Chapter III, endocrine, nutritional and metabolic diseases and immunity disorders.

Table 10.2 and Figure 10.1 show the SMRs for infectious and parasitic diseases overall and the main causes of death within this ICD chapter. Over the three years 1991–93, some 1,387 deaths occurring to men aged 20–64 in England and Wales were coded to this chapter of the ICD. There was no single dominant disease. As recently as 1981 about half of the deaths to men aged 20–64 coded to infectious and parasitic diseases were due to some form of tuberculosis. This is now less than a fifth of all deaths in this ICD chapter. Septicaemia accounts for about 16 per cent and viral hepatitis for about 11 per cent. As can be seen from Figure 10.1, tuberculosis still shows a strong social class gradient, but neither of the other two main causes of death does. For septicaemia, only Class V has an SMR significantly different from 100, having raised mortality with an SMR of 171. Viral hepatitis has a different pattern again with Class IIIN showing raised mortality, SMR 180, and Class IIIM having low mortality, SMR 56. About 15 per cent of the deaths in this code had no social class information. These patterns in individual diseases results in no overall pattern of differences across the infectious and parasitic diseases chapter of the ICD.

TABLE 10.2

SMRs by social class, men aged 20–64, chapter I of the ICD

England and Wales, 1991–93

| Social class | Chapter I – infectious and parasitic diseases (excluding HIV infection) | | | |
	All diseases (001–139, ex 042–044)	Tuberculosis (010–018, 137)	Septicaemia (038)	Viral hepatitis (070)
I – Professional	75*	32*	98	87
II – Managerial and Technical	90*	47*	82	96
IIIN – Skilled (non–manual)	126*	75	112	180*
IIIM – Skilled (manual)	82*	94	84	56*
IV – Partly skilled	106	141*	113	117
V – Unskilled	156*	285*	171*	93
England and Wales	100	100	100	100
Number of deaths	1,387	252	227	159

* 95 per cent confidence interval does not include 100

FIGURE 10.1

SMRs by social class,
men aged 20–64, chapter
I of the ICD

England and Wales, 1991–93

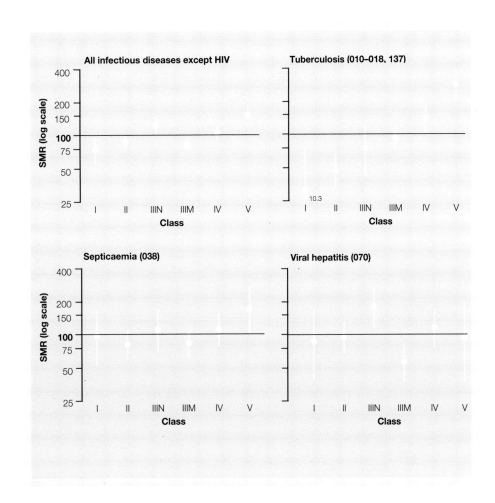

ICD Chapter II: Neoplasms (140–239)

There were 55,827 deaths of men aged 20–64 in England and Wales in 1991–93 which were coded to Chapter II of the ICD, neoplasms. This is over 30 per cent of all the deaths to men in these age groups. Malignant neoplasms made up about 99 per cent of these deaths. Table 10.3 and Figure 10.2 show the SMRs for malignant neoplasms overall and for a number of causes within this. There is a social class gradient in malignant neoplasms. This is mainly due to the fact that nearly 30 per cent of deaths identified within codes 140–208 in this age group are malignant neoplasms of trachea, bronchus and lung – commonly known as lung cancer. This single cause of death was responsible for nearly 10 per cent of all deaths to men aged 20–64 in England and Wales in 1991–93.

As mentioned in Chapter 8, lung cancer has a strong social class gradient. The effect that this disease has on the gradient for all malignant neoplasms is obvious from Figure 10.2, as is the manual/non-manual difference in lung cancer mortality. The manual classes have SMRs significantly higher than 100 and the non-manual classes have SMRs significantly lower than 100. No other single ICD code within this chapter accounts for even 10 per cent of the deaths due to malignant neoplasms. Thus lung cancer plays a very large part in the social class gradient seen for malignant neoplasms overall.

TABLE 10.3

SMRs by social class,
men aged 20–64, chapter
II of the ICD
England and Wales, 1991–93

Social class:	Chapter II – Neoplasms		
	Malignant neoplasms [140–208]	MN of bronchus, trachea and lung [162]	Non–Hodgkin's lymphoma [200,202]
I – Professional	78*	45*	107
II – Managerial and Technical	79*	61*	98
IIIN – Skilled (non–manual)	101	87*	117*
IIIM – Skilled (manual)	126*	138*	105
IV – Partly skilled	116*	132*	102
V – Unskilled	165*	206*	114
England and Wales	100	100	100
Number of deaths	55,205	16,082	2,208

Social class:	MN of oesophagus [150]	MN of stomach [151]	MN of colon [153]	MN of rectum rectosigmoid etc. [154]
I – Professional	80*	64*	113	90
II – Managerial and Technical	76*	69*	95	84*
IIIN – Skilled (non–manual)	98	89	118*	106
IIIM – Skilled (manual)	127*	133*	115*	129*
IV – Partly skilled	119*	127*	101	111*
V – Unskilled	177*	193*	133*	141*
England and Wales	100	100	100	100
Number of deaths	2,898	3,240	3,969	2,452

Social class:	MN of pancreas [157]	MN of prostate [185]	MN of brain [191]
I – Professional	94	111	119*
II – Managerial & Technical	88*	103	95
IIIN – Skilled (non–manual)	108	108	120*
IIIM – Skilled (manual)	122*	120*	113*
IV – Partly skilled	105	103	96
V – Unskilled	153*	132*	99
England and Wales	100	100	100
Number of deaths	2,437	1,995	2,648

* 95 per cent confidence interval does not include 100

Four cancers of different parts of the body each account for about 5 per cent of the deaths discussed in this section. These are malignant neoplasm of colon, of stomach, of oesophagus and of brain. Stomach and oesophageal cancers show increasing SMRs with lower social class. Cancer of the colon shows no real pattern and brain cancer has the opposite gradient to most cancers, having significantly raised mortality in Social Classes I and IIIN.

Malignant neoplasms of the rectum, pancreas and prostate each have about 4 per cent of the deaths coded to malignant neoplasms. This is also true for non-Hodgkin's lymphoma. Rectal cancer and pancreatic cancer show a tendency to increasing mortality with lower social class. Prostate cancer is raised in Classes IIIM and V, but no clear pattern is obvious. Non-Hodgkin's lymphoma has no clear pattern.

FIGURE 10.2

SMRs by social class,
men aged 20–64, chapter
II of the ICD
England and Wales, 1991–93

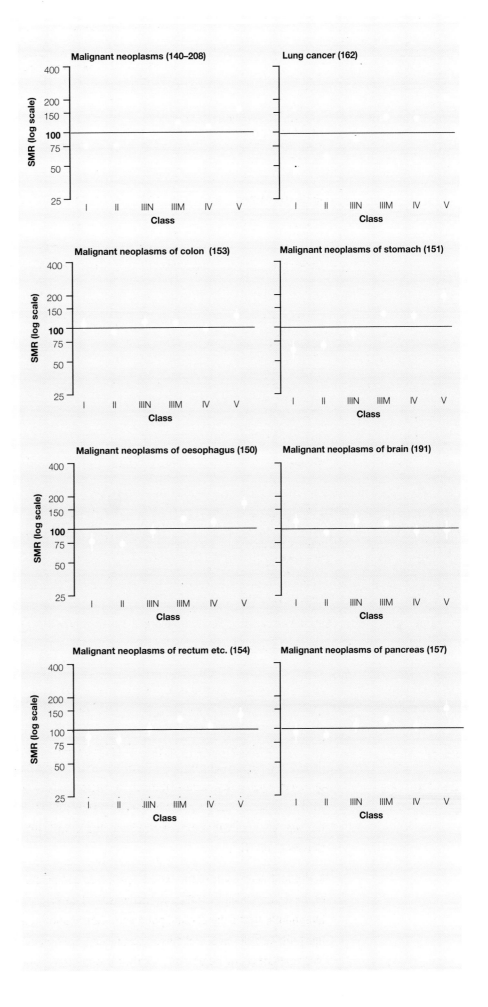

FIGURE 10.2 - *continued*

SMRs by social class,
men aged 20–64, chapter
II of the ICD

England and Wales, 1991–93

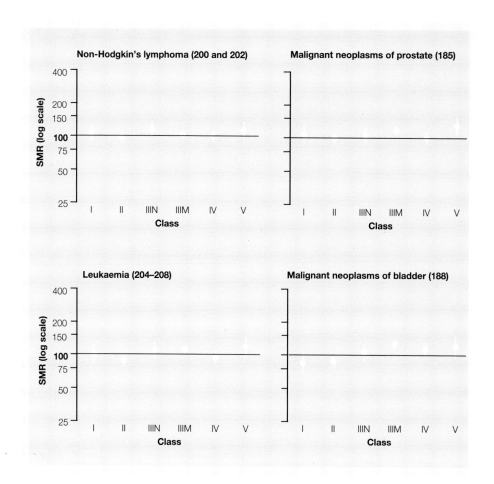

ICD Chapter III: Endocrine, nutritional and metabolic diseases and immunity disorders including HIV infections
(240–279 and 042–044)

As mentioned, deaths coded to ICD 042–044, HIV infection, were recoded to 279.1, deficiency of cell-mediated immunity, in order to have all three years 1991–93 coded on the same basis. This moved about 500 deaths in 1993 for men aged 20–64 to this chapter of the ICD from Chapter I, infectious and parasitic diseases.

There were 3,946 deaths coded to diseases included in this chapter of the ICD. Of these, nearly 50 per cent were diabetes mellitus. About 35 per cent of deaths in this chapter are coded to 279.1 in 1991–92 and to codes 042–044 in 1993. This is an approximate coding for HIV infection for these years. However, not all deaths which are HIV related are coded to this range. This is discussed in detail in an article in *Population Trends* by Anna McCormick. [2]

As can be seen in Table 10.4 and Figure 10.3, both diabetes and HIV infection give rise to significantly raised mortality in Social Class IIIN. Mortality from diabetes shows a strong social class gradient with very high mortality in Social Class V and low mortality in Classes I and II. This contributes to the raised SMR in Social Class V for the whole chapter of the ICD. HIV has a non-manual bias, Classes II and IIIN having raised mortality with Classes IIIM, IV and V having low SMRs. HIV infection had only seven and a half per cent of deaths registered with no or insufficient occupational information from which to derive a social class. Thus the number of deaths in the unclassified and unoccupied groups are not large enough to affect the overall pattern of social class differences in this disease. The differing patterns of SMRs for diabetes and HIV contribute greatly to the complicated pattern of mortality across the social classes for this ICD chapter overall.

TABLE 10.4

SMRs by social class,
men aged 20–64, chapter
III of the ICD
England and Wales, 1991–93

Social class:	Chapter III – endocrine, nutritional and metabolic diseases, and immunity disorders (including HIV infection)		
	All diseases [240–279,042–044]	Diabetes mellitus [250]	HIV infection [279.1, 042–044]
I – Professional	72*	54*	99
II – Managerial and Technical	98	70*	141*
IIIN – Skilled (non–manual)	141*	126*	172*
IIIM – Skilled (manual)	89*	110*	55*
IV – Partly skilled	94	114*	72*
V – Unskilled	152*	214*	62*
England and Wales	100	100	100
Number of deaths	*3,946*	*1,853*	*1,351*

* 95 per cent confidence interval does not include 100

FIGURE 10.3

SMRs by social class,
men aged 20-64, chapter
III of the ICD
England and Wales, 1991–93

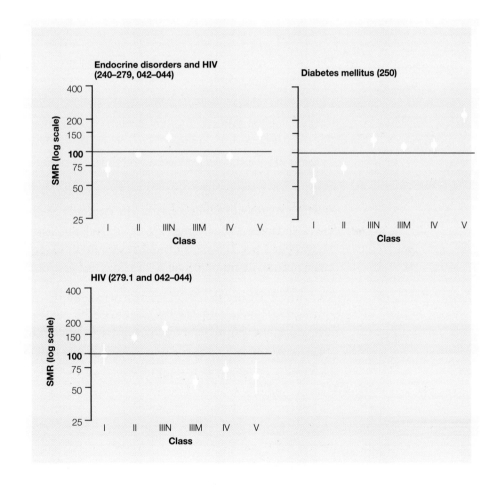

ICD Chapter IV: Diseases of the blood and blood-forming organs
(280– 289)

FIGURE 10.4

SMRs by social class,
men aged 20-64, chapter
IV of the ICD
England and Wales, 1991–93

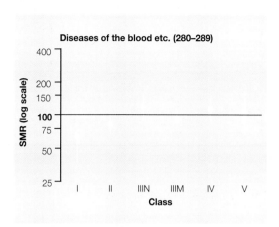

Diseases of the blood etc. (280–289)

SMR (log scale)

Class

Over the three years 1991–93,
only 457 deaths were coded to
this chapter for men aged 20–
64. As can be seen from Figure
10.4, there is no clear social
class pattern in these deaths.

ICD Chapter V: Mental disorders (290–319)

This chapter includes psychoses, alcohol dependence, drug dependence and non-
dependent abuse of drugs. There were 1,396 deaths coded to this chapter in 1991–93.
Of these, the majority were in the codes 304 and 305, drug dependence and non-
dependent abuse of drugs. Together these accounted for 60 per cent of the deaths in
this chapter of the ICD. Just over 15 per cent of deaths from mental disorders were
coded to 303 – alcohol dependence syndrome.

Table 10.5 and Figure 10.5 show the SMRs by social class for mental disorders overall
and for the causes mentioned earlier. The large difference between Social Class V and
the other classes is due to drug dependence and non-dependent abuse of drugs. Only
Social Class V has a significantly raised SMR for these diseases. There was a near four-
fold differential between Class V and Class IV, let alone any other social class, for these
causes. Unusually, over a quarter of deaths in these two ICD codes were in the group
called 'unoccupied'. This means their occupations on the deaths database were coded
to 9 – full-time care of home and/or dependent relative, housewife/husband, full-time
student, independent means, permanently sick, no previous occupation or not stated
(economically inactive or no information at all).

TABLE 10.5

SMRs by social class,
men aged 20–64, chapter
V of the ICD,
England and Wales, 1991–93

	Chapter V – mental disorders		
Social class:	All diseases	Drug dependence and non–dependent abuse of drugs	Alcohol dependence syndrome
	[290–319]	[304–305]	[303]
I – Professional	27*	18*	73
II – Managerial and Technical	41*	32*	58*
IIIN – Skilled (non–manual)	67*	54*	89
IIIM – Skilled (manual)	81*	77*	95
IV – Partly skilled	98	100	110
V – Unskilled	323*	388*	253*
England and Wales	100	100	100
Number of deaths	1,396	844	227

* 95 per cent confidence interval does not include 100

FIGURE 10.5

SMRs by social class,
men aged 20-64, chapter
V of the ICD

England and Wales, 1991–93

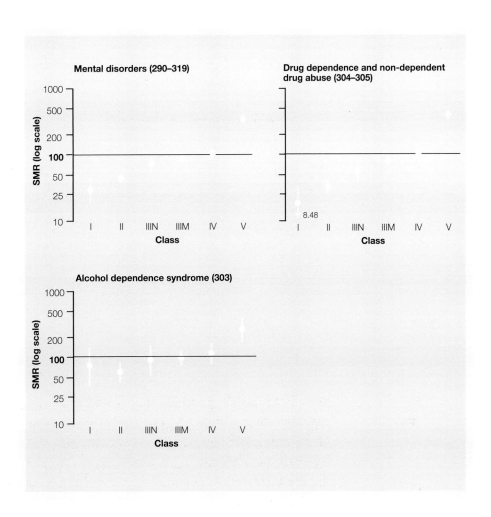

ICD Chapter VI: Diseases of the nervous system and sense organs
(320–389)

Table 10.6 and Figure 10.6 show that there is some evidence of a social class gradient in deaths from diseases of the nervous system and sense organs. However, over a fifth of deaths coded within this ICD chapter lack occupational information on which to base social class. Classes I and II have significantly low SMRs, Classes IIIN, IIIM and IV have SMRs near 100 and Class V has a significantly raised SMR. Of the 3,578 deaths coded to this chapter of the ICD, nearly 30 per cent were due to epilepsy. Nearly a fifth were due to motor neurone disease. A further 15 per cent were from multiple sclerosis.

Epilepsy has a strong social class gradient. Social Class V has an SMR of 275 with nearly three times the number of deaths as would have been expected if the overall England and Wales death rates applied to this class. Classes I and II have low SMRs, but the numbers of deaths in Class I are small. Very unusually, about a third of deaths from epilepsy has no social class information. This may be because those with severe epilepsy have difficulty in having a full-time occupation. Motor neurone disease and multiple sclerosis do not exhibit such social class differences. So, the differences in this ICD chapter as a whole are mostly due to the gradient in epilepsy.

TABLE 10.6

SMRs by social class,
men aged 20–64, chapter
VI of the ICD,

England and Wales, 1991–93

| | Chapter VI – diseases of the nervous system and sense organs | | | |
Social class:	All diseases [320–389]	Epilepsy [345]	Motor neurone [335.2]	Multiple sclerosis [340]
I – Professional	62*	37*	106	80
II – Managerial and Technical	57*	30*	97	66*
IIIN– Skilled (non–manual)	103	81	123	152*
IIIM – Skilled (manual)	85*	57*	122*	112
IV – Partly skilled	96	129*	82	85
V – Unskilled	181*	275*	113	145*
England and Wales	100	100	100	100
Number of deaths	*3,578*	*1,036*	*655*	*526*

* 95 per cent confidence interval does not include 100

FIGURE 10.6

SMRs by social class,
men aged 20-64, chapter
VI of the ICD

England and Wales, 1991–93

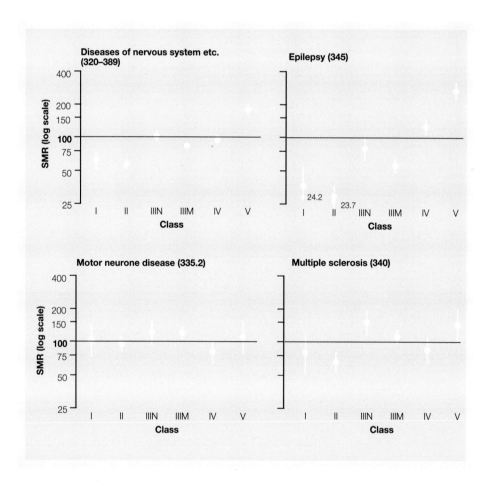

Circulatory disease is still the major killer in men of these ages with 69,384 deaths in the years 1991–93. Nearly 40 per cent of all deaths to men aged 20–64 in 1991–93 in England and Wales are coded to causes within this ICD chapter. Only neoplasms, with about 30 per cent of deaths, has so large a proportion of deaths in a single ICD chapter. Ischaemic heart disease is the cause of three quarters of the deaths in this chapter of the ICD and of nearly 30 per cent of all deaths to men aged 20–64. Cerebrovascular disease accounts for another 12 per cent of the deaths from diseases of the circulatory system. The SMRs for causes within this chapter are shown in Table 10.7

TABLE 10.7

SMRs by social class, men aged 20–64, chapter VII of the ICD

England and Wales, 1991–93

Social class:	Chapter VII – diseases of the circulatory system		
	All diseases	Ischaemic heart disease	Cerebrovascular disease
	[390–459]	[410–414]	[430–438]
I – Professional	65*	63*	70*
II – Managerial and Technical	72*	73*	67*
IIIN – Skilled (non–manual)	106*	107*	96
IIIM – Skilled (manual)	123*	125*	118*
IV – Partly skilled	121*	121*	125*
V – Unskilled	186*	182*	219*
England and Wales	100	100	100
Number of deaths	*69,384*	*52,219*	*8,350*

* 95 per cent confidence interval does not include 100

FIGURE 10.7

SMRs by social class, men aged 20-64, chapter VII of the ICD

England and Wales, 1991–93

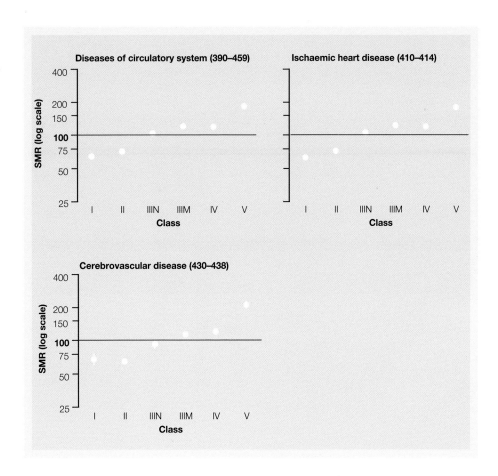

Patterns in social class gradients for circulatory diseases, ischaemic heart disease and cerebrovascular disease can be seen in Figure 10.7. The patterns are very similar for both ischaemic heart disease and for cerebrovascular disease. As these are the major contributors to the whole ICD chapter, diseases of the circulatory system overall also show the same increasing mortality with decreasing social class. Mortality in Social Class V is nearly three times that in Social Class I for ischaemic heart disease. For cerebrovascular disease, the differential is slightly over three with Social Class V having an SMR of 219 and Social Class I having an SMR of 70. Overall in this ICD chapter, the differential, not surprisingly, is nearly three with Social Class I having an SMR of 65 and Social Class V an SMR of 186.

ICD Chapter VIII: Diseases of the respiratory system (460–519)

Diseases of the respiratory system made up about 6 per cent of all the deaths in the age group 20–64 for men in England and Wales in 1991–93 (9,704 deaths). Of this, pneumonia accounted for 30 per cent and chronic airways obstruction another 30 per cent. In 1993, ONS introduced an automated cause coding system. This changed the way in which pneumonia was coded.[3]

General patterns can be seen in Table 10.8 and Figure 10.8. There is no evidence to suggest that a social class bias would be introduced in pneumonia deaths by the new system. There are clear social class gradients in all the respiratory diseases shown in Figure 10.8. Many respiratory causes of deaths can be linked to smoking habits. However, bronchitis and emphysema and asthma can also be occupationally related diseases. They tend to be related to occupations in manual areas and so the gradient is not unexpected. Chronic airways obstruction may also be occupationally acquired and so the gradient is not unexpected.

TABLE 10.8

SMRs by social class, men aged 20–64, chapter VIII of the ICD

England and Wales, 1991–93

Social class:	Chapter VIII – diseases of the respiratory system and sense organs		
	All diseases [460–519]	Pneumonia [480–486]	Chronic airway obstruction nec [496]
I – Professional	42*	58*	21*
II – Managerial and Technical	56*	69*	42*
IIIN– Skilled (non–manual)	92*	106	78*
IIIM– Skilled (manual)	115*	93*	131*
IV – Partly skilled	128*	108	146*
V – Unskilled	248*	197*	298*
England and Wales	100	100	100
Number of deaths	*9,704*	*2,916*	*3,095*
Social class:	Bronchitis and emphysema [490–492]	Asthma [493]	
I – Professional	44*	51*	
II – Managerial and Technical	43*	55*	
IIIN – Skilled (non–manual)	81*	90	
IIIM – Skilled (manual)	125*	128*	
IV – Partly skilled	137*	114	
V – Unskilled	268*	229*	
England and Wales	100	100	
Number of deaths	*1,331*	*910*	

* 95 per cent confidence interval does not include 100

FIGURE 10.8

SMRs by social class,
men aged 20-64, chapter
VIII of the ICD

England and Wales, 1991–93

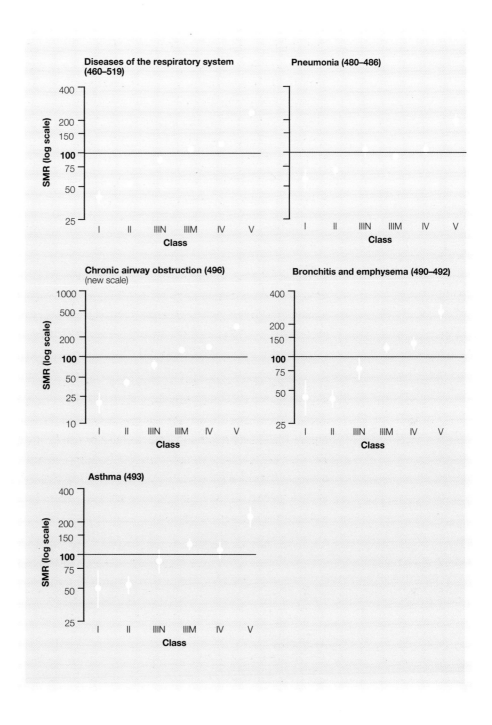

ICD Chapter IX: Diseases of the digestive system (520–579)

This chapter of the ICD had 6,453 deaths to men aged 20–64 in England and Wales in 1991–93. Of these, half were from chronic liver disease and cirrhosis. Another 14 per cent were from ulcers.

From Table 10.9 and Figure 10.9, we can see that Classes IV and V have elevated SMRs for both chronic liver disease and for ulcers. These lead to there being a strong social class gradient overall in diseases of the digestive system. The SMR for Class V for chronic liver disease and cirrhosis is more than three and a half times that for Social Class I. Drinking patterns are known to have a social class gradient and will contribute to this pattern of mortality. For ulcers, the differential is even larger at more than five times. The SMR for Class V is 296 and for Class I is 54.

TABLE 10.9

SMRs by social class, men aged 20–64, chapter IX of the ICD,

England and Wales, 1991–93

Social class:	Chapter IX – diseases of the digestive system		
	All diseases	Chronic liver disease and cirrhosis	Ulcers
	[520–579]	[571]	[531–533]
I – Professional	68*	67*	54*
II – Managerial and Technical	68*	75*	50*
IIIN – Skilled (non–manual)	105	115*	85
IIIM – Skilled (manual)	100	97	106
IV – Partly skilled	118*	119*	125*
V – Unskilled	246*	242*	296*
England and Wales	100	100	100
Number of deaths	*6,453*	*3,270*	*896*

* 95 per cent confidence interval does not include 100

FIGURE 10.9

SMRs by social class, men aged 20-64, chapter IX of the ICD

England and Wales, 1991–93

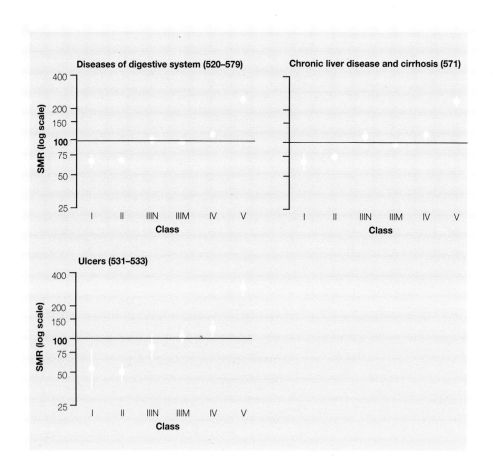

ICD Chapter X: Diseases of the genitourinary system (580–629)

There were 715 deaths coded to this chapter in 1991–93. There is some evidence for a social class gradient with Class V having a raised mortality ratio and Classes I and II have low mortality ratios. Table 10.10 and Figure 10.10 show this pattern.

Renal failure, ICD codes 584–586, account for 36 per cent of the deaths in this chapter of the ICD.

TABLE 10.10

SMRs by social class, men aged 20–64, chapter X of the ICD,

England and Wales, 1991–93

| Social class: | Chapter X – diseases of the genitourinary system | |
	All diseases [580–629]	Renal failure [584–586]
I – Professional	39*	58
II – Managerial and Technical	58*	63*
IIIN – Skilled (non–manual)	111	119
IIIM – Skilled (manual)	100	104
IV – Partly skilled	119	117
V – Unskilled	208*	221*
England and Wales	100	100
Number of deaths	*715*	*258*

* 95 percent confidence interval does not include 100

FIGURE 10.10

SMRs by social class, men aged 20-64, chapter X of the ICD

England and Wales, 1991–93

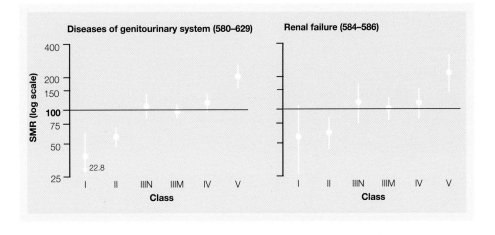

ICD Chapter XII: Diseases of the skin and subcutaneous tissue (608–686)

FIGURE 10.11

SMRs by social class, men aged 20-64, chapter XII of the ICD

England and Wales, 1991–93

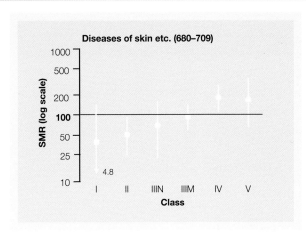

There were only 81 deaths coded to this chapter. This really is too few to make meaningful comparisons across social classes. Figure 10.11 shows the pattern. As there are so few deaths, no individual disease has been singled out for comment.

ICD Chapter XIII: Diseases of the musculoskeletal system and connective tissue (710–739)

There were only 445 deaths coded to this chapter. Table 10.11 and Figure 10.12 show the pattern of SMRs by social class. There is some evidence for a social class gradient, but the large confidence intervals makes this difficult to see clearly.

TABLE 10.11

SMRs by social class, men aged 20–64, Chapter XIII of the ICD

England and Wales, 1991-93

| Social class: | Chapter XIII - diseases of the musculoskeletal system and connective tissue | |
	All diseases (710-739)	Rheumatoid arthritis (714)
I - Professional	52*	34*
II - Managerial and Technical	62*	59*
IIIN - Skilled (non-manual)	103	94
IIIM - Skilled (manual)	115	147*
IV - Partly skilled	113	119
V - Unskilled	159*	161
England and Wales	100	100
Number of deaths	445	154

* 95 percent confidence interval does not include 100

FIGURE 10.12

SMRs by social class, men aged 20–64, chapter XIII of the ICD

England and Wales, 1991–93

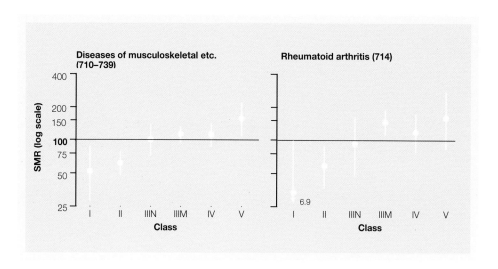

ICD Chapter XIV: Congenital anomalies (740–759)

Although there are 823 deaths coded within this chapter of the ICD, it is difficult to comment on the social class gradients as the occupational information for about 40 per cent of the deaths are code 9 – full-time care of home and/or dependent relative, housewife/husband, full-time student, independent means, permanently sick, no previous occupation or not stated (economically inactive or no information at all). Figure 10.13 shows the pattern for deaths from congenital anomalies overall and for deaths from congenital heart defect. Congenital anomalies of the heart and circulatory system make up over half of the deaths within this chapter of the ICD. SMRs from these causes are shown in Table 10.12.

TABLE 10.12

SMRs by social class,
men aged 20–64, chapter
XIV of the ICD

England and Wales, 1991–93

| | Chapter XIV –congenital anomalies | |
Social class:	All diseases [740–759]	Congenital anomalies of the heart [745–747]
I – Professional	44*	53*
II – Managerial and Technical	44*	55*
IIIN – Skilled (non–manual)	109	127
IIIM – Skilled (manual)	66*	84
IV – Partly skilled	71*	76
V – Unskilled	91	106
England and Wales	100	100
Number of deaths	*823*	*441*

* 95 per cent confidence interval does not include 100

FIGURE 10.13

SMRs by social class,
men aged 20-64, chapter
XIV of the ICD

England and Wales, 1991–93

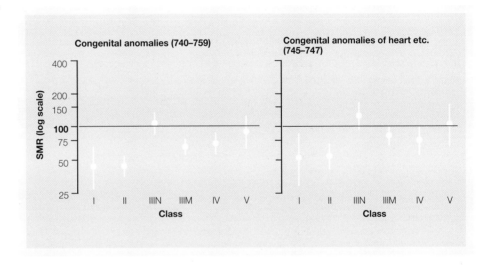

ICD Chapter XVI: Symptoms, signs and ill-defined conditions (780–799)

In general, this chapter includes the more ill-defined conditions which cannot be assigned to a more specific ICD code either because the symptoms point equally to two or more diseases or because there is insufficient study of the medical history to make a final diagnosis. There are only 592 deaths in this category. As the causes of death coded here are so peculiar, no discussion of the SMRs by social class are given for this ICD chapter.

External causes of injury and poisoning (E800–E999)

All external causes of injury and poisoning, some 21,043 deaths to men aged 20–64 in England and Wales in 1991–93, account for 12 per cent of the deaths. Of these, nearly half are accidents of some sort. Suicide and undetermined injury make up a further 46 per cent of this ICD chapter.

Table 10.13 and Figure 10.14 show that there are strong social class gradients in both accidents and in suicide etc. The patterns are very similar with Social Class V having SMRs more than double that of England and Wales as a whole. Accidents has a four-fold difference between the top and the bottom of the social scale with Class V having an SMR of 226 and Class I having an SMR of 54. Suicide etc. also has a four-fold differential, as was commented on in Chapter 8. As these two make up the vast majority of all deaths coded to external causes, it is not surprising the whole group also has a four-fold differential.

Half of all accidents to men aged 20–64 in 1991–93 were motor vehicle traffic accidents. Again these show a strong social class gradient. Social Class V has an SMR of 185, meaning there were nearly twice as many deaths in this group as would be expected if they had the same mortality rates for motor accidents as England and Wales as a whole. Class V had three times the mortality of Class I, SMR 66.

Over 10 per cent of the deaths from accidents were from falls. These too show increased mortality in manual classes. Class V had an SMR of 273, giving a four and a half fold difference with Class I.

About 13 per cent of deaths from accidents were due to accidental poisoning. Again there is a strong social class gradient. Two thirds of the accidental poisonings are due to accidental poisoning by drugs. Nearly 30 per cent of the deaths from accidental drug poisoning did not have enough information to be given a social class. Even so, Class V has mortality more than three times the England and Wales value.

TABLE 10.13

SMRs by social class, men aged 20–64, external causes of death
England and Wales, 1991–93

Social class:	External causes of injury and poisoning			
	All causes	Accidents	Suicide and undetermined	Homicide
	[E800–E999]	[E800–E949]	[E950–E959, E980–E989 exc E988.8]	[E960–E969]
I – Professional	53*	54*	55*	25*
II – Managerial and Technical	59*	57*	63*	43*
IIIN – Skilled (non–manual)	79*	74*	87*	72
IIIM – Skilled (manual)	101	107*	96	80*
IV – Partly skilled	107*	106*	107*	116
V – Unskilled	224*	226*	215*	300*
England and Wales	100	100	100	100
Number of deaths	*21,043*	*10,275*	*9,725*	*482*

Social class:	Motor vehicle traffic accidents [E810–E819]	Accidental falls [E880–E888]	Accidents caused by fire and flames [E890–E899]
I – Professional	66*	61*	25*
II – Managerial and Technical	65*	56*	41*
IIIN – Skilled (non–manual)	86*	60*	66*
IIIM – Skilled (manual)	113*	109	91
IV – Partly skilled	101	117*	90
V – Unskilled	185*	273*	384*
England and Wales	100	100	100
Number of deaths	*5,155*	*1,196*	*369*

Social class:	Accidental poisoning [E850–E869]	by drugs [E850–E858]	by other substances [E860–E869]
I – Professional	28*	28*	28*
II – Managerial and Technical	36*	32*	45*
IIIN – Skilled (non–manual)	46*	46*	46*
IIIM – Skilled (manual)	90*	81*	108
IV – Partly skilled	117*	111	129*
V – Unskilled	329*	332*	320*
England and Wales	100	100	100
Number of deaths	*1,301*	*876*	*425*

* 95 per cent confidence interval does not include 100
Notes:
Codes E850–E858 cover accidental poisoning by drugs, medicaments and biologicals.
Codes E860–E869 cover accidental poisoning by other solids and liquid substances, gases and vapours.

FIGURE 10.14

SMRs by social class,
men aged 20-64, external
causes of death

England and Wales, 1991–93

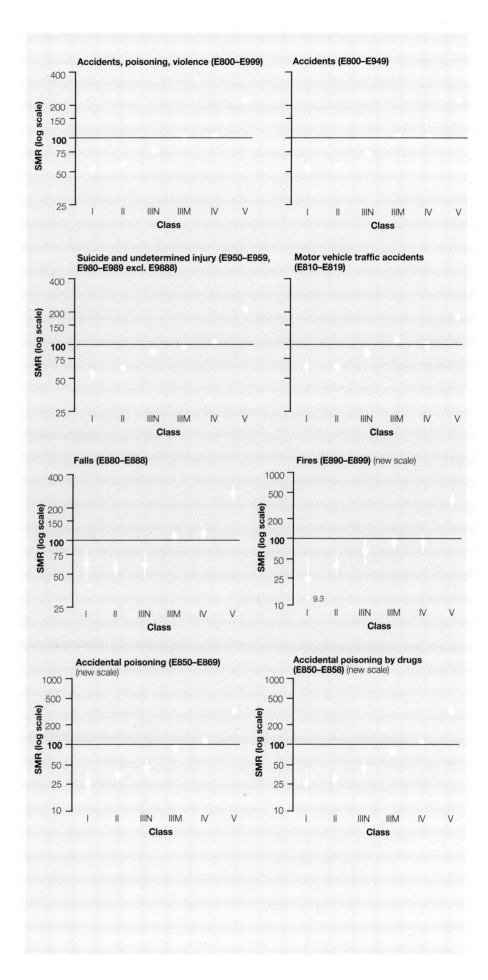

FIGURE 10.14 - *continued*

SMRs, by social class, men
aged 20-64, external causes
of death

England and Wales, 1991–93

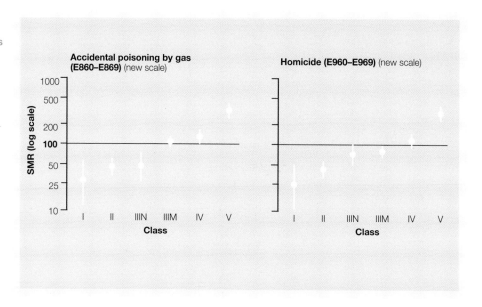

Conclusion

A large number of different diseases has been examined in this analysis. Even more data are available for further analyses on the electronic media accompanying this volume. The major causes of death in men aged 20–64 are, not surprisingly, those which have been picked out by the Department of Health as priority areas in their *Health of the Nation* strategy and are discussed in detail in Chapter 8. These show significant social class gradients with the higher end of the social spectrum having lower mortality, but this is not the whole picture, malignant neoplasm of the brain and HIV infection being the most noticeable examples of a 'reverse' gradient.

References

1 World Health Organisation (1977) *Ninth version of the International Classification of Diseases,* WHO, Geneva.

2 McCormick, A (1994) The impact of human immunodeficiency virus on the population of England and Wales, *Population Trends*, 76: 40–45.

3 Rooney, C and Devis, T (1996) Mortality trends by cause of death in England and Wales 1980–94: the impact of introducing automated causes coding and related changes in 1993, *Population Trends* , 86: 29–35.

11

Mortality trends using the Longitudinal Study

Seeromanie Harding, Ann Bethune, Roy Maxwell and Joanna Brown

Summary

This chapter uses data from the Longitudinal Study to investigate social class trends in mortality among women and men present at the 1971 Census and followed up to the end of 1992. Mortality at ages 35-64 is compared for time periods 1976-81, 1981-85, and 1986-92. Details of occupation and employment status are taken from the 1971 Census.

Particular emphasis is placed on mortality differences among women. Married women are classified by their partner's occupation, and single women by their own.

For the period 1986-92 the mortality of women in Social Classes I and II is 24 per cent lower than that of Social Class IIIM, while for Classes IV and V it is 17 per cent higher. The pattern is similar for men but the differences are slightly greater; 27 per cent and 22 per cent respectively.

The differentials between manual and non-manual classes are much greater among non-married than married women.

There is clear evidence of widening social class differences in female and male mortality over the period 1981-92, due to the larger declines in death rates among non-manual classes as compared with manual.

Increasing differences between social classes in ischaemic heart disease mortality was a major determinant of the widening of the all-cause mortality gradient. Among women, a flattening of the gradient for breast cancer in 1986-92 was another contributory factor.

Unemployment is unlikely to explain the widening social class differences observed here, although with longer follow-up it may become an important factor.

There is consistent evidence of social class gradients in mortality in the UK.[1, 2, 3, 4, 5] Similar gradients have been observed in other industrialised nations.[6, 7] Recently, the focus has been on whether the magnitude of class differences has increased over time.[8, 9, 10] It been argued that larger declines in mortality rates among the more affluent could account for these trends.[11, 12] Over the last two decades, unemployment has increased and its impact has been felt most by men in manual occupations. Mortality of the unemployed [13, 14] is higher than that of the employed but the effects of their higher mortality on social class trends have not been explored.

Analyses of data in the Longitudinal Study (LS) have made important contributions to these discussions.[15, 16] The last published analysis, covering the years up to 1989, showed some evidence of an increase in relative social class differences in mortality among men, but it was uncertain whether these differences were due to a rise in the death rates of those in manual occupations, or to a more rapid decline of death rates of those in non-manual occupations.[17]

In this chapter we address the following questions, placing special emphasis on mortality differences among women:

- What are the current patterns in social class mortality?
- Have the gaps in mortality between social classes widened or narrowed over the last two decades?
- Are changes due to a more rapid improvement or a deterioration in mortality for some classes?
- Which major causes of death account for the social class trends?
- Does the higher mortality of the unemployed contribute to these trends?

Methods related to the LS are described in Appendix A and in detail in Hattersley and Creeser.[18] The main analysis in this chapter is based on men and women present at the 1971 Census and followed up to the end of 1992 (1971 Census Cohort; see Box 11.1). Although social class can be obtained for persons aged 15–34, they are excluded from this analysis to allow comparisons of the same ages at death over the three time periods –1976 to Census day 1981, post-1981 Census day to 1985, and 1986 to 1992. As is now conventional for class analyses of longitudinal data, the first five years of follow-up are excluded because of the effects of health selection[15] (see Box 11.1). Details of occupation and employment status were taken from the 1971 Census. Unemployed men are defined as those seeking work or waiting to take up a job in the week before census.

Detailed tables with 95% confidence intervals for rate ratios and standard errors for rates are available on the electronic media accompanying this volume.

Death rates for each class category were standardised by the direct method to the World Health Organisation European Standard Population, derived for all-cause mortality and for major causes of death. The age-specific rates were calculated using the deaths and person years at risk (see Box 11.1) for each of the three time periods. To ensure that the age-specific rates from the study population were statistically robust, we could not adjust for both age in five-year bands and yearly variations in the death rates. For similar reasons we aggregated Classes I and II and Classes IV and V. The additional advantage of these groupings is that the comparison of rates across classes was not confined to extreme points, that is Class I and Class V, in the distribution. Age-adjusted rate ratios were derived using the largest class (IIIM) as the baseline category (RR=1). We also produced manual versus non-manual ratios (RR=1 for Classes I/II and IIIN) adjusted for the variations in death rates of the individual class categories.

Current patterns in all-cause mortality of women by social class

Examining mortality of women by social class is usually problematic in England and Wales because of the large proportions who cannot be classified.[19] LS data allow examination of mortality differentials among women, as a greater percentage of women can be allocated a class from details in the census. In addition, occupational details of partners are linked to members' records in the LS, enabling the classification

---

Box 11.1   Definitions

Person years at risk

In the LS, we can calculate the exact fraction of a year in which each individual is at risk of death after adjusting for people leaving and entering the study. This cumulative total is known as the person years at risk and is used to calculate death rates per 100,000 person years at risk. In contrast, in a routine cross-sectional analysis, the baseline population for the calculation of death rates is obtained from the mid-year estimate of population derived from the census.

Health selection

In a longitudinal study, health selection may affect mortality differentials in the early period of follow-up. Health selection refers to the process whereby individuals are included or excluded from a group because of their health status. Employed individuals are generally assigned to a social class. They also tend to be healthier than those out of work. The effects of health selection on mortality differences by social class wear off with increased follow-up.

1971 Census Cohort

The 1971 cohort comprises all persons present at the 1971 Census and traced in the National Health Service Central Register. In this analysis, they were classified by their occupation details at the 1971 Census and followed-up to the end of 1992.

1981 Census Cohort

The 1981 cohort comprises all persons present at the 1981 Census and traced in the National Health Service Central Register. They include mainly those in the 1971 cohort who survived the first 10 years of follow-up but also a small proportion of immigrants who entered England and Wales between censuses. This cohort would usually include new births but because this analysis is based on 35–64 year olds, they are not part of the study sample. The 1981 cohort were classified by their information at the 1981 Census and followed-up to the end of 1992.

of women who did not record an occupation at the census. In this analysis, women are classified by their partners' occupation details, or if these are absent, by their own. Marital status is known to be an important predictor of mortality differences and in this chapter we also consider these differences by social class, classifying married women by their husbands' social class and single women by their own.

Table 11.1 shows that mortality of women aged 35–64 varies systematically with social class for the period 1986–92. Mortality of women in Class I/II is 24 per cent lower than that of the reference Class IIIM, while for Class IV/V it is 17 per cent higher. Table 11.2 shows that mortality differences are greater among women who are not married. Because of the constraint of small numbers of deaths at this level of disaggregation, the social classes are aggregated into non-manual (I, II and IIIN) and manual (IIIM, IV and V) classes. Among married women, mortality of those in manual classes is 31 per cent higher than for non-manual women. However, for women in manual classes who are not married, mortality is 70 per cent higher than their non-manual counterparts.

<table>
<tr><td>Social class:</td><td>RR</td><td>deaths</td></tr>
<tr><td>I/II</td><td>0.76*</td><td>450</td></tr>
<tr><td>IIIN</td><td>0.86*</td><td>294</td></tr>
<tr><td>IIIM</td><td>1.00</td><td>783</td></tr>
<tr><td>IV/V</td><td>1.17*</td><td>558</td></tr>
<tr><td>Manual v non–manual</td><td>1.35*</td><td>2,085</td></tr>
</table>

* Rate ratio differs significantly from 1.00

TABLE 11.1

Mortality rate ratios (RR) by social class, women aged 35–64

1971 LS cohort.
England and Wales, 1986–92

<table>
<tr><td>Social class:</td><td>RR</td><td>deaths</td></tr>
<tr><td>All</td><td>1.35*</td><td>2,085</td></tr>
<tr><td>Married</td><td>1.31*</td><td>1,785</td></tr>
<tr><td>Not married</td><td>1.70*</td><td>300</td></tr>
</table>

* Rate ratio differs significantly from 1.00

TABLE 11.2

Mortality rate ratios (RR) of manual to non-manual classes, by marital status, women aged 35–64

1971 LS cohort
England and Wales, 1986–92

Trends in women's social class mortality, 1976 to 1992

During the entire period of follow-up 1976–92, 5,908 deaths were linked to women in this study. Table 11.3 shows the trends in mortality over three time periods. It can be seen that differences between manual and non-manual classes narrowed between 1976–81 and 1981–85 and then increased in 1986–92. The widening of the differential in 1986–92 was the result of the improved relative mortality of Classes I/II and IIIN and the worsening mortality of Class IV/V.

Table 11.4 shows age-standardised death rates of women in each social class and percentage changes between 1976–81 and 1981–85 and between 1981–85 and 1986–92. Between 1976–81 and 1981–85, there was little change in mortality rates of non-manual women but those of manual women declined accounting for the narrowing of relative differences seen in Table 11.3. By 1986–92, however, mortality declined among non-manual women and the fall was larger than that of manual women resulting in a steeper class gradient for the latest period (see Figure 11.1). Table 11.5 shows that the

TABLE 11.3

Mortality rate ratios (RR) by social class, women aged 35–64

1971 LS cohort.
England and Wales, 1976–92.

Social class:	1976–81[a]		1981–85[a]		1986–92[a]	
	RR	deaths	RR	deaths	RR	deaths
I/II	0.72*	428	0.87*	405	0.76*	450
IIIN	0.79*	267	0.98	248	0.86*	294
IIIM	1.00	759	1.00	617	1.00	783
IV/V	1.09*	633	1.12*	466	1.17*	558
Manual v non–manual	1.38*	2,087	1.15*	1,736	1.35*	2,085

[a]1981 refers to census day in first time period and post census day in second time period
* Rate ratio differs significantly from 1.00

Table 11.4

Age-standardised death rates per 100,000 people, by social class, women aged 35–64

1971 LS cohort.
England and Wales, 1976–92

Social class:	1976–81[a]	1981–85[a]	% change[b]	1986–92	% change[c]
I/II	338	344	2	270	–22
IIIN	371	387	4	305	–21
IIIM	467	396	–15	356	–10
IV/V	508	445	–12	418	– 6
Non–manual	355	366	3	287	–22
Manual	488	421	–14	387	– 8

[a]1981 refers to census day in first time period and post census day in second time period
[b] between 1976–81 and 1981–85
[c] between 1981–85 and 1986–92

FIGURE 11.1

Percentage change in death rates by social class, women aged 35-64

1971 LS cohort.
England and Wales

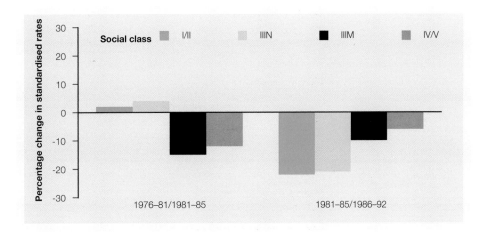

widening of the gradient in 1986–92 was not only related to class but also to marital status. Non-manual women experienced large declines in death rates between 1981–85 and 1986–92, regardless of marital status. Manual women who were not married, however, fared worse than their married counterparts in that their death rates rose between 1981–85 and 1986–92.

Patterns and trends in all-cause mortality of men by social class for 1976 to 1992

As for women, mortality varied consistently with social class for men in the late 1980s (see Table 11.6). Relative differences in the 1980s were wider among men than among women. In 1986–92, mortality of men in Class I/II was 27 per cent lower, and that of those in Class IV/V was 22 per cent higher, than that of men in Class IIIM.

During the follow-up period 1976–92, 10,611 deaths were linked to men classified to Classes I to V. There was a progressive increase in mortality differences between non-manual and manual men during this period. As with women, the widening of the

TABLE 11.5

Age–standardised death
rates per 100,000 people,
by marital status and
manual/non–manual
social class, women aged
35–64

1971 LS cohort
England and Wales, 1976–92

Social class:	1976–81[a]	1981–85[a]	% change[b]	1986–92	% change[c]
All					
Non–manual	355	366	3	287	–22
Manual	488	421	-14	387	-8
Married					
Non–manual	358	364	2	283	-22
Manual	471	420	-11	371	-12
Not married					
Non–manual	354	406	15	305	-25
Manual	620	420	-32	519	24

[a] 1981 refers to census day in first time period and post census day in second time period
[b] between 1976–81 and 1981–85
[c] between 1981–85 and 1986–92

TABLE 11.6

Mortality rate ratios (RR),
by social class and
employment status, men
aged 35–64

1971 LS cohort
England and Wales, 1976–92

Social class:	1976–81[a]		1981–85[a]		1986–92	
	RR	deaths	RR	deaths	RR	deaths
I/II	0.77*	775	0.78*	622	0.73*	750
IIIN	1.07*	450	0.95*	320	0.78*	349
IIIM	1.00	1,470	1.00	1,198	1.00	1,575
IV/V	1.19*	1,164	1.19*	863	1.22*	1,075
Manual v non–manual	1.18*	3,859	1.27*	3,003	1.48*	3,749

[a] 1981 refers to census day in first time period and post census day in second time period
* Rate ratio differs significantly from 1.00

TABLE 11.7

Age-standardised death
rates per 100,000 people
by social class, men aged
35–64

1971 LS cohort
England and Wales, 1976–92

Social class	1976-81[a]	1981-85[a]	% change[b]	1986-92	% change[c]
I/II	621	539	-13	455	-16
IIIN	860	658	-23	484	-26
IIIM	802	691	-14	624	-10
IV/V	951	824	-13	764	-7
Non-manual	741	598	-19	470	-21
Manual	877	757	-14	694	-8

[a] 1981 refers to census day in first time period and post census day in second time period
[b] between 1976-81 and 1981-85
[c] between 1981-85 and 1986-92

FIGURE 11.2

Percentage change in
death rates by social
class, men aged 35-64

1971 LS cohort
England and Wales

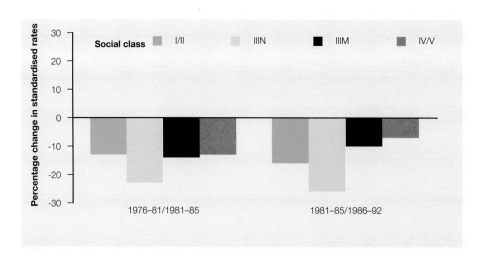

differential in 1986–92 was the result of both the improved relative mortality of Class I/II and IIIN and of the relative worsening in the position of Class IV/V. The improvement in the relative mortality in Class IIIN was such that it contributed to the differences between non-manual and manual classes becoming more marked in 1986–92.

Table 11.7 shows age-standardised death rates of men in each social class and percentage changes between 1976–81 and 1981–85 and between 1981–85 and 1986–92. The death rates in each social class declined from 1976–81 to 1986–92. The wider class differences in mortality in the late 1980s were due to the larger declines in death rates of men in non-manual classes compared with those in manual classes (Figure 11.2). The mortality decline was greatest for men in Class IIIN and smallest for those in Class IV/V, contributing to the marked increase in relative differences between non-manual and manual classes noted in Table 11.6.

Trends for major causes of death

Ischaemic heart disease was a main cause of death, accounting for more deaths among men (38 per cent) than among women (17 per cent). There is a consistent relationship between social class and deaths from ischaemic heart disease in the 1980s for both women and men, with mortality rising with declining social class (Table 11.8). The gradient for women narrowed in 1981–85 and then widened in 1986–92, such that mortality of manual women was more than twice that of non-manual women. Among men, mortality differences between non-manual and manual classes increased over the three time periods. The improvement in the relative position of men in Class I/II between 1976–81 and 1981–85, and that of men in Class IIIN across all three time periods, contributed to the progressive widening of differences between non-manual and manual men.

Among women breast and lung cancers were the next main causes of deaths, contributing 14 per cent and 8 per cent respectively. In 1976–81, mortality from breast cancer was highest in Class IIIN, and in 1981–85 in Class I/II. In 1986–92 however, the gradient flattened, as relative mortality of women in Class IV/V rose. For lung cancer, the difference in relative mortality between non-manual and manual women increased progressively from the late 1970s. Respiratory diseases showed large non-manual/manual differences among women in all three time periods, with mortality more than twice as high for manual than for non-manual women.

Among men, the class gradients for lung cancer and respiratory diseases (which contributed 12 per cent and 6 per cent respectively of the total deaths), were steeper in the late 1980s because of the improvement in the relative mortality of the non-manual classes. In contrast, the gradient for cerebrovascular diseases narrowed between 1981–85 and 1986–92.

Death rates for major causes

Table 11.9 shows that among women, the changes in ischaemic heart disease and breast cancer death rates contributed to the narrowing of the all-cause mortality differentials between 1976–81 and 1981–85 and the subsequent widening in 1986–92.

TABLE 11.8

Mortality rate ratios (RR)
by social class, major
causes of death, men and
women aged 35–64

1971 LS cohort .
England and Wales, 1976–92

Cause of death	Women			Men		
Social class:	1976-81[a]	1981-85[a]	1986-92	1976-81[a]	1981-85[a]	1986-92
Ischaemic heart disease						
I/II	0.45*	0.67*	0.50*	0.80*	0.69*	0.69*
IIIN	0.66*	0.84*	0.66*	1.24*	0.99	0.70*
IIIM	1.00	1.00	1.00	1.00	1.00	1.00
IV/V	1.23*	1.13*	1.33*	1.18*	1.09*	1.15*
Manual v non-manual	2.21*	1.49*	2.21*	1.18*	1.34*	1.59*
Cerebrovascular diseases						
I/II	0.72*	0.61*	0.76*	1.10*	0.62*	0.88*
IIIN	1.00	0.93*	1.22*	0.92*	1.03*	0.84*
IIIM	1.00	1.00	1.00	1.00	1.00	1.00
IV/V	1.19*	1.30*	1.89*	1.32*	1.31*	1.23*
Manual v non-manual	1.39*	1.68*	1.88*	1.17*	1.59*	1.33*
Respiratory diseases						
I/II	0.47*	0.49*	0.47*	0.30*	0.63*	0.35*
IIIN	0.52*	0.43*	0.50*	1.28*	1.04*	0.57*
IIIM	1.00	1.00	1.00	1.00	1.00	1.00
IV/V	1.00	1.27*	1.23*	1.38*	1.57*	1.33*
Manual v non-manual	2.03*	2.51*	2.41*	2.00*	1.80*	2.89*
Lung cancer						
I/II	0.84*	0.68*	0.47*	0.57*	0.58*	0.45*
IIIN	0.96*	0.30*	0.50*	0.76*	0.93*	0.64*
IIIM	1.00	1.00	1.00	1.00	1.00	1.00
IV/V	1.82*	1.06*	1.35*	1.24*	1.13*	1.04*
Manual v non-manual	1.75*	1.90*	2.60*	1.82*	1.55*	1.99*
Breast cancer						
I/II	0.85*	1.30*	1.14*			
IIIN	1.23*	1.24*	1.06*			
IIIM	1.00	1.00	1.00			
IV/V	0.78*	0.88*	1.17*			
Manual v non-manual	0.87*	0.72*	1.00			

[a]1981 refers to census day in first time period and post census day in second time period
* Rate ratio differs significantly from 1.00

Among women in non-manual classes, death rates from ischaemic heart disease and breast cancer rose between 1976–81 and 1981–85. By 1986–92, the proportionate decline for both diseases among non-manual women was substantial whereas among manual women there was virtually no change in the mortality rates. For lung cancer, the numbers of deaths to individual class categories are small especially in Class IIIN, but the non-manual/manual split suggests that the rise in lung cancer death rates among manual women also contributed to the steeper gradient observed in all-cause mortality in 1986–92.

Among men, death rates for ischaemic heart disease fell in each social class between the three time periods. The fall between 1981–85 and 1986–92 among non-manual classes was more than twice that of the manual classes. Death rates for lung cancer and respiratory diseases also declined between 1981–85 and 1986–92 in each social class, with greater reductions among non-manual classes than among manual classes.

TABLE 11.9

Age-standardised death
rates per 100,000 people,
by social class, major
causes of death, men and
women aged 35–64

1971 LS cohort .
England and Wales, 1976–92

Cause of death Social class:	Women					Men				
	1976-81[a]	1981-85[a]	% change[b]	1986-92	% change[c]	1976-81[a]	1981-85[a]	% change[b]	1986-92	% change[c]
Ischaemic heart disease										
I/II	39	45	15	29	-36	246	185	-25	160	-14
IIIN	56	57	2	39	-32	382	267	-30	162	-39
IIIM	85	67	-21	59	-12	309	269	-13	231	-14
IV/V	105	76	-28	78	3	363	293	-19	266	-9
Non-manual	44	49	11	33	-33	291	212	-27	161	-24
Manual	98	73	-25	72	-1	345	285	-17	255	-11
Cerebrovascular diseases										
I/II	26	19	-27	14	-26	45	28	-38	29	4
IIIN	36	29	-19	22	-24	38	46	21	27	-41
IIIM	36	32	-11	18	-44	41	45	10	33	-27
IV/V	42	41	-2	34	-17	54	59	9	40	-32
Non-manual	29	23	-21	17	-26	42	34	-19	28	-18
Manual	40	38	-5	29	-24	50	54	8	38	-30
Respiratory diseases										
I/II	17	11	-35	11	0	16	24	50	13	-46
IIIN	19	9	-53	12	33	66	39	-41	21	-46
IIIM	36	22	-39	23	5	52	38	-27	36	-5
IV/V	36	28	-22	29	4	72	59	-18	48	-19
Non-manual	18	10	-44	11	10	33	29	-12	15	-48
Manual	36	26	-28	27	4	65	49	-25	44	-10
Lung cancer										
I/II	21	23	10	16	-30	63	54	-14	35	-35
IIIN	24	10	-58	17	70	84	86	2	50	-42
IIIM	25	35	40	34	-3	110	92	-16	77	-16
IV/V	45	37	-18	47	27	136	104	-24	80	-23
Non-manual	22	19	-14	16	-16	70	64	-9	40	-38
Manual	39	36	-8	42	17	128	100	-22	79	-21
Breast cancer										
I/II	52	74	42	52	-30					
IIIN	75	71	-5	49	-31					
IIIM	61	57	-7	46	-19					
IV/V	47	50	6	54	8					
Non-manual	59	73	24	51	-30					
Manual	52	52	0	51	0					

[a] 1981 refers to census day in first time period and post census day in second time period
[b] between 1976-81 and 1981-85
[c] between 1981-85 and 1986-92

The impact of male unemployment

We now turn to the question of whether the higher mortality of the unemployed contributed to the observed social class trends. Deaths among employed men accounted for 94 per cent, and among unemployed for 4 per cent, of all deaths in the study (9,969 deaths and 409 deaths respectively). Table 11.10 shows the mortality of those in work and those unemployed. Mortality varied consistently by social class in the 1980s among the employed. The relationship is also generally apparent among the unemployed. Relative differences between non-manual and manual classes widened in the late 1980s for both employed and unemployed men, more so for the unemployed. The improvement in the relative position of those in Class IIIN among both the employed and unemployed contributed to a more pronounced non-manual/manual split. Among the unemployed there was also a deterioration in the relative mortality of men in Class IV/V.

Table 11.11 shows that in each social class the absolute level of mortality of employed men was lower than that of the unemployed. Among the employed, the larger reduction in death rates of non-manual men compared with that of manual men accounted for the wider gradient in 1986–92 (see Figure 11.3). In contrast, mortality of unemployed men in Classes IIIM and IV/V rose in the latest period, thus accounting for the wider differences between the employed and unemployed in 1986–92 (see Figure 11.4).

Social class and employment status at the 1981 Census

Occupational and economic activity details were also recorded at the 1981 Census for those present in the LS study at the 1981 Census. These people, known as the 1981 cohort, included the original members of the LS who entered the study in 1971 and who had survived to 1981, as well as additional individuals who had entered the study through immigration (see Box 11.1). The trend analysis of this cohort is limited because of shorter follow-up (1981–92) and the effects of health selection (see Box 11.1) during the first five years of follow-up.[14,16]

TABLE 11.10

Mortality rate ratios (RR) by social class and employment status, men aged 35–64

1971 LS cohort.
England and Wales, 1976–92

	Employed			Unemployed		
Social Class:	1976-81[a]	1981-85[a]	1986-92	1976-81[a]	1981-85[a]	1986-92
I/II	0.79*	0.78*	0.73*	0.69*	0.89	0.75*
IIIN	1.09*	0.96*	0.77*	1.10	0.93	0.68*
IIIM	1.00	1.00	1.00	1.00	1.00	1.00
IV/V	1.18*	1.20*	1.19*	1.02	1.05	1.28*
Manual v non-manual	1.17*	1.26*	1.45*	1.13	1.12	1.59*

[a] 1981 refers to census day in first time period and post census day in second time period
* Rate ratio differs significantly from 1.00

TABLE 11.11

Age standardised death rates per 100,000 people by social class and employment status, men aged 35–64

1971 LS cohort.
England and Wales, 1976–92.

	Employed					Unemployed				
Social class:	1976-81[a]	1981-85[a]	% change[b]	1986-92	% change[c]	1976-81[a]	1981-85[a]	% change[b]	1986-92	% change[c]
I/II	611	530	-13	448	-15	850	836	-2	782	-6
IIIN	845	647	-23	472	-27	1,362	876	-36	711	-19
IIIM	777	676	-13	611	-10	1,234	941	-24	1,041	11
IV/V	921	809	-12	725	-10	1,264	984	-22	1,333	35
Non-manual	728	589	-19	460	-22	1,106	856	-23	746	-13
Manual	849	742	-13	668	-10	1,249	962	-23	1,187	23

[a] 1981 refers to census day in first time period and post census day in second time period
[b] between 1976-81 and 1981-85
[c] between 1981-85 and 1986-92

FIGURE 11.3

Percentage change in death rates by manual/non-manual classes, employed men aged 35-64

1971 LS cohort.
England and Wales, selected years

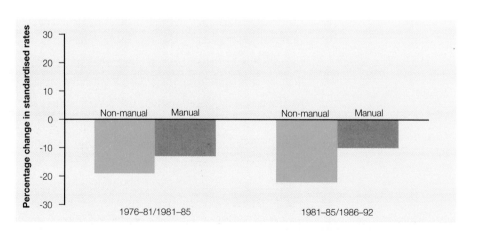

FIGURE 11.4
Percentage change in
death rates, by manual/
non-manual classes,
unemployed men, aged
35–64

1971 LS cohort.
England and Wales, selected
years

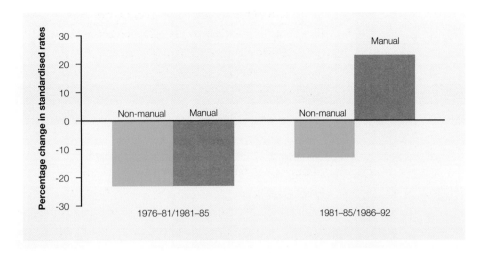

Between 1981 and 1992, 6,726 deaths were linked to men in the 1981 Census cohort, of which 78 per cent (5,223 deaths) were to those employed in 1981 and 9 per cent (600 deaths) to those unemployed. Mortality by social class at the 1981 Census also varied systematically and the class gradient widened between 1981–85 and 1986–92 due to the rise in relative mortality of men in Class IV/V (see Table 11.12). The widening of differences among the employed was the major determinant as differences narrowed among the unemployed. Table 11.13 shows that among the employed, the rise in death rates of Class IV/V contributed to the widening gradient, whereas among the unemployed the large rise in the death rates of non-manual men accounted for the narrowing of the gradient.

Comparing the 1971 and 1981 cohorts, the range of mortality differences by class in 1971 and by class in 1981 are similar in 1981–85. In 1986–92, however, relative mortality of Class IV/V was higher by class in 1981 than by class in 1971 (see Table 11.12). These differences could be partly due to the effects of initial health selection (see Box 11.1). Despite changes in coding practices, relatively large proportions of those out of work continued to be unclassified in 1981. Other analyses have given considerable attention to the effects of health selection in the years immediately following the 1981 Census.[16] Briefly, the class gradient is expected to widen after the first five years of follow-up because the effect of the exclusion of the permanently sick wears off. In addition, it can be argued that the lower proportion employed in 1981 (84 per cent) compared with 1971 (91 per cent) strengthened the healthy worker effect

TABLE 11.12
Mortality rate ratios (RR)
by social class and
employment status,
men aged 35–64

1981 LS cohort.
England and Wales, 1981–92.

Social class:	All[a]				Employed				Unemployed			
	1981-85		1986-92		1981-85		1986-92		1981-85		1986-92	
I/II	0.78*	(0.78)	0.78*	(0.73)	0.83*	(0.78)	0.81*	(0.73)	0.75*	(0.89)	0.92*	(0.75)
IIIN	0.91*	(0.95)	0.94*	(0.78)	0.98*	(0.96)	0.95*	(0.77)	0.62*	(0.93)	1.19*	(0.68)
IIIM	1.00	(1.00)	1.00	(1.00)	1.00	(1.00)	1.00	(1.00)	1.00	(1.00)	1.00	(1.00)
IV/V	1.17*	(1.19)	1.28*	(1.20)	1.12*	(1.20)	1.23*	(1.19)	1.29*	(1.05)	1.24*	(1.28)
Manual v non-manual	1.35*	(1.27)	1.43*	(1.48)	1.18*	(1.26)	1.31*	(1.45)	1.51*	(1.12)	1.30*	(1.59)

* Rate ratio differs significantly from 1.00
[a] includes economically inactive men
Note:1971 cohort rate ratios in parentheses. See also Table 11.10

TABLE 11.13

Age-standardised death
rates per 100,000 people
by social class and
employment status, men
aged 35–64

1981 LS cohort.
England and Wales, 1981–92.

Social class:	All [a]			Employed 1981 Census			Unemployed 1981 Census		
1981 Census	1981-85	1986-92	% change[b]	1981-85	1986-92	% change[b]	1981-85	1986-92	% change[b]
I/II	530	459	-13	471	435	-8	571	779	36
IIIN	620	553	-11	558	510	-9	470	1,008	114
IIIM	683	592	-13	567	539	-5	762	848	11
IV/V	796	758	-5	636	661	4	984	1,055	7
Non-manual	560	490	-13	498	480	-4	520	894	72
Manual	759	703	-7	589	628	7	877	1,008	15

[a] includes economically inactive men
[b] between 1981-85 and 1986-92

in the 1980s. The death rates of men employed in 1981 for the period 1981–85 (see
Table 11.13) are lower than for men employed in 1971 (see Table 11.11) for the same
period. In Chapter 12, Ann Bethune argues that in times of rising unemployment,
those in work are likely to be even healthier. These data lend some support to this
supposition.

Conclusion

With over 20 years of follow-up in the LS, we are able to report on patterns and trends
in mortality differences between social classes with a large degree of confidence. There
has been an overall reduction in death rates with larger declines observed in the non-
manual classes. This resulted in a widening of the social class gradients. Increasing
differences between social classes in ischaemic heart disease mortality was a major
determinant of the widening of the all-cause mortality gradient. Among women, a
flattening of the gradient in breast cancer in 1986–92 was another contributory factor.

Social class mobility or changes in classification[16,20] are unlikely to explain these
trends in mortality. Recent analyses of longitudinal data on morbidity[21] and mortality[22, 23] have shown that social mobility does not have a major effect on the social class
gradient. Although persons moving down show worse health than that of their class of
origin, they show better health than that of their class of destination. The resulting
effect was to reduce rather than to exaggerate the gradient. The study by Blane and
colleagues[22] used one classification of occupations so that the observed effects were not
the result of classification changes.

As expected, mortality of unemployed men was higher than the employed and the class
variations were evident irrespective of when economic activity status or class was
measured.[13, 14] Class differences widened for both those employed and unemployed in
1971. A similar trend was noted for those in employment in 1981 but differences
narrowed among the unemployed as a result of the large increases in the death rates
of non-manual men.

A comparison between the first and second five years of follow-up of those unemployed
in 1971 showed that the changes in their death rates were less unfavourable (I/II
showed a decline of 23 per cent, IIIN a rise of 53 per cent) than those unemployed in
1981. The proportion of unemployed men doubled between 1971 and 1981 and these
immediate effects may be associated with a change in the nature of unemployment.[14]

Our interpretation of these patterns is that even though with longer follow-up unemployment may become an important factor, it is unlikely to explain the widening of social class differences in these data. The proportion economically inactive, however, increased between the two censuses, from 5 per cent to 8 per cent, and it is plausible that their higher mortality may have some impact on the gradient (see Chapter 12).

In summary, these findings show clear evidence of widening social class differences in mortality over the period 1976–92, due to the larger declines in death rates among non-manual classes compared with that of manual classes.

References

1   Townsend, P and Davidson, N (1982) *Inequalities in Health: the Black Report.* London; Penguin.

2   Townsend, P, Davidson, N and Whitehead, M (1990) *Inequalities in Health: the Black Report and the Health Divide.* London; Penguin.

3   Goldblatt, P and Jones, D (1990) Methods. In: *Longitudinal Study 1971–81: mortality and social organisation.* London; HMSO.

4   Blane, D, Power, C and Bartley, M (1996) Illness behaviour and the measurement of class differentials in morbidity, *Royal Statistical Society,* 159 (1): 77–92.

5   Marmot, M and Shipley, M (1996) Do socio-economic differences in mortality persist after retirement? 25 year follow-up of civil servants from the first Whitehall study, *BMJ* 313: 1177–80.

6   Davey Smith, G and Egger, M (1992) Socio-economic differences in mortality in Britain and the United States, *American Journal of Public Health,* 82 (8): 1079–81.

7   Kunst, A, Calelaars, A, Groenhof, F, Geurts, J and Mackenbach, J (1996) EU Working group on socio–economic inequalities in health. *Socio–economic inequalities in morbidity and mortality in Europe: a comparative study.* Rotterdam, Erasmus University.

8   Drever F, Whitehead, M. and Roden, M (1996) Current patterns and trends in male mortality by social class (based on occupation), *Population Trends,* 86:15–20.

9   Filakti, H and Fox, J (1995) Differences in mortality by housing tenure and by car access from the OPCS Longitudinal Study, *Population Trends,* 81: 27–30.

10 McCarron, P, Davey Smith, G and Womersley, J (1994) Deprivation and mortality in Glasgow: changes from 1980 to 1992, *BMJ* 309: 1481–82.

11 Phillimore, P, Beattie, A and Townsend, P (1994) Widening inequality of health in northern England, 1981–91. *BMJ* 308:1125–28.

12 McLoone, P and Boddy, F (1994) Deprivation and mortality in Scotland, 1981 and 1991, *BMJ* 309: 1465–70.

13 Moser, K, Goldblatt, P, Fox, J and Jones, D (1990) Unemployment and mortality. In: Goldblatt, P (ed.) *Longitudinal Study 1971–81: mortality and social organisation.* London; HMSO.

14 Bethune, A (1996) Economic activity and mortality of the 1981 Census cohort in the OPCS Longitudinal Study, *Population Trends* 83: 37–43.

15 Fox, J, Goldblatt, P and Jones, D (1985) Social–class mortality differentials – artefact, selection or life circumstances, *Journal of Epidemiology and Community Health.* 39: 1–8.

16 Goldblatt, P (1989) Mortality by social class, 1971–85. *Population Trends,* 56: 6–15.

17 Harding, S (1995) Social class differences in mortality of men: recent evidence from the OPCS Longitudinal Study, *Population Trends,* 80: 31–37.

18 Hattersley, L and Creeser, R (1995) *Longitudinal Study 1971–1991: history, organisation and quality of data.* London; HMSO.

19 Moser, K, Pugh, H and Goldblatt, P (1990) Mortality and social classification of women. In: Goldblatt, P (ed.) *Longitudinal Study 1971–81: mortality and social organisation.* London; HMSO.

20 Goldblatt, P (1988) Changes in social class between 1971 and 1981: could these affect mortality differences among men of working ages? *Population Trends,* 51: 9–17.

21 Bartley, M and Plewis, I (1997) *The relationship between social mobility and illness in England and Wales 1971–1991: evidence from the ONS Longitudinal Study.* (In press).

22 Blane, D, Harding, S and Rosato, M (1996) *Social class mobility and mortality among middle aged men in England and Wales.* Royal Statistical Society Conference.

23 Power, C, Matthews, S and Manor, O (1996) Inequalities in self rated health in the 1958 birth cohort: lifetime social circumstances or social mobility? *BMJ* 313: 449–53.

12 Unemployment and mortality

Ann Bethune

Summary

Longitudinal Study data are used to investigate mortality 1981-92 of men (aged 16-64) and women (aged 16-59) seeking work at 1981 Census. Findings for men are compared with data from the 1970s.

Unemployment carries a risk of premature mortality. Men and women unemployed in 1981 had excess mortality of about 33 per cent over the period 1981-92. The risk was particularly high among younger unemployed (ages 16-44) where men had a 58 per cent and women a 69 per cent excess.

Adjusting for the social class distribution of the unemployed reduces their excess mortality from 32 per cent to 25 per cent for men and from 33 per cent to 21 per cent for women.

Employed women had lower than average mortality even if their husbands were unemployed, while unemployed women had higher mortality even if their husbands were in work. This suggests a woman's own economic activity may have the stronger influence on her mortality. Unemployed women with unemployed husbands had a 35 per cent mortality excess.

Both employed and unemployed men in the 1980s had lower mortality than the equivalent groups in the 1970s. The difference in their mortality narrowed from the 1970s to the 1980s.

Men unemployed at both 1971 and 1981 Censuses had mortality double that of all men in the same age range; men unemployed at only one census had an excess mortality of 27 per cent. Almost double the proportion of men were unemployed in both 1981 and 1991 compared with both 1971 and 1981. If the mortality pattern of the 1990s follows that of the 1980s this should be a cause for concern.

Mortality from all major causes was consistently higher than average among unemployed men. Among younger men mortality from injuries and poisonings, including suicide, was particularly high. Unemployed women had high mortality from ischaemic heart disease and injuries and poisonings, including suicide.

Neither pre-existing ill health, nor social class, nor marital status (for women) could account for the raised mortality of the unemployed. This lends support to the hypothesis that unemployment has an independent causal effect on mortality.

The 1980s spanned a period of major labour market change throughout the UK. Unemployment, rising since the mid-1970s, peaked at over 3 million in 1986 before beginning to decline.[1] By 1990 it had fallen to around 1.6 million, although there was a second peak in 1991, as documented in Chapter 3.

The relationship between unemployment and ill health has been widely reported[2, 3, 4, 5, 6] and the high mortality risk associated with unemployment continues to be a focus for concern. An earlier study of the 1971 Census Longitudinal Study (LS) cohort established that there was an excess of deaths among unemployed men of working ages.[2] Too few women were unemployed in 1971 to allow a similar study. Analysis of the 1981 Census cohort of men using deaths data to the end of 1989[7] was associated with a 28 per cent excess of deaths in unemployed men and confirmed previous findings for the early 1980s.[8]

In the 1980s there was a continued increase in women's labour market participation. The decline in industries such as heavy engineering and coalmining, along with expansion of the services sector and an increase in part-time work, accentuated this trend.[9] As with men, mortality to the end of 1989 was lower than average among women who were in employment and higher among women who were seeking work at the 1981 Census.[7] Scandinavian studies have also found higher mortality among unemployed women.[10, 11, 12]

This chapter updates mortality analyses of the 1981 Census cohort to 1992. It explores in greater detail the mortality of men and women who were seeking work in 1981 in an attempt to understand why they should be at risk of premature death, and sets out to address the following questions:

- Do unemployed men and women continue to have a higher risk of mortality?

- Is the pattern of mortality among the unemployed a reflection of social class distribution rather than an effect of unemployment?

- What are the time trends in unemployment and mortality?
   - How does the mortality of economically active men in the 1980s compare with men in the 1970s?
   - Do men who were unemployed at both censuses have an even greater risk of mortality?

- What is the influence of marital status on the mortality of economically active women?

- Do the major causes of death suggest why unemployed men and women die prematurely?

- Are there implications for mortality in the 1990s if those who were unemployed in 1981 are more likely also to be unemployed in 1991?

The analysis covers men and women of working ages, 16–64 and 16–59 respectively, at the 1981 Census, followed to the end of 1992. When the 1981 cohort of men is compared with the 1971 cohort (aged 15–64), follow-up is to the end of 1989 and to the end of 1979 respectively. Standardised mortality ratios (SMRs) for deaths to the end of 1992 were calculated using person years at risk. The method is described in detail in Appendix A. Death rates directly standardised to the European Population were calculated to examine the differences between the 1971 and 1981 male cohorts.[13] Further information on direct standardised rates can be found in Appendix A. Findings are shown for the main causes of death. The 95% confidence intervals for the SMRs are included on the electronic media accompanying this volume.

At the 1971 and 1981 Censuses a person was defined as unemployed if he or she was recorded as seeking work, or waiting to take up a job, in the week preceding the census. Anyone recorded as unable to seek work due to temporary sickness was excluded from the analysis.

Social class is defined by occupation at the 1981 Census. For women, using husbands' social class reduced the proportion classified as unoccupied[14] and it is argued that husbands' occupations have the greater influence on social conditions. Moser and colleagues[14] also found that among employed women, husbands' social class identified a wider range of mortality levels than did social class based on their own occupation. This analysis presents findings for women by their husbands' social class if married, or their own if single. A separate analysis of women's mortality by their own social class has also been carried out.

Mortality by economic activity

There were 166,302 men and 151,847 women of working age in the 1981 LS Census cohort (see Table 12.1). Of these, 81 per cent of men and 56 per cent of women were in employment at the census. Thirty-seven per cent of employed women worked part time. Nine per cent of men and 4 per cent of women were seeking work or waiting to take up a job, double that of the 1971 cohort, 4 and 2 per cent respectively. Almost a third of women were looking after the home and/or family. Men under 25 were most likely to be seeking work and 20 per cent of men and women in this age group were

TABLE 12.1

Percentage distribution of economic activity of men and women by age at the 1981 Census

1981 LS cohort.
England and Wales

Economic activity:	Men					
	16-24	25-34	35-44	45-54	55-64	16-64
Employed	65.0	87.0	89.7	88.4	73.1	80.5
Seeking work	13.1	9.7	7.3	7.0	8.9	9.4
Temporarily sick	0.3	0.6	0.9	1.2	1.9	0.9
Permanently sick/disabled	0.5	0.7	1.3	2.8	8.4	2.5
Retired	0.1	—	—	0.3	7.4	1.3
Student	20.0	1.4	0.4	0.1	—	5.0
Other inactive[a]	0.9	0.5	0.4	0.2	0.3	0.5
Total	37,702	37,927	32,630	30,088	27,955	166,302

	Women					
	16-24	25-34	35-44	45-59		16-59
Employed	54.9	50.0	62.4	58.1		56.2
Seeking work	8.3	3.7	2.4	2.3		4.1
Temporarily sick	0.4	0.5	0.5	0.7		0.5
Permanently sick/disabled	0.4	0.6	0.9	2.5		1.2
Retired	—	—	0.1	1.1		0.3
Looking after home/family	15.0	44.3	33.3	35.2		32.2
Student	20.7	0.9	0.4	0.1		5.3
Other inactive[a]	0.7	0.6	0.6	0.5		0.7
Total	36,396	37,798	31,673	45,980		151,847

[a] includes not stated, independent means

TABLE 12. 2

All-cause mortality of
men and women
ofworking ages by
economic activity at the
1981 Census

1981 LS cohort.
England and Wales 1981–92

Economic activity:	Men (16-64)		Women (16-59)	
	Deaths	SMR	Deaths	SMR
Employed	5,557	84*	2,389	80*
Seeking work	812	132*	106	133*
Temporary sick	247	269*	48	282*
Permanently sick/disabled	908	338*	234	587*
Retired	173	160*	—	—
Looking after home/family	—	—	997	108*
Other inactive[a]	119	94	55	114
Total	7,816	100	3,829	100

[a] includes students, 'not stated'
* 95 per cent confidence interval for SMR excludes 100

FIGURE 12.1

SMRs by economic
activity at the 1981
Census, men and women
by age at death

1981 LS cohort.
England and Wales, 1981-92

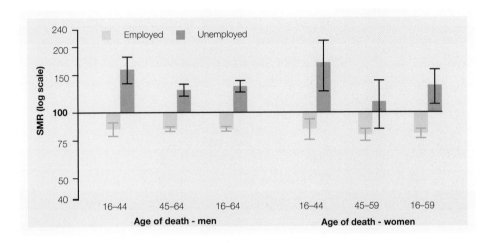

students. The lower proportion of men aged 55–64 in employment in 1981 is largely
due to an increase in those permanently sick/disabled or prematurely retired.

Table 12.2 sets the all-cause mortality of economically active men and women in the
context of all LS men and women of working age at the 1981 Census. Employed men
and women had lower mortality than all men and all women, with SMRs of 84 and 80
respectively. In contrast, both men and women in every other group, with the exception of 'other inactive' men, had higher than average mortality. The high proportion
of students, 92 per cent, among the 'other inactive' men accounts for the lower
mortality in this category. Women looking after the home and/or family had a statistically significant 8 per cent mortality excess. Unemployed men and women had a
mortality excess of the order of 33 per cent.

Figure 12.1 presents mortality of men and women by age at death. Mortality was
substantially higher for the unemployed at younger working ages, 16–44, with a
statistically significant 58 per cent excess among unemployed men and a 69 per cent
excess among unemployed women.

Social class and unemployment

The difference in the social class distribution of unemployed men and of all men in
the LS is shown in Figure 12.2. Unemployment was largely concentrated among the
less skilled groups, with 21 per cent of men in Social Class V seeking work compared
with around 3 per cent in Social Class I. Social Class V contains only 6 per cent of all

FIGURE 12.2

Social class distribution
at the 1981 Census, by
employment status, men
aged 16-64

1981 LS cohort.
England and Wales, 1981

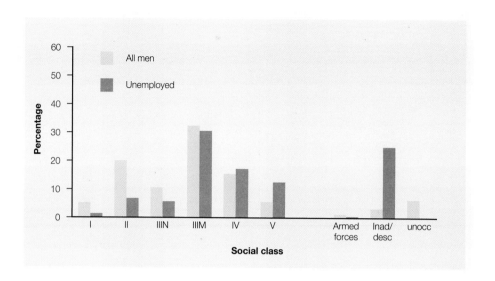

TABLE 12.3

Mortality of men aged 16–
64 by social class and
economic activity at the
1981 Census

1981 LS cohort.
England and Wales, 1981–92

Social class:	Employed		Unemployed	
	Deaths	SMR	Deaths	SMR
I	228	56*	11	92
II	1,253	74*	58	102
IIIN	593	82*	46	118
IIIM	1,945	86*	242	118*
IV	1,078	97	156	139*
V	388	112*	131	176*
Armed forces	28	71	5	267
Inadequately described	41	127	163	145*
Unoccupied	3	95	—	—
Total	5,557	84*	812	132*
Adjusted for Social Classes I-V				125*

* 95 per cent confidence interval for SMR excludes 100

TABLE 12.4

Mortality of women aged
16–59 by own and
husband's social class
and economic activity at
the 1981 Census

1981 LS cohort.
England and Wales,1981–92

	Own social class				Husband's own social class			
Social class:	Employed		Unemployed		Employed		Unemployed	
	Deaths	SMR	Deaths	SMR	Deaths	SMR	Deaths	SMR
I	6	36*	—	—	40	50*	2	122
II	267	73*	8	123	290	68*	15	161
IIIN	450	73*	20	121	241	83*	17	139
IIIM	116	83	5	87	388	79*	14	79
IV	377	96	29	180*	284	101	29	193*
V	121	89	2	59	70	98	3	67
Armed forces	—	—	—	—	7	83	—	—
Inadequately described	13	100	42	135	30	97	26	139
Non-manual	723	72*	28	120	571	71*	34	147*
Manual	614	92*	36	142	742	88*	46	123
Total	1,350	80*	106	133*	1,350	80*	106	133*
Adjusted for Social Classes I-V					87*		121*	
Adjusted for marital status					80*		122	

* 95 per cent confidence interval for SMR excludes 100

FIGURE 12.3

Social class distribution
at the 1981 Census, by
employment status,
women aged 16–59

1981 LS cohort.
England and Wales, 1981

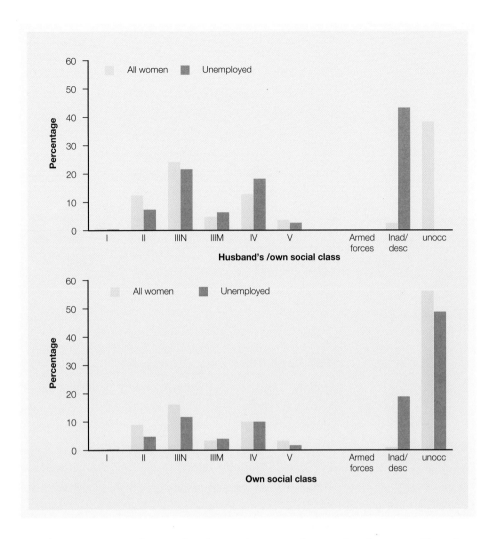

men but 13 per cent of unemployed men. A quarter of unemployed men could not be allocated to a social class as their most recent occupation was inadequately described at the 1981 Census.

Figure 12.3 shows the equivalent distribution for women both by their own and by their husbands'/own social class. The distributions of unemployed women in each social class are fairly similar to those of all women in the same class, although fewer unemployed women had a social class of their own. According to their own social class, almost half, 49 per cent of the unemployed women were in the unoccupied group, while according to their husbands'/own classification the highest proportion, 43 per cent, was in the inadequately described category.

Mortality by social class for men employed or seeking work at the 1981 Census compared with that of all men is presented in Table 12.3. There is a classic mortality gradient among employed men, with SMRs ranging from 56 in Social Class I to 112 in Social Class V. A social class gradient is also seen for unemployed men, ranging from an SMR of 92 in Social Class I to 176 in Social Class V. Mortality is higher among unemployed men in every social class. Adjusting for the social class distribution of the unemployed lowers the SMRs of unemployed men from 132 to 125. Thus, although some of their excess mortality is accounted for by their social class, a 25 per cent excess remains.

Among women (see Table 12.4) there are no clear mortality gradients by social class, whether measured by their own occupations or by their husbands' occupations if married. However, employed women in all social classes except Class IV, according to husbands'/own classification, had lower than average mortality. Unemployed women largely had higher than average mortality. When the classes are aggregated as non-manual and manual, employed women have lower mortality by both classifications. The mortality pattern of women seeking work differs little between the two classifications and although their own social class produces a classic non-manual/manual gradient the SMRs are not statistically significant. By husbands'/own social class a reverse gradient emerges, with a significant mortality excess among non-manual women (SMR 147). As with men, adjusting for the social class distribution of women seeking work explains some of their mortality, although a significant 21 per cent excess remains.

Mortality trends

1971 and 1981 cohorts of men

Mortality rates for men employed or seeking work in the 1971 and 1981 Census cohorts are shown in Table 12.5. Deaths are over a similar time-span for each cohort, that is to the end of 1979 and the end of 1989 respectively. Both employed and unemployed men in the 1980s had lower mortality than their 1970s counterparts, and the difference in mortality rates between the employed and unemployed narrowed from 108 per 100,000 persons in the 1970s to 92 per 100,000 persons in the 1980s.

Economic activity change 1971–1981

In Finland, persons experiencing more than one period of unemployment have been found to have higher mortality than those in continuous employment.[12] This is explored for England and Wales in Table 12.6, which presents SMRs for the 1981 cohort of men aged 25–64 who were present at the 1971 Census compared with all

TABLE 12.5

Mortality rates of men of working ages by economic activity at the 1971 and 1981 Censuses

1971 and 1981 LS cohorts. England and Wales, 1971–79, 1981–89

Economic activity:	Rates per 100,000 people	
	1971-79	1981-89
Employed	302	227
Unemployed	410	319

TABLE 12.6

Mortality of men aged 25–64 by change in economic activity between the 1971 and 1981 Censuses

1981 LS cohort present in 1971. England and Wales, 1981–92

Economic activity: 1971 Census	1981 Census	Number in 1981	Mortality 1981–92 Deaths	SMR
Employed	employed	90,831	4,660	83*
Employed	unemployed	7,007	512	127*
Unemployed	employed	2,172	124	127*
Unemployed	unemployed	1,094	100	194*
Total		101,104	5,396	

* 95 per cent confidence interval for SMR excludes 100

similarly aged men present at both censuses. The majority of men were employed at both censuses, and only 2 per cent of men in work in 1981 had been unemployed ten years earlier. Fourteen per cent of those unemployed at the 1981 Census had also been seeking work in 1971. Men unemployed at one or other census had a significant 27 per cent mortality excess, while the mortality of those seeking work at both censuses was almost double that of all similarly aged men (SMR 194).

Mortality of married women by their own or their husbands' economic activity

Married women are generally found to be healthier than unmarried women.[15] The current analysis shows that after adjustment for marital status, mortality of unemployed women remained higher than expected but was not statistically significant (see Table 12.4).

Raised mortality has been found previously among the wives of men seeking work,[8] and women who were not in employment at the 1971 Census had higher than average mortality if their husbands were unemployed.[2] The effect of their husbands' economic activity on the mortality of married women in the 1981 cohort is illustrated in Figure 12.4. This group of women were aged 16–59 and lived with husbands aged 16–64. Their mortality up to 1992 is compared with that of all married women living with husbands in the 16–64 age group. Employed women had lower than average mortality even if their husbands were unemployed, while unemployed women had higher mortality even if their husbands were in work. This suggests that a woman's own economic activity may have the stronger influence on her mortality. The mortality advantage was greatest when both husband and wife were in employment. This group of women had a statistically significant SMR of 77. In contrast, among unemployed women with unemployed husbands there was a 35 per cent mortality excess.

Unemployment and cause of death

Table 12.7 shows mortality at younger and older working ages for the major causes of death and the largest subgroups of causes among men seeking work in 1981.

For men of working age, mortality from every cause was consistently higher than average among unemployed men, with circulatory diseases the main cause of death,

FIGURE 12.4

SMRs for women by own and husband's economic activity

1981 LS cohort.
England and Wales, 1981-92

TABLE 12.7

Mortality of men aged
16–64, unemployed at the
1981 Census, cause of
death

1981 LS cohort.
England and Wales 1981–92

Cause of death	Age 16-44		Age 45-64		Age 16-64	
	Deaths	SMR	Deaths	SMR	Deaths	SMR
All causes	179	158*	633	127*	812	132*
Malignant neoplasms	28	138	197	121*	225	123*
Lung cancer	6	238	90	147*	96	151*
Circulatory diseases	32	143	305	124*	337	126*
Ischaemic heart disease	21	140	244	130*	265	131*
Respiratory diseases	8	220	47	154*	55	161*
Injuries and poisonings						
including suicide	91	190*	31	158*	122	181*
Suicide	42	205*	14	147	56	187*

* 95 per cent confidence interval for SMR excludes 100

TABLE 12.8

Mortality of women aged
16–59, unemployed at
the1981 Census, by
cause of death

1981 LS cohort.
England and Wales, 1981–92

Cause of death	Deaths	SMR
All causes	106	133*
Malignant neoplasms	44	116
Lung cancer	6	129
Breast cancer	12	106
Circulatory diseases	25	155
Ischaemic heart disease	16	189*
Respiratory diseases	2	51
Injuries and poisonings including suicide	22	226*
Suicide	14	312*

* 95 per cent confidence interval for SMR excludes 100

accounting for 42 per cent of all deaths. The high mortality from malignant neo-plasms (SMR 123) is largely attributable to deaths from lung cancer, which accounted for 43 per cent of cancer deaths among all men seeking work. Among the older men, aged 45–64, circulatory diseases (SMR 124) accounted for 48 per cent of deaths, mainly due to ischaemic heart disease (SMR 130). The only statistically significant mortality excess among younger unemployed men was for injuries and poisonings, including suicide, with an SMR of 190. This accounted for about half the deaths (51 per cent) in the age group, compared with 15 per cent at all ages. Among these younger men, 46 per cent of the deaths in the injuries and poisonings category were from suicide.

As the number of deaths among women seeking work is small, their causes of death are shown for all working ages only (see Table 12.8). Mortality was higher than that of all women for every major cause with the exception of respiratory diseases. There were significant excesses from ischaemic heart disease (SMR 189) and accidents and poisonings including suicide (SMR 226) of which 64 per cent were suicide. Unlike men, lung cancer was not a main contributor towards all cancer deaths. Interestingly, among the wives, aged 16–59, of unemployed men of working ages in 1981, lung cancer deaths were double those of all women married to men of working ages (SMR 215, 95 per cent confidence interval 125 to 345, 17 deaths).

Economic activity change 1981–1991

Economic activity at the 1991 Census is shown in Table 12.9 for the surviving men and women of the 1981 cohort who were employed or seeking work at the 1981 Census. This is an attempt to complete the employment picture of people still of working age at the end of the decade and to question whether the high mortality associated with being out of work at both the 1971 and 1981 Censuses is likely to be repeated.

TABLE 12.9

Percentage distribution of economic activity at 1991 Census of men and women employed or seeking work at 1981 Census

1981 LS cohort.
England and Wales, 1991

Economic activity 1991:	Economic activity 1981			
	Men (16-54 in 1981)		Women (16-49 in 1981)	
	Employed %	Seeking work %	Employed %	Seeking work %
Employed	84	55	73	50
Seeking work[a]	6	26	3	10
Permanently sick	5	12	3	6
Retired	4	2	2	1
Looking after home/family	1	2	18	32
Other[b]	1	2	1	2
Total	98,496	10,094	61,068	4,731

[a] temporarily sick not excluded at 1991 Census
[b] includes students, government training scheme, not stated

Most people employed in 1981 were in employment ten years on, 84 per cent of men and 73 per cent of women. Half those unemployed in 1981 were employed in 1991, although a quarter of men, 26 per cent, were again seeking work. Almost a third of women who were unemployed in 1981 were looking after the home and/or family ten years later compared with only 18 per cent of women who were employed in 1981.

As shown earlier, men unemployed at both 1981 and 1971 Censuses, 14 per cent, had almost double the expected mortality (see Table 12.6). If this pattern is repeated for those unemployed at 1981 and 1991 Censuses, even more men will face an increased risk of premature death.

Possible explanations

In addressing the questions set out in the introduction, possible explanations have been sought as to why unemployed men and women were more likely to die prematurely than all men or women in the Longitudinal Study. The analysis, with follow-up extended to the end of 1992, reinforces earlier findings on mortality of the 1981 LS cohort by their economic activity at the 1981 Census[7, 8] and confirms the continuing mortality disadvantage of unemployed men and women.

The argument that people become unemployed because of existing ill health has been considered an inadequate explanation of the excess mortality associated with unemployment.[2, 10, 16] The men and women in this analysis were a potentially healthy group who defined themselves as seeking work at the 1981 Census, rather than as temporarily or permanently sick. At times of high unemployment men have been found more likely to describe themselves as retired or permanently sick and thus leave the labour market altogether[8, 17] while the fittest remain employed or seeking work. The higher mortality among the economically inactive groups, apart from the group that was mainly students, suggests this was the case with the 1981 cohort of men (Table 12.2).

In any analysis of unemployment and mortality it is important to standardise for social class. The social class mortality gradient in the LS is well established[18, 19, 20] and unemployment among both men and women was largely concentrated in the less skilled social classes. This social class bias in unemployment did not, however, account for all the raised mortality associated with unemployment in this analysis, for either men or women. Classifying women by their own occupations, or by a combination of own for single and husbands' for married women, produced very similar results.

Although unemployment at census is self-defined and therefore unaffected by changes in administrative definitions, it depicts economic activity only during one week in 1981. However, being unemployed at one point in time has been shown to increase the risk of further unemployment [6, 21, 22] and men unemployed at the 1981 Census were more likely to have also been unemployed in 1971. Their mortality was almost double that of all men. This is consistent with Finnish findings that men and women who experienced periods of unemployment had higher mortality than those continuously employed.[12] The raised mortality of LS men and women seeking work is also similar to that of long-term unemployed Swedish men and women.[11]

With the proportion of men unemployed in both 1981 and 1991 almost twice that of men unemployed in 1971 and 1981, 26 per cent and 14 per cent respectively, if the mortality pattern of the 1990s follows that of the 1980s this should be a cause for concern.

It has been suggested that the association between unemployment and mortality might be expected to weaken with the rising unemployment in the 1980s, when the fittest people appeared more likely to continue seeking work.[8, 17] In this analysis, the lower mortality among both employed and unemployed men in the 1980s compared with their 1970s counterparts, and the narrowing of the mortality difference between employed and unemployed, will also be influenced by the overall secular decline in mortality. However, the findings would seem to lend support to the hypothesis that the unemployed in the 1980s were healthier than those in the 1970s.

Married women are known to be in better health and to have lower mortality than those who remain single or become widowed, divorced or separated.[15] Waldron and colleagues[23] found marriage had a protective effect among women who were not employed. However, marital status in the analysis presented here failed to account for all the mortality excess among women seeking work at the 1981 Census. It has also been claimed that women may suffer less during unemployment than men, the traditional housewife role providing a sense of purpose and status,[24] although in this analysis their relative mortality was found to differ little from that of men. However, at the 1991 Census, almost twice as many women who had been unemployed in 1981 considered themselves to be in the 'traditional housewife role' compared with women who were employed in 1981.

The causes of death among unemployed men and women may contribute to the search for possible explanations of their premature mortality. Ischaemic heart disease was the main cause of death among unemployed men and also an important cause among unemployed women. Lung cancer was an important cause of death among unemployed men, but not women. However, lung cancer has been found to be a significant cause of death among the wives of unemployed men. Although ischaemic heart disease and lung cancer are associated with health-related behaviours, findings using data from the British Regional Heart Study showed that differences in mortality between employed and unemployed men remained after adjustment for factors including smoking and alcohol consumption.[21] It is therefore unlikely that health damaging behaviour is an adequate explanation for the excess mortality associated with unemployment .

Suicide was the main cause of death among younger, 16–44, unemployed men and women and it has been suggested that unemployment may trigger underlying psychiatric conditions.[5]

Conclusion

Neither pre-existing ill health nor higher rates of unemployment among the less skilled social classes, nor women's marital status, could adequately explain the relationship between unemployment and the risk of premature mortality found in this analysis. This lends support to the hypothesis that unemployment has an independent causal effect on mortality.[2, 16, 21, 22] The risk of unemployment runs on into the 1990s, with men and women unemployed ten years earlier more likely to be seeking work at the 1991 Census. Whether their mortality risk continues to the end of the century remains to be seen.

References

1 Lawlor, J (1990) Monthly employment statistics: maintaining a consistent series. *Employment Gazette*, December: 601–608.

2 Moser, K, Goldblatt, P, Fox,J and Jones, D (1990) Unemployment and mortality. In: Goldblatt, P (ed.) *Longitudinal Study 1971-1981: mortality and social organisation*. London, HMSO.

3 Cook, D G, Cummins, R O, Bartley, M J and Shaper, A G (1982) Health of unemployed middle-aged men in Britain, *The Lancet,* i: 1920–24.

4 Stern, J (1983) The relationship between unemployment, morbidity and mortality in Britain, *Population Studies,* 37: 61–74.

5 Platt, S (1984) Unemployment and suicidal behaviour: a review of the literature, *Social Science and Medicine,* 19(2): 93–115.

6 Bartley, M (1994) Unemployment and ill health: understanding the relationship, *Journal of Epidemiology and Community Health,* 48: 333–7.

7 Bethune, A (1996) Economic activity and mortality of the 1981 Census cohort in the OPCS Longitudinal Study, *Population Trends,* 83: 37-42.

8 Moser, K A, Goldblatt, P O, Fox, A J and Jones, D R (1987) Unemployment and mortality: comparison of the 1971 and 1981 longitudinal study census samples, *British Medical Journal,* 294: 86-90.

9 Taylor, S, Davies, N and McCrea, P (1995) Demographic and employment trends. In: Drever, F (ed.) *Occupational health: decennial supplement*. DS 10. London, HMSO.

10 Iversen, L, Andersen, O, Andersen, P K, Christoffersen, K and Keiding, N (1987) Unemployment and mortality in Denmark, 1970-80, *British Medical Journal,* 295: 879–84.

11 Stefansson, C-G (1991) Long-term unemployment and mortality in Sweden, 1980–1986, *Social Science and Medicine,* 32(4): 419–23.

12 Martikainen, P T and Valkonen, T (in press) Excess mortality of unemployed men and women during rapidly increasing unemployment, *The Lancet.*

13 Breslow, N E and Day, N E (1987) *Statistical methods in cancer research*, Vol. II. International Agency for Research on Cancer, Lyon, WHO.

14 Moser, K A, Pugh, H S and Goldblatt, P O (1990) Mortality and the social classification of women. In: Goldblatt, P (ed.) *Longitudinal Study 1971–1981: mortality and social organisation*. London, HMSO.

15 Arber, S (1991) Class, paid employment and family roles: making sense of structural disadvantage, gender and health status, *Social Science and Medicine,* 32(4): 425–36.

16 Martikainen, P T (1990) Unemployment and mortality among Finnish men, 1981–85, *British Medical Journal,* 301: 407–11.

17 Laczko, F, Dale, A, Arber, S and Gilbert, G N (1988) Early retirement in a period of high unemployment,*Journal of Social Policy,* 17(3): 313–33.

18 Fox, A J and Goldblatt, P O (1982) *Longitudinal Study: socio-demographic mortality differentials 1971-75.* London, HMSO.

19 Fox, A J, Goldblatt, P O and Jones, D R (1985) Social class mortality differentials: artefact, selection or life circumstances,*Journal of Epidemiology and Community Health,* 39: 1-8.

20 Harding, S (1995) Social class differences in mortality of men: recent evidence from the OPCS Longitudinal Study, *Population Trends,* 80: 31–37.

21 Morris, J K, Cook, D G and Shaper, A G (1994) Loss of employment and mortality, *British Medical Journal,* 308: 1135–39.

22 Arrow, J O (1996) Estimating the influence of health as a risk factor on unemployment: a survival analysis of unemployment durations for workers surveyed in the German socio-economic panel (1984–1990). *Social Science and Medicine,* 42(12): 1651–59.

23 Waldron, I, Hughes, M E and Brooks, T L (1996) Marriage protection and marriage selection - prospective evidence for reciprocal effects of marital status and health, *Social Science and Medicine,* 43(1): 113–23.

24 Jahoda, M (1982) *Employment and Unemployment*. Cambridge, Cambridge University Press.

13 Mortality of women and men using alternative social classifications

Jillian Smith and Seeromanie Harding

Summary

This chapter uses Longitudinal Study data to investigate trends in mortality of women and men using alternative social classifications, in particular housing tenure and access to cars. Mortality at ages 35 and above is compared for time periods 1971-81 and 1981-92. Particular emphasis is placed on mortality differences among women and older age groups.

Mortality in the 1970s and 1980s was higher among people in local authority housing or without access to a car, and lower among owner occupiers or those with access to a car. For example in 1981-92, at ages 35-59, the mortality of women in owner occupied housing was 17 per cent lower than that of all women, but among local authority tenants it was 26 per cent higher.

The relative differences in mortality between the least and most advantaged groups were smaller at older ages, but the absolute differences were larger than at working ages.

For women and men of late working ages, and women at older ages, mortality differentials by housing tenure or car access increased between the two decades. Death rates declined in all categories but the falls were larger among the most advantaged groups.

Among women and men those in less advantaged groups had highest mortality for most major causes of death, but the greatest social differential was found for lung cancer and respiratory disease mortality. For both sexes and most age groups differentials in mortality from ischaemic heart disease increased over time by housing tenure or car access.

Some of the widening of the mortality differences observed here are likely to be influenced by changes in housing tenure at younger ages, but not at older working ages.

A variety of social indicators has been used to compare the health of people living in different social and economic circumstances. Of these indicators, housing tenure and access to cars have proved to be useful indirect indicators of household assets and long-term command over resources. Analyses of data from both the Whitehall study[1, 2] and the Longitudinal Study [3, 4] have shown that housing tenure and car access are successful in defining variations in health.

In addition these indicators have special value for studies which look at the health of women and the elderly who are often not classified under the social class schema. Car access and housing tenure represent the circumstances of all members in a household, rather than one individual and they apply regardless of economic activity status or age. Table 13.1 shows that, for example, of the 1971 LS sample, only 53 per cent of women aged 65 and over could be allocated to a social class from the details available at census. However, 95 per cent could be classified from details of their housing tenure and car access.

In this chapter we focus on the following issues:

1   The patterns of mortality by tenure and car access, with special emphasis on women and older age groups.

2   The trends in mortality differences between the 1970s and 1980s.

3   The major causes of death contributing to these patterns and trends.

4   How changes in housing tenure status influence the mortality gradient.

The main analysis is based on those present at the 1971 Census (the 1971 cohort) using their 1971 housing tenure and car access status. This cohort is followed up for a total of 22 years from 1971 to 1992. We also show findings for those present at the 1981 Census (the 1981 cohort), using their 1981 tenure and car access status, followed up for almost 12 years, from 1981 to 1992. This cohort includes people surviving the first ten years of the study and small numbers entering the study through immigration.[5]

TABLE 13.1

Proportions classified by social class, by car access and housing tenure at the 1971 Census, women and men

1971 LS cohort.
England and Wales

	Social Class I to V	Car access and tenure	Numbers
	%	%	
Women			
35-64 years	92	99	78,940
65+ years	53	95	57,367
35+ years	76	97	136,307
Men			
35-64 years	96	98	91,979
65+ years	85	96	26,246
35+ years	93	98	118,225

Note:
Those not classified to Social Class I-V were inadequately described, unoccupied or in the armed forces. Those not classified to car access and housing tenure lived in non-private households.

In order to compare the same age-ranges over time, those under 35 years of age are excluded from the analysis. The tenure categories used are owner occupied, privately rented and local authority housing. The three car access categories used are no access to a car, access to one car, and access to two or more cars.

Standardised mortality ratios (SMR) were derived using age and cause-specific death rates for all men and women in the LS cohorts.[6, 7] Major causes of death shown are lung cancer, breast cancer for women, ischaemic heart disease, cerebrovascular disease, respiratory disease and deaths from injuries and poisonings. To assess the trend in death rates over the two decades, age adjusted death rates directly standardised to the European population were calculated for the periods 1971–81 and 1981–92.

Socio-economic indicators of health

While social class (based on occupation) is a useful measure, it is increasingly recognised that housing tenure and access to cars reflect additional aspects of social conditions. The association of social class, grouped as manual and non-manual, with mortality is evident in Table 13.2, but there is also systematic variation by housing tenure and car access.[8] Mortality is uniformly higher among both men and women without access to a car than among those with access to a car, with the exception of women aged 75 and over who were in local authority housing and who were in a non-manual social class. Owner occupation generally shows the lowest mortality in all groups.

Patterns and trends in mortality among women

Figure 13.1 shows all-cause SMRs by age at death for women, for the follow-up periods 1971–81 and 1981–92. Housing tenure and car access are taken from the 1971 Census. There is a clear relationship between housing tenure and mortality and

TABLE 13.2

SMRs, by social class, access to cars and housing tenure at the 1971 Census, women and men all causes

1971 LS cohort.
England and Wales, 1971–92

Social Class	Age					
Access to cars	45-64		65-74		75+	
Housing tenure	Women	Men	Women	Men	Women	Men
Non-manual social class						
car						
owner occupied	70*	72*	71*	75*	81*	82*
privately rented	82*	83*	84*	89*	90*	82*
local authority	93	96	86*	90*	97	95
no car						
owner occupied	91	99	84*	95	90*	98
privately rented	105	129*	108	111	95	102
local authority	125*	120*	98	118*	92	107
Manual social class						
car						
owner occupied	85*	82*	86*	83*	88*	93*
privately rented	100	93	91*	100	100	104
local authority	101	104	101	104	97	105
no car						
owner occupied	99	101	101	103	96*	102
privately rented	128*	132*	110*	114*	104	109*
local authority	131*	126*	122*	122*	107*	116*

* 95 per cent confidence interval excludes 100

between car access and mortality in both time periods. Mortality was lowest among those in owner occupied housing and among those with access to two cars. For example in 1981–92, at ages 35–59, mortality of those in owner occupied housing was 17 per cent lower than that of all women but among local authority tenants it was higher by 26 per cent. Although relative differences narrow with age the gradients are also evident at older ages. At ages 60 and over in 1981–92, mortality of those in owner occupied housing was 8 per cent lower than that of all women but among local authority tenants it was higher by 12 per cent.

Trends in mortality between 1971–81 and 1981–92

At ages 35–59, the gradient for housing tenure was steeper in 1981–92 than in 1971–81, mainly as a result of the relative increase in the SMR for local authority tenants. This trend was not apparent by car access.

Table 13.3 further subdivides the age-range and shows that mortality differences by tenure narrowed in the 35–44 year age group but widened in the age group 45–59 and, to a lesser extent, in the older age groups. For car access the picture is again less clear but there was a narrowing of the difference among the 35–44 year olds and some widening after the age of 60 years at death.

FIGURE 13.1

SMRs by housing and access to cars, women at age at death, all causes

1971 LS cohort.
England and Wales, 1971–92

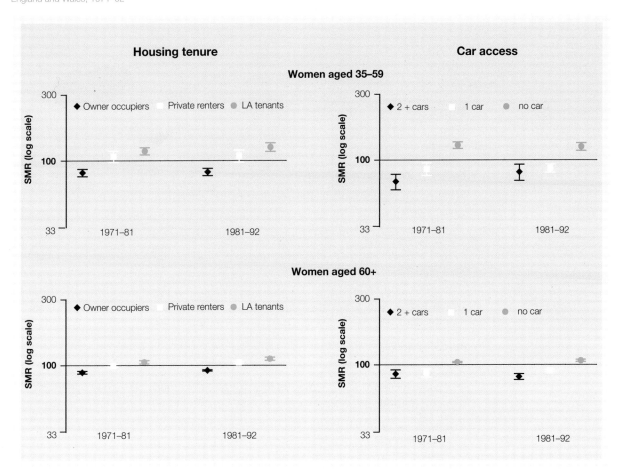

TABLE 13.3

SMRs by housing tenure
and by access to cars at
the 1971 Census, women,
all causes

1971 LS cohort.
England and Wales, 1971–92

Period of death	35-44 Deaths	35-44 SMR	45-59 Deaths	45-59 SMR	60-74 Deaths	60-74 SMR	75+ Deaths	75+ SMR
	Age at death							

Housing tenure

Period of death	Deaths	SMR	Deaths	SMR	Deaths	SMR	Deaths	SMR
1971-81								
Owner occupiers	163	81*	1,056	82*	3,836	86*	7,592	91*
Private renters	58	114	409	107	1,854	105	3,683	97
LA tenants	122	127*	967	117*	2,616	112*	4,133	103
1981-92								
Owner occupiers	173	91	925	82*	3,895	86*	11,377	94*
Private renters	90	104	316	110	1,543	106*	4,811	104*
LA tenants	121	115	755	128*	3,176	120*	5,970	109*
1971-92								
Owner occupiers	336	86*	1,981	82*	7,731	86*	18,969	93*
Private renters	148	108	725	108*	3,397	105*	8,494	101
LA tenants	243	121*	1,722	122*	5,792	116*	10,103	106*

Access to cars

	Deaths	SMR	Deaths	SMR	Deaths	SMR	Deaths	SMR
1971-81								
2+ cars	29	69	270	70*	417	76*	509	96
1 car	178	89	1,041	87*	2,451	85*	3,033	91*
No car	146	131*	1,223	129*	5,887	110*	13,598	103*
1981-92								
2+ cars	36	86	218	81*	939	77*	975	88*
1 car	177	88	984	88*	3,481	88*	6,141	92*
No car	181	119*	832	128*	4,340	121*	15,493	104*
1971-92								
2+ cars	65	78*	488	75*	1,356	77*	1,484	91*
1 car	355	89*	2,025	88*	5,932	87*	9,174	92*
No car	327	124*	2,055	128*	10,227	115*	29,091	104*

* 95 per cent confidence interval for SMR excludes 100

Changes in death rates over time

To make valid comparisons of mortality over time, we calculated the direct age-standardised death rates, using the European Standard Population (see Appendix A for method). In addition, this enabled us to compare absolute size of mortality difference. Table 13.4 gives mortality by housing tenure and shows that although relative differences narrowed with age, the absolute size of the inequality was larger at older ages. For example in 1981–92, at ages 35–44, the difference in mortality rates between owner occupiers and local authority tenants is 0.2 per 1,000 persons, and increases to 2 per 1,000 at ages 45–59, and 6 per 1,000 at ages 60–74.

Between 1971–81 and 1981–92, death rates fell in all categories of housing tenure. At ages 35–44, the largest falls in mortality were for those in local authority accommodation, 26 per cent compared with seven per cent for owner occupiers, which accounts for the narrowing of relative differences observed above in Table 13.3. In contrast, at ages 45–59 there were larger declines in mortality among those in owner occupied housing, 25 per cent compared with 17 per cent for local authority tenants, so that the gradient widened. The trends for women aged 60–74 and 75 and over also suggest that the increase in mortality differences was due to smaller declines in mortality among those in the most disadvantaged categories.

TABLE 13.4

Age-standardised death rates per 1,000 people, by housing tenure, women, all causes

1971 LS cohort.
England and Wales, 1971–92

Age at death	Period of death		
Housing tenure	1971-81	1981-92	change[a] %
35-44 years			
Owner occupiers	0.99	0.92	-7
Private renters	1.37	1.04	-24
LA tenants	1.56	1.16	-26
45-59 years			
Owner occupiers	4.28	3.22	-25
Private renters	5.62	4.32	-23
LA tenants	6.09	5.07	-17
60-74 years			
Owner occupiers	17.19	14.65	-15
Private renters	21.13	18.38	-13
LA tenants	22.50	20.53	-9
75+ years			
Owner occupiers	89.48	77.83	-13
Private renters	95.63	86.88	-9
LA tenants	98.50	89.80	-9

[a] percentage change in 1971 cohort mortality rates between 1981–92 and 1971–81, in terms of 1971-81 figures

Variation by cause of death

Figure 13.2 shows mortality for women by housing tenure and car access in 1971 for major causes of death in the follow-up periods 1971–81 and 1981–92. Detailed results are available on the electronic media accompanying this volume. Consistent gradients can be seen for most major causes of death, with the highest mortality among the less advantaged groups. As has been found in previous studies using the LS,[9] the widest range of mortality levels was found for lung cancer and respiratory diseases.

Ischaemic heart disease, a main cause of death (13 per cent of all deaths), shows a consistent widening over time in mortality differences among those aged 35–59 and 60–74 by both indicators. In contrast to these other diseases, mortality from breast cancer does not appear to differ significantly between socio-economic groups. Where the results differ between housing tenure and car access, as is the case for cerebrovascular diseases for women under 60, we suggest that this relates to the problems of attempting to summarise peoples' socio-economic circumstances, particularly those of women, using a single measure.

Patterns and trends in mortality among men

Figure 13.3 shows all-cause mortality for men for the follow-up periods 1971–81 and 1981–92 with housing tenure and car access taken from the 1971 Census. As for women, the same relationship between the indicators and mortality is seen, with a narrowing in the differences at older age groups. Again the widening of relative differences by tenure at ages 35–64 is apparent because of the rise in mortality for local authority tenants between the two decades. Table 13.5 shows that, as with women, the widening between 1971–81 and 1981–92 occurred at ages 45–64, with mortality differences narrowing at ages 35–44. For car access, differences also narrowed at ages 35–44, but the trends were less clear at older ages.

FIGURE 13.2
SMRs by housing tenure
access to cars women by
age at death, selected
causes
1971 LS cohort.
England and Wales, 1971–92

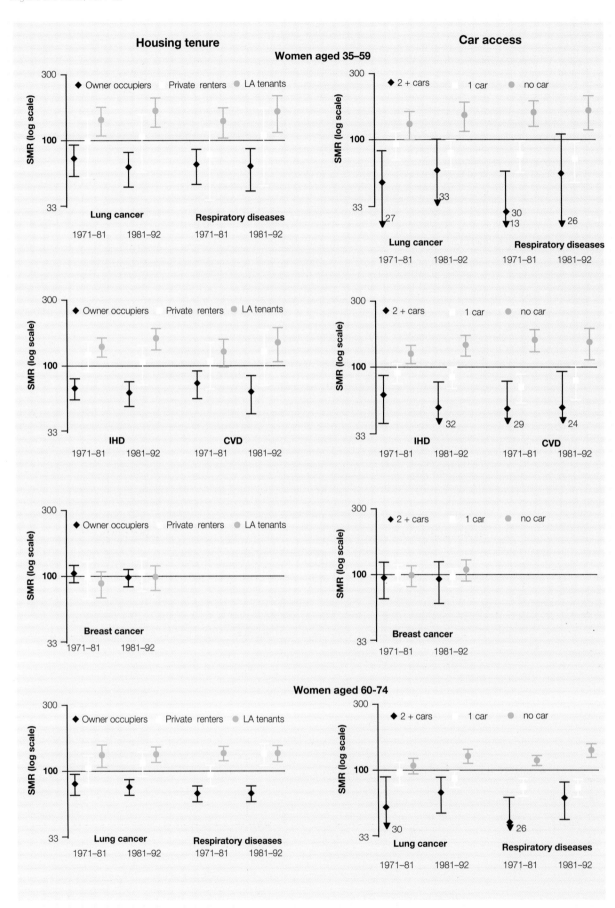

FIGURE 13.2 - *continued*

SMRs by housing tenure
access to cars women by age
at death, selected causes

1971 LS cohort.
England and Wales, 1971–92

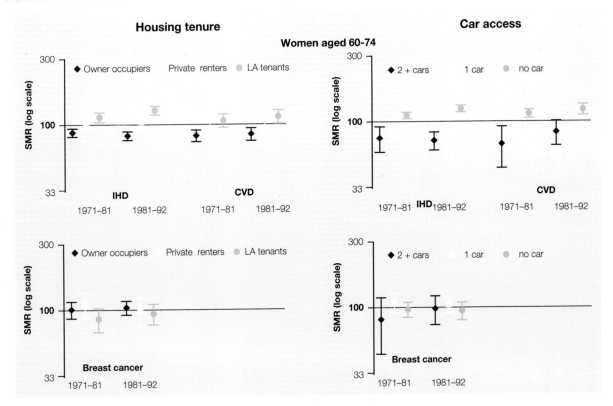

FIGURE 13.3

SMRs by housing tenure and
access to cars men by age at
death, all causes

1971 LS cohort.
England and Wales, 1971–92

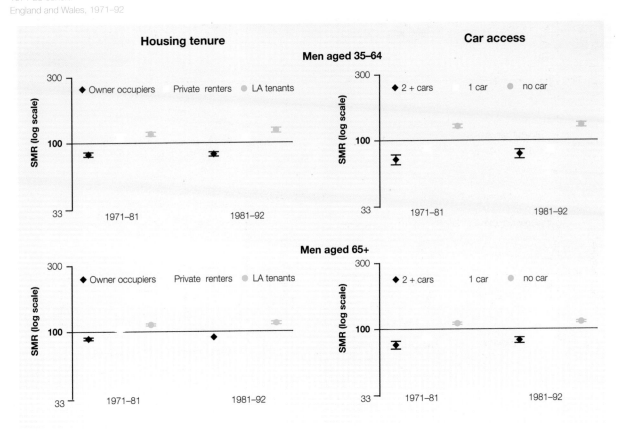

TABLE 13.5

SMRs by age and by
housing tenure and by car
access, men at the 1971
Census, all causes

1971 LS cohort.
England and Wales, 1971-92

	Age at death							
	35-44		45-64		65-74		75+	
Period of death	Deaths	SMR	Deaths	SMR	Deaths	SMR	Deaths	SMR
Housing tenure								
1971-81								
Owner occupiers	275	80*	3,161	84*	4,595	87*	5,476	91*
Private renters	108	111	1,345	110*	2,111	107*	2,286	102
LA tenants	194	126*	2,645	115*	3,004	116*	2,653	109*
1981-92								
Owner occupiers	244	88	2,926	82*	4,592	86*	8,259	94*
Private renters	125	93	1,077	112*	1,808	109*	2,976	104
LA tenants	200	117*	2,395	124*	3,517	117*	3,885	113*
1971-92								
Owner occupiers	519	84*	6,087	83*	9,187	87*	13,735	93*
Private renters	233	100	2,422	111*	3,919	108*	5,262	103
LA tenants	394	121*	5,040	119*	6,521	117*	6,538	111*
Access to cars								
1971-81								
2+ cars	53	75*	784	73*	591	72*	381	88*
1 car	282	82*	3,211	89*	3,441	87*	2,650	85*
No car	272	143*	3,451	125*	6,045	115*	8,094	107*
1981-92								
2+ cars	73	74*	749	81*	1,281	82*	1,196	85*
1 car	251	88*	3,118	87*	4,521	91*	5,992	93*
No car	286	128*	2,689	131*	4,353	121*	8,205	109*
1971-92								
2+ cars	126	74*	1,533	77*	1,872	78*	1,577	86*
1 car	533	84*	6,329	88*	7,962	89*	8,642	90*
No car	558	135*	6,140	128*	10,398	117*	16,299	108*

* 95 per cent confidence interval for SMR excludes 100

TABLE 13.6

Age-standardised death
rates per 1,000 people, by
housing tenure, men, all
causes

1971 LS cohort.
England and Wales, 1971–92

Age at death	Period of death		
Housing tenure	1971-81	1981-92	change[a] %
35-44 years			
Owner occupiers	1.60	1.34	-16
Private renters	2.24	1.41	-37
LA tenants	2.51	1.80	-28
45-64 years			
Owner occupiers	9.99	7.50	-25
Private renters	13.19	10.28	-22
LA tenants	13.76	11.44	-17
65-74 years			
Owner occupiers	43.31	34.76	-20
Private renters	53.20	44.56	-16
LA tenants	57.77	47.16	-18
75+ years			
Owner occupiers	130.55	113.28	-13
Private renters	144.73	122.90	-15
LA tenants	153.23	132.78	-13

[a] percentage change in 1971 cohort mortality rates between 1981-92 and 1971-81, in terms of
1971-81 figures

Changes in death rates over time

Table 13.6 shows direct age-standardised rates for men by housing tenure. As noted for women, absolute differences were larger at older ages than at younger ages. Also, levels of mortality fell between the 70s and the 80s in all categories. The narrowing of the gradient at ages 35–44 was a result of larger mortality declines among renters, in particular among private renters (37 per cent), and the widening of the gradient at ages 45–64 was due to the larger declines among owner occupiers (25 per cent).

Variation by cause of death

Figure 13.4 shows mortality for men by housing tenure and by car access for major causes of death in the follow-up periods 1971–81 and 1981–92. Detailed results are available on the electronic media accompanying this volume. The consistent patterns, noted for women, can be seen for most major causes of death, with highest mortality among the less advantaged groups. For men aged 35–64, the widest ranges of mortality levels were found for lung cancer and respiratory diseases.

Ischaemic heart disease, a major contributory cause (36 per cent of all deaths), shows a consistent increase over time in mortality differences by both housing tenure and car access. However for other causes, among men aged 65–74, the trends are not always consistent for the two indicators. For example, housing tenure suggests a decrease in differences for lung cancer between 1971–81 and 1981–92, but car access shows a widening.

The effect of changes in housing tenure

We now look at how changes in housing tenure status between 1971 and 1981 have affected mortality.

Table 13.7 shows direct age-standardised death rates for women present at the 1981 Census (the 1981 cohort) and followed up from 1981 to 1992, with tenure taken from the 1981 Census. Their death rates are compared to the rates for the 1971 cohort for the follow-up period 1971–81, with tenure taken from the 1971 Census. In all tenure categories the death rate declined. However women in the 35–44 year age group now show the smallest fall in mortality rates to be among local authority tenants, 8 per cent. This results in an increase rather than a reduction in differences between the 1970s and 1980s, in contrast to the analysis of the 1971 cohort over the same two periods (see Table 13.4). For this age-group, in 1971–81, mortality of local authority tenants is 58 per cent higher than that of owner occupiers. In 1981–92, by tenure at the 1971 Census differences appear to decrease as the death rate of local authority tenants is 26 per cent higher (Table 13.4) but by tenure at the 1981 Census it increases as the death rate is 78 per cent higher (Table 13.7). The implication is that moves between housing tenure categories affected the results for women in this younger age group.

At ages 45–59, however, the largest falls in mortality are among women in owner occupied housing, whether tenure status is taken from the 1971 Census (see Table 13.4) or the 1981 Census (see Table 13.7). This is clear evidence that mortality

FIGURE 13.4
SMRs by housing tenure
and access to cars, men
by age at death, selected
causes
1971 LS cohort
England and Wales, 1971–9292

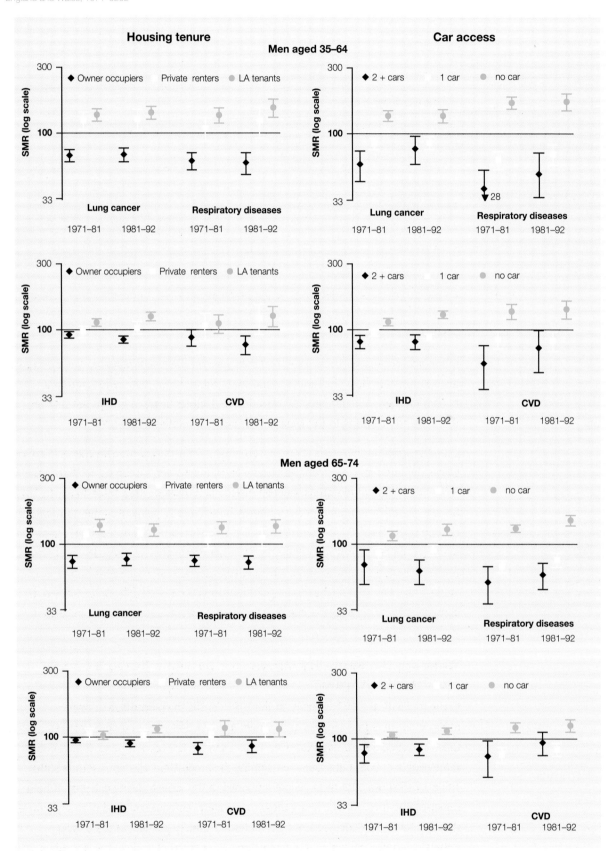

TABLE 13.7

Age-standardised death
rates per 1,000 people, by
housing tenure, women,
all causes

1971 and 1981 LS cohorts.
England and Wales, 1971–92.

| Age at death | 1971 cohort[a] | 1981 cohort[b] | |
| Housing tenure | Period of death: | | change[c] |
	1971-81	1981-92	%
35-44 years			
Owner occupiers	0.99	0.81	-18
Private renters	1.37	1.08	-21
LA tenants	1.56	1.44	-8
45-59 years			
Owner occupiers	4.28	3.18	-26
Private renters	5.62	4.80	-15
LA tenants	6.09	5.09	-16
60-74 years			
Owner occupiers	17.19	14.30	-17
Private renters	21.13	18.34	-13
LA tenants	22.50	20.95	-7
75+ years			
Owner occupiers	89.48	75.08	-16
Private renters	95.63	81.20	-15
LA tenants	98.50	87.90	-11

[a] tenure status from 1971 Census
[b] tenure status from 1981 Census
[c] percentage change between 1981 cohort mortality rates (1981–92) compared to 1971 cohort rates (1971–81), in terms of 1971-81 figures

differences by tenure status have increased between the two decades for women in this age group, regardless of changes in the composition of the sample in relation to housing tenure. At older ages the variation in declines between groups are smaller, therefore contributing to the general narrowing of relative differences.

The corresponding analysis for men, comparing the 1981 cohort with the 1971 cohort, shows the same apparent contradiction seen in the women's analysis, in that in the 35–44 age group differentials widened instead of narrowing (see Table 13.8). In 1971–81, the mortality of men in local authority housing is 57 per cent higher than owner occupiers. In 1981–92, by tenure at the 1981 Census mortality of local authority tenants is 68 per cent higher than that of owner occupiers (see Table 13.8) whereas for the same period by tenure at the 1971 Census, mortality is 34 per cent higher (see Table 13.6). For men in the 45–64 year age group the largest fall, as for women, is consistently among owner occupiers regardless of when tenure status is measured.

What are the mortality differences between housing tenure movers and stayers?

Compared with the 1971 Census, at the 1981 Census the percentage in owner occupation increased for men and women aged 35-64 with a compensatory fall among those in rented accommodation (see Table 13.9). In the LS, it is possible to identify the same people at both Censuses and examine the proportions changing tenure status. Table 13.10 shows that most people remained in the same housing category at both censuses, the most mobile being those in privately rented accommodation. By tenure status at the 1981 Census, 81 per cent of female and 79 per cent of male local authority tenants, 80 per cent of female and 79 per cent of male owner occupiers, and

TABLE 13.8

Age-standardised death rates per 1,000 people, by housing tenure, men, all causes

1971 and 1981 LS cohorts. England and Wales, 1971–92

Age at death Housing tenure	1971 cohort[a]	1981 cohort[b]	
	period of death		
	1971-81	1981-92	change[c] %
35-44 years			
Owner occupiers	1.60	1.21	-24
Private renters	2.24	1.68	-25
LA tenants	2.51	2.03	-19
45-64 years			
Owner occupiers	9.99	7.30	-27
Private renters	13.19	10.55	-20
LA tenants	13.76	12.26	-11
65-74 years			
Owner occupiers	43.31	34.64	-20
Private renters	53.20	43.67	-18
LA tenants	57.77	48.29	-16
75+ years			
Owner occupiers	130.55	112.05	-14
Private renters	144.73	126.73	-12
LA tenants	153.23	132.28	-14

[a] tenure status from 1971 Census

[b] tenure status from 1981 Census

[c] percentage change between 1981 cohort mortality rates (1981-92) compared to 1971 cohort rates (1971-81), in terms of 1971-81 figures

65 percent of female and 65 per cent of male private renters were in the same category of housing as at the 1971 Census. Similar proportions of private renters and local authority tenants moved into owner occupied housing in 1981. Among those who moved into local authority housing, more came from privately rented accommodation than owner occupied housing.

We now assess whether the mortality gradient differs if tenure is taken from the 1971 Census than from the 1981 Census for people present at both censuses. Because of the differences in temporal trends at ages 35–44 observed earlier, we disaggregate these results by age in Table 13.11. In both age-groups, the gradient is wider if tenure status is taken from the 1981 Census than from the 1971 Census. This is especially marked at ages 35–44 because the SMRs for local authority tenants are much higher if tenure is taken from the 1981 Census than from the earlier census.

There are two main possible explanations. First, since most people tend to remain in the same tenure, and therefore largely determine the gradient, the widening may be due to a deterioration in the mortality of those staying in local authority housing. Second, this could be due to a higher mortality among those moving into local authority housing.

Table 13.12 shows SMRs for people who remained in the same housing tenure or moved between categories. Taking both women and men, the distribution of the number of deaths confirms that mortality gradients by housing tenure are mainly influenced by the consistent differences seen for those who remained in the same housing category. At ages 35–44, compared to those remaining in owner occupied housing, mortality is higher among those moving out of, and lower or similar among those moving into owner occupied housing. The net effect is to lower the SMR for those in owner occupied housing in 1981. At the other end of the spectrum, compared

TABLE 13.9

Housing tenure and car access distributions at the 1971 and 1981 Censuses, women and men

1971 and 1981 LS cohorts. England and Wales

	Age			
	35-59 (35-64 for men)		60+ (65+ for men)	
	1971 %	1981 %	1971 %	1981 %
Women				
Owner occupiers	52	64	49	52
Private renters	15	8	21	13
LA tenants	31	26	25	31
Non-private households	1	1	5	5
Tenure not stated[a]	-	-	-	-
Total (100%)	78,940	77,831	57,367	62,570
Men				
Owner occupiers	52	63	51	55
Private renters	16	9	20	13
LA tenants	30	26	25	28
Non-private households	2	2	4	4
Tenure not stated[a]	-	-	-	-
Total (100%)	91,979	90,967	26,246	30,994

[a] For the 1981 Census 'not stated' codes were imputed to other categories.

TABLE 13.10

Housing tenure mobility distributions at the 1971 and 1981 Censuses, women and men

1971 LS cohort present at 1981 England and Wales

1971 Census	1981 Census:			
	Owner occupiers %	Private renters %	LA tenants %	Total (100%)
Women				
Owner occupiers	80 (91)	19 (4)	6 (4)	38,111 (100)
Private renters	10 (49)	65 (28)	12 (23)	10,102 (100)
LA tenants	9 (30)	14 (5)	81 (64)	19,986 (100)
Total[a] (100%)	44,409	5,418	18,487	68,961
Men				
Owner occupiers	79 (90)	19 (4)	7 (4)	44,370 (100)
Private renters	10 (47)	65 (30)	13 (22)	12,874 (100)
LA tenants	10 (30)	13 (5)	79 (63)	23,152 (100)
Total[a] (100%)	52,095	6,979	21,474	81,693

Notes:
  Figures in brackets are row percentages.
  LS members were present at both censuses.
[a] Includes those in communal households

TABLE 13.11

SMRs by housing tenure at the 1971 and 1981 Censuses, women and men

1971 LS cohort present at 1981. England and Wales, 1981–92

Age at death Tenure	Women		Men	
	1971	1981	1971	1981
35-44				
Owner occupiers	92	81	88	80
Private renters	100	94	96	112
LA tenants	114	144	115	133
45-59 (64)				
Owner occupiers	82	81	82	80
Private renters	115	122	114	117
LA tenants	126	129	123	131

Note: LS members were present at both censuses.

TABLE 13.12

SMRs by changes in housing tenure between the 1971 and 1981 Censuses, all causes, women and men

1971 LS cohort present at 1981 England and Wales, 1981-92

1971 Census	1981 Census:							
	Owner occupiers Deaths SMR		Private renters Deaths SMR		LA tenants Deaths SMR		Total[a] Deaths SMR	
Women								
35-44								
Owner occupiers	132	83*	10	115	13	127	164	92
Private renters	37	84	11	74	27	149	78	100
LA tenants	31	76	5	84	77	148*	114	114
Total[a]	202	81*	29	94	118	144*	366	100
45-59								
Owner occupiers	758	76*	31	112	48	159*	863	82*
Private renters	104	102	117	122*	70	123	295	115*
LA tenants	114	103	29	140	538	127*	700	126*
Total[a]	983	81*	178	122*	664	129*	1890	100
Men								
35-44								
Owner occupiers	181	82*	16	114	14	97	222	88
Private renters	47	71*	28	124	29	119	110	96
LA tenants	56	82	10	96	104	137*	179	115
Total[a]	293	80*	56	112	157	133*	541	100
45-64								
Owner occupiers	2,437	78*	101	113	149	144*	2,738	82*
Private renters	277	90	402	114*	277	146*	987	114*
LA tenants	318	93	90	133*	1,781	128*	2,237	123*
Total[a]	3,056	80*	608	117*	2,234	131*	6,094	100

Note: LS members were present at both censuses.
* 95 per cent confidence interval for SMR excludes 100.
[a] includes those in communal households.

to those remaining in local authority housing mortality is lower among those moving in or out of this category. The overall effect is to widen the gradient if tenure is taken at the 1981 Census. At ages 45–59/64 these mortality differences are not so apparent, and the overall effect on the gradient in 1981 is less.

Conclusion

This analysis has shown that mortality in the 1970s and 1980s was higher among less advantaged groups, such as people in local authority housing or without a car, and lower among the more advantaged, such as owner occupiers and those with access to cars. The gradients are remarkably stable at older ages and although relative differences between the least and most advantaged groups became smaller at older ages, absolute differences in mortality rates were larger than at working ages.

Previous work using the LS suggested that mortality differences have widened between socio-economic groups.[3] This chapter shows corroborative evidence, but also highlights that changes in housing tenure are likely to influence the trends at younger ages. From this analysis we are unable to say whether movement to local authority housing was a result of illness or unemployment or some other factor. At older working ages, tenure changes are unlikely to explain the widening of differences observed in the analysis. Further work is underway to quantify these effects on the gradients. However, other work using social class suggests that at older working ages, mobility is unlikely to have a major effect on the mortality gradient.[10]

To summarise, among women and men of late working ages and women at older ages, there is evidence of an increase in mortality differences by these two indicators between the two decades. Death rates declined in all tenure and car access categories, but the falls were larger among the most advantaged groups.

References

1   Davey Smith, G, Shipley, M and Rose, G (1990) Magnitude and causes of socio-economic differentials in mortality: further evidence from the Whitehall Study, *Epidemiology and Community Health,* 44: 265–70.

2   Marmot, M, and Shipley, M (1996) Do socio-economic differences in mortality persist after retirement? 25 year follow-up of civil servants from the first Whitehall Study, *BMJ,* 313: 1177–80.

3   Filakti, H and Fox, J (1995) Differences in mortality by housing tenure and by car access from the OPCS Longitudinal Study, *Population Trends,* 81: 27–30.

4   Moser, K, Goldblatt, P, Fox, J and Jones, D (1990) Unemployment and mortality. In: Goldblatt, P (ed.) *Longitudinal Study 1971-81: mortality and social organisation.* London, HMSO.

5   Hattersley, L, and Creeser, R (1995) *Longitudinal Study 1971-1991: History, organisation and quality of data.* London, HMSO.

6   Fox, J, and Goldblatt, P (1982) *Socio-demographic mortality differentials: Longitudinal Study 1971-75.* London, HMSO.

7   Goldblatt, P (1990) *Longitudinal Study 1971-81: mortality and social organisation.* London, HMSO.

8   Harding, S, Bethune, A and Rosato, M (1997) Second study supports results of Whitehall Study after retirement. *BMJ,* 314:1130.

9   Harding, S (1995) Social class differences in mortality of men: recent evidence from the OPCS Longitudinal Study, *Population Trends,* 80, 31–37.

10   Blane, D, Harding, S and Rosato, M (1996) *Social class mobility and mortality among middle aged men in England and Wales.* Royal Statistical Society conference.

Part Three

Morbidity

14 Children's health and lifestyle – a review

Beverley Botting and Julia Bunting

Summary

Here we review data on the socio-economic differentials in childhood morbidity, health service use, and health-related behaviours. A variety of sources have been used, largely continuous and ad hoc surveys.

The prevalence of childhood chronic sickness is higher in 1995 than 1985, for both sexes, and both manual and non-manual groups.

Children in manual classes are more likely to suffer from chronic sickness than children in non-manual classes; the difference is greater for boys than for girls.

Children from manual households are more likely to suffer from tooth decay, and to have a greater number of teeth affected, than children from non-manual households.

Consulting ratios in general practice are higher among children in council housing than those in owner occupied housing for most major causes of consultation. The differences are largest for conditions classed as serious, where consulting ratios among children in council housing are 20% higher than those in owner occupied housing. Consultations for diseases of the nervous system show a reverse social class gradient.

There was little social class variation in the percentage of children who had ever-smoked, but smokers in manual households consumed more cigarettes per week than those in non-manual households.

Drinking prevalence (ever-drinking, and regular drinking) is higher for children in non-manual households than manual. However children in manual households tend to drink more heavily.

Chapter 7 discussed socio-economic differentials in infant and childhood mortality. However, death is an extreme measure of health and makes up only a small part of the total health experience. Each year in England and Wales less than 1 in 1,500 people aged under 20 years dies. In contrast to the long-term trend of decreasing infant and childhood mortality, measures of morbidity suggest that there has been an increase in the prevalence of ill-health in childhood. It has long been recognised that the socio-economic environment exerts a powerful influence on health[1] and that the effects on health of adverse environments in childhood may well persist into adult life.[2] This chapter looks at the pattern of morbidity, health service use and health-related behaviours among children by socio-economic status. Data on socio-economic status are not routinely collected within primary or secondary care, so the information available for use in this chapter is mainly derived from continuous and ad hoc surveys.

Morbidity

This section looks at patterns of childhood morbidity, including dental health and congenital anomalies, by socio-economic status. Data are presented from a number of sources including the General Household Survey[3] (GHS) and the Children's Dental Health Survey.[4]

The GHS has asked questions on a variety of health-related topics since its inception in 1971. Child health data are supplied by adult survey respondents if there is a child in the household aged under 16 for whom they are responsible. Data on self-reported health status must always be interpreted with care because of varying expectations of health among different subgroups. However, when the perception of an individual's health is reported by another, for example, a child's health status being reported by a parent, even greater care must be taken over interpretation. The GHS uses two measures of reported sickness; chronic sickness is defined as a long-standing illness, disability or infirmity while acute sickness is defined as the restriction of normal activities, as a result of illness or injury, during the two weeks prior to interview. Respondents who reported that a child suffered from a long-standing illness were asked if it limited their activities in any way.

Chronic sickness – long-standing and limiting long-standing illness

For ease of interpretation, data on childhood chronic sickness by socio-economic status of the head of the household are presented as non-manual (Social Classes I, II and IIIN) and manual groups (Social Classes IIIM, IV and V). Figure 14.1 shows the prevalence of reported long-standing illness for children in Great Britain in 1985 and 1995. The reported prevalence of chronic sickness is higher in 1995 than 1985 for each group. Among girls in the non-manual group, for example, the reported prevalence increased from 11 to 15 per cent between 1985 and 1995. The figure also shows that at each time period and in each social class group, boys have a higher reported prevalence than girls. In 1995, for example, 20 per cent of boys in the manual group were reported to suffer from a chronic illness compared with 16 per cent of girls. Looking specifically at differences by socio-economic group, the ratio of prevalence in the manual to the non-manual group is higher among boys than among girls. Boys in the manual group are about 20 per cent more likely to be reported suffering from a chronic illness than boys in the non-manual group. The corresponding difference between girls is less than 10 per cent.

Figure 14.2 shows that, overall, under 10 per cent of children who were reported to have a chronic sickness were limited in their activities. Again, the reported prevalence of restricted activity among children with a chronic illness has increased over time. Among girls in the manual group, for example, the prevalence of a limiting long-standing illness is higher in 1995 than 1985, 7 per cent and 5 per cent respectively. As with long-standing illness, the reported prevalence of a limiting long-standing illness is higher for boys than girls. In 1995 in the manual group, for example, the prevalence is 9 per cent for boys and 7 per cent for girls. The ratio of prevalence of limiting long-standing illness in the manual and non-manual group is about the same for boys in the two time periods. However, for the girls there has been an increase.

FIGURE 14.1

Prevalence of reported long-standing illness, boys and girls aged under 16 years

Great Britain, 1985 and 1995

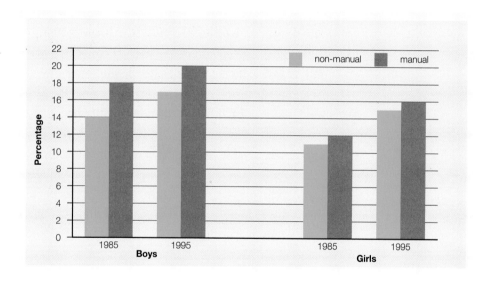

FIGURE 14.2

Prevalence of reported limiting long-standing illness, boys and girls aged under 16

Great Britain, 1985 and 1995

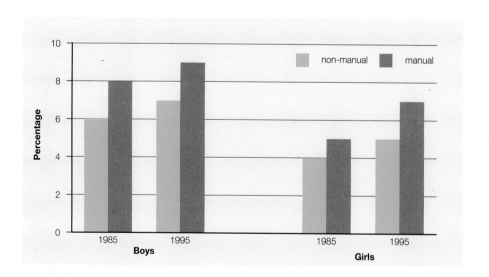

Dental health

Data presented are from the Children's Dental Health Survey conducted in the United Kingdom in 1993. This is the third national survey of children's dental health carried out by the Social Survey Division of the Office of Population Censuses and Surveys, the previous two being conducted in 1973 and 1983. The 1993 survey examined the teeth of over 17,000 children attending primary and secondary schools in the United Kingdom. Table 14.1 presents data on a variety of dental health conditions for children aged 12 and 15 by the social class of the household. For every condition the percentage is higher for children from unskilled manual households (IV/V) than those from non-manual households (I/II/IIIN). Among children aged 12 years, for example, 45 per cent from non-manual households suffered from any form of decay, compared to 68 per cent from unskilled manual households. The difference between the top and bottom social classes in the percentage of children with tooth decay increases with increasing severity of the condition. Among 12 year olds the difference is nearly two-fold for the percentage with actively decayed teeth and five-fold for the percentage with teeth missing as a result of decay. By age 15, the difference in the percentage suffering from any condition has decreased between the top and bottom of the social scale.

Children from unskilled manual households are not only more likely to suffer from tooth decay, they are also likely to have a higher number of teeth affected than children from non-manual households. The mean number of teeth affected by any form of decay among children aged 15, for example, is just under three and a half for the unskilled manual classes compared to two for the non-manual classes.

TABLE 14.1

Children's dental health by household social class

United Kingdom, 1993

Source: Children's Dental Health Survey 1993

Condition	% children with condition			mean number of teeth affected		
	I, II, IIIN	IIIM	IV,V	I, II, IIIN	IIIM	IV,V
Age 12						
Any known decay	45	51	68	1.1	1.4	2.0
Actively decayed	17	27	32	0.3	0.5	0.6
Filled	35	38	50	0.7	0.7	1.1
Missing due to decay	3	6	15	0.1	0.1	0.3
Age 15						
Any known decay	58	68	72	2.0	2.7	3.4
Actively decayed	25	25	36	0.5	0.6	0.9
Filled	48	59	59	1.4	2.0	2.2
Missing due to decay	4	6	19	0.1	0.1	0.3

Congenital anomalies

Data on congenital anomaly notifications are taken from the Office for National Statistics (ONS) publications.[5] The data are collected through the National Congenital Anomaly System which was established in England and Wales in 1964 following the thalidomide epidemic. Although the data are primarily for monitoring changes in frequency of anomaly notifications, it is the most extensive source of data on prevalence levels. The notification form also collects information on a number of factors including parents occupation and mother's age and parity. However, the disadvantage of the monitoring system for epidemiological studies is that notifications are voluntary and, more importantly, in 1994 covered only those anomalies identified in the first ten days after birth. Some conditions, such as cardiovascular anomalies,

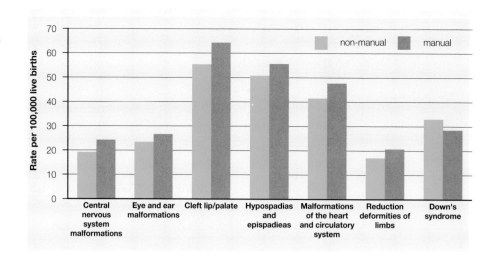

are not identified until some time after birth. Data on social class are based on the occupation of the father. In 1994, there were over five and a half thousand congenital anomaly notifications, of which 60 per cent had occupational information for the father. More than 75 per cent of these (2,518) had sufficient occupational information to categorise them to Social Classes I to V, the rest were assigned to Social Class 'Other'. Because of the small numbers involved data were aggregated for the five years 1990–94 and into manual and non-manual social classes. Figure 14.3 presents the notification rate per 100,000 live births by social class of the father. Although care must be taken when interpreting the results it can be seen that, in general, the notification rate is higher in manual than non-manual social classes. For central nervous system malformations, for example, the notification rate per 100,000 live births is 23 in manual classes compared to 19 in non-manual. The exception to this pattern is Down's syndrome where the notification rate is higher in non-manual than manual classes, 33 and 29 per 100,000 live births respectively. It is possible that the higher mean age of childbearing among non-manual women influences this pattern. The incidence of Down's syndrome increases with maternal age and women in non-manual social classes have a higher mean age at childbearing than those in manual social classes.

Health service utilisation

This section presents data on health service utilisation using the fourth national Morbidity Statistics from General Practice Study.[6] The measures presented are age-standardised patient consulting ratios (SPCR). SPCRs are the same type of measure as standardised mortality ratios (SMRs) used elsewhere in this volume. The SPCR for the study population is 100. SPCRs below 100 indicate lower consultation rates than expected, SPCRs greater than 100 indicate higher than average consultation rates. Table 14.2 shows the SPCR for children aged under 16 by severity of condition by housing tenure and social class of the parent/guardian. In general, for all severity of conditions, SPCRs are higher among children in council housing than for those in owner occupied housing. Among girls, at each of the three levels of severity, the SPCR for the owner occupied group is significantly lower than the overall ratio and that for the council housing group is significantly higher. Among boys, the only significant ratios are seen for conditions categorised as serious. When the consultation ratios are examined by parental social class, girls in Social Class I/II show significantly lower SPCRs for each severity level. Significantly lower SPCRs are also seen for boys in Social Class I/II for both serious and minor conditions but not for intermediate conditions. The only significantly raised SPCR by social class is for serious conditions for boys in Class IIIM.

Table 14.3 shows SPCRs by housing tenure and social class of parent/guardian for disease chapters of the Ninth Revision of the International Classification of Diseases (ICD–9).[7] Only ICD chapters where the overall rate of consultations with a doctor for children under 16 was higher than 500 per 10,000 person years at risk have been included. By housing tenure, the general pattern is for children in council housing to have higher SPCRs than those in owner occupied housing. The majority of these ratios are significantly different from 100. The exception to this general pattern are diseases of the nervous system and sense organs. For this chapter of the ICD, boys in owner occupied housing have a significantly raised SPCR of 104 and both boys and girls in council housing have significantly lower SPCRs, 91 and 96 respectively. The biggest significant difference between the owner occupied and council house groups is among girls for diseases of the genitourinary system, SPCRs 93 and 123 respectively.

TABLE 14.2

Age standardised patient consulting ratios (SPCR) by severity of condition, children aged under 16 years by housing tenure and social class of parent/guardian

England and Wales 1991–92

Source: Morbidity Statistics from General Practice: Fourth national study 1991–1992 Series MB5 no.3

Severity of condition		Housing tenure		Social class			
		Owner occupied	Council housing	I&II	IIIN	IIIM	IV&V
All diseases and conditions ICD I-XVIII	Boys	99	101	99	100	100	101
	Girls	98	103*	98*	101	101	101
Serious	Boys	95*	115*	92*	98	106*	106
	Girls	95*	115*	92*	105	104	107
Intermediate	Boys	99	102	98	100	102	101
	Girls	98*	106*	96*	102	101	103
Minor	Boys	99	103	97*	100	101	102
	Girls	98*	104*	97*	101	101	103

SPCR for study population = 100
*95 per cent confidence interval does not include 100

TABLE 14.3

Age standardised patient consulting ratios (SPCR) by ICD chapter, children aged under 16 years by housing tenure and social class

England and Wales 1991–92

Source: Morbidity Statistics from General Practice: Fourth national study 1991–1992 Series MB5 no.3

	ICD Chapter		Housing tenure		Social class			
			Owner occupied	Council housing	I & II	IIIN	IIIM	IV & V
I	Infectious and parasitic diseases (001-0139)	Boys	96*	113*	92*	99	104	108*
		Girls	93*	119*	88*	99	104	112*
VI	Diseases of nervous system and sense organs (320-389)	Boys	104*	91*	103	101	100	96
		Girls	102	96*	102	101	101	93*
VIII	Diseases of the respiratory system (460-519)	Boys	98	107*	96*	101	102	104*
		Girls	97*	109*	94*	101	101	107*
IX	Diseases of the digestive system (520-579)	Boys	95	119*	90*	97	106	112*
		Girls	93*	122*	89*	103	104	115*
X	Diseases of genitourinary system (580-629)	Boys	99	103	94	95	106	105
		Girls	93*	123*	86*	107	103	115*
XII	Diseases of skin and subcutaneous tissue (680-709)	Boys	97*	108*	94*	98	103	104
		Girls	96*	111*	94*	102	101	107*
XIII	Diseases of musculoskeletal system and connective tissue (710-739)	Boys	98	107	100	95	100	101
		Girls	94	118*	88*	109	100	110
XVI	Symptoms, signs and ill-defined conditions (780-799)	Boys	95*	114*	93*	104	100	113*
		Girls	92*	119*	89*	105	102	112*
XVII	Injury and poisoning (800-999)	Boys	95*	111*	92*	99	104	107*
		Girls	94*	111*	94*	98	102	106

SPCR for study population = 100
*95 per cent confidence interval does not include100

By social class, the majority of ratios are lower in Social Class I/II, with girls being more likely than boys to have ratios significantly lower than 100. Again, the exception is diseases of the nervous system and sense organs, which are higher, although not significantly so, for both boys and girls in Social Class I/II. However, the SPCR is significantly lower than 100, at 93, for boys in Social Class IV/V. The biggest differences between Social Class I/II and IV/V for both boys and girls are for diseases of the digestive system and symptoms, signs and ill-defined conditions.

Health-related behaviours

This section presents data on a number of health-related behaviours including smoking, alcohol consumption and diet and nutrition by socio-economic status. Much of the data on the health-related behaviours of children are from a Health Education Authority (HEA) survey called Tomorrow's Young Adults.[8] The survey questioned 10,293 children aged 9 to 15 years in a representative sample of 475 primary, middle and secondary schools in England. The survey categorised children using the marketing industry's socio-economic status categories AB, C1, C2 and DE.

Smoking

A reduction in the prevalence of smoking among children aged 11-15 years is one of the *Health of the Nation* targets[9]. The target was to reduce the prevalence of regular smoking, defined as smoking one or more cigarettes per week, from 8 per cent in 1988 to less than 6 per cent in 1994. By 1994 however, 12 per cent of secondary school children reported smoking regularly. Table 14.4 shows information on various measures of smoking behaviour by socio-economic status from the HEA survey. While the highest percentage of children who have ever tried smoking, 35 per cent, are in group AB, there is little variation between the socio-economic groups. However, cigarette consumption in the last week is related to social status with children who smoke in group DE smoking on average 50 per cent more cigarettes per week than children in AB. When asked about their future expectations of smoking, there is a continual increase in the percentage who considered that they would, or might, be smokers at age 20 with decreasing socio-economic status. Some 23 per cent of children in group DE thought they would or might be a smoker at age 20, compared to 18 per cent of children in group AB.

TABLE 14.4

Smoking behaviour of 9–15 year olds by socio-economic group of household

England 1989

Source: HEA, Tomorrow's young adults, 1992

Socio-economic group	% ever- smoked[a]	Cigarette consumption[b]	% will/might be smokers at age 20[a]
AB	35	16	18
C1	30	19	20
C2	32	22	21
DE	31	23	23
All	31	19	

[a] of all respondents
[b] average number of cigarettes smoked in previous week by smokers in previous week

TABLE 14.5

Smoking education of
9–15 year olds by socio-
economic group of
household

England 1989

Source: HEA,⁶

Socio-economic group	% Had lessons at school	% Talked to parents
AB	52	60
C1	46	60
C2	43	53
DE	39	53
All	43	56

Table 14.5 shows the percentage of children who had received smoking education either at home or at school by socio-economic status. Overall, a higher percentage of children received advice from parents than at school. Children in group AB are the most likely to have received smoking education both at home and at school. At school, 52 per cent in group AB reported having smoking education compared to 39 per cent in group DE. When it comes to talking to parents about smoking, the differential between the top and bottom socio-economic groups is smaller with 60 per cent in AB and 53 per cent in DE reporting that they have discussed smoking with their parents.

Alcohol

Table 14.6 presents data on alcohol consumption from the HEA survey. The percentage of children aged 9 to 15 who have ever tried alcohol is highest in the AB group, 70 per cent, and lowest in the DE group at 58 per cent. A similar pattern is seen for the percentage who report that they are regular drinkers. Some 16 per cent of children in socio-economic group AB report that they drink at least once a week, more than double the percentage in group DE. More children in group AB than group DE, however, report to be occasional drinkers, that is drink less than once or twice a month. Therefore there is a more diverse range of drinking behaviours among children in socio-economic group AB than among group DE. Also shown is the percentage of children who report drinking more than the 1992 recommended safe limits for adults. One per cent of children in group AB reported that they exceeded this recommendation compared to 5 per cent in group DE and 6 per cent in group C2.

TABLE 14.6

Drinking prevalence
among 9–15 year olds by
socio-economic group of
household

England 1989

Source: HEA,⁶

Socio-economic group	% ever tried alcohol	% regular drinkers[a]	% occasional drinkers[b]	% drinking over the safe adult limit[c]
AB	70	16	20	1
C1	66	13	18	4
C2	67	13	16	6
DE	58	7	13	5
All	63	12	16	4

[a] at least one drink a week
[b] not more than once or twice a month
[c] among 11-15 year olds girls 14 units, boys 21 units per week

Table 14.7 presents figures on preference for soft drinks compared to alcoholic drinks. There is no evidence of variation by socio-economic status in the percentage of children who said that they liked soft drinks more than alcohol, with just under 70 per cent of all children reporting this to be the case. However, there is a socio-economic pattern in the percentage of children reporting that they like the taste of alcohol. Some 30 per cent of children in group AB reported liking the taste of alcohol, nearly double the percentage in group DE. The percentage of children in each socio-economic group who report to be regular drinkers, Table 14.6, is only half the percentage who say that they like the taste of alcohol.

Socio-economic group	% like soft drinks more than alcoholic	% enjoy the taste of alcohol
AB	69	30
C1	68	26
C2	67	24
DE	68	18
All	68	23

Drugs

The HEA survey presented children with a list of nine drugs which were categorised into solvents, Class A drugs which included heroin and cocaine and Class B which included cannabis and amphetamines. The respondents were asked which drugs they had been offered and which drugs they had tried. Table 14.8 presents the findings from this question by socio-economic group. Overall, about 7 per cent of children aged between 9 and 15 years claimed to have been offered Class A drugs and Class B drugs. However, there was very little difference by socio-economic group.

Socio-economic group	% exposed		
	Class A[a]	Class B[b]	Solvents
AB	9	8	7
C1	7	8	8
C2	8	7	6
DE	7	7	5
All	7	7	6

[a] acid, heroin, ecstasy, cocaine, crack
[b] cannabis, amphetamines, tranquilisers

Diet and nutrition

This section presents data on the incidence of breastfeeding by social class, and food consumption of children aged $1\frac{1}{2}$ to $4\frac{1}{2}$ years by manual/non-manual social class of head of household. It is well documented that the dietary behaviour established in early life is not only fundamentally important for a child's growth and development, but also lays the foundation for later life.[10] Diet and nutrition also have a key role in achieving the targets for reducing the number of deaths from coronary heart disease and stroke set out in the *Health of the Nation*.

Breast feeding

Government policy has consistently supported breastfeeding as the best way of ensuring a healthy start for newborns.[11] Overall, there has been a slight increase in the incidence of initial breastfeeding between 1985 and 1995, 64 to 66 per cent. However, these overall figures mask considerable variation by social class. Data on the incidence of breastfeeding by social class of the husband/partner for the years 1985, 1990 and 1995 are shown in Figure 14.4. In 1985, women in Social Class I were more than twice as likely to breastfeed as women in Social Class V, 87 and 43 per cent respectively. By 1995, there had been a slight reduction in this differential with 50 per cent of women in Social Class V initially breastfeeding compared to 90 per cent in Social Class I. Table 14.9 presents data on the duration of breastfeeding by social class. The differential between Social Class I and V in the percentage of mothers who breastfeed increases with increasing age of the child. At birth, women in Social Class I are 1.8 times more likely to breastfeed than those in Social Class V; by two weeks this differential has increased to 2.3 times. In the 1970s a working party of the Committee on Medical Aspects of Food and Nutrition Policy recommended that mothers should be encouraged to breastfeed, preferably for four to six months.[12] In 1995, 56 per cent of mothers in Social Class I were still breastfeeding at four months, compared with only 13 per cent in Social Class V.

FIGURE 14.4
Incidence of breast-feeding by social class of husband/partner
Great Britain, selected years

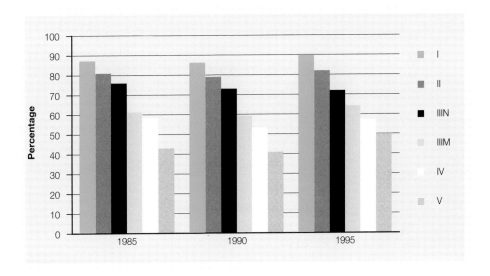

TABLE 14.9
Prevalence of breastfeeding by social class of husband/ partner
Great Britain, 1995
Source: Infant feeding 1995

	I	II	IIIN	IIIM	IV	V
Birth	90	82	72	64	57	50
1 week	84	72	64	52	46	40
2 weeks	83	68	60	48	43	36
6 weeks	73	59	48	36	33	23
4 months	56	41	30	21	21	13
6 months	42	31	23	16	17	11
9 months	31	19	18	10	11	5

Toddler's food consumption

Information on food consumption for children aged $1^1/_2$ to $4^1/_2$ years was collected for the National Diet and Nutrition Survey. The survey was conducted on a nationally representative sample of 2,101 children living in private households over a 12-month period beginning July 1992. Table 14.10 presents patterns of food consumption for selected food types by social class of head of household. Nearly 100 food categories are

TABLE 14.10

Food consumption,
selected types by social
class of head of house-
hold, children aged 1$^1/_2$–
4$^1/_2$ years

Great Britain, 1992–93

*Source: National Diet and Nutrition
Survey*

Types of food [a]	Non-manual	Manual	All
	quantities in grams per week		
White bread	199	245	226
Wholegrain/high fibre breakfast cereals	127	121	125
Other breakfast cereals	85	97	92
Biscuits	119	118	118
Whole milk	1,841	1,909	1,872
Other vegetables (not raw)	111	91	102
Potato chips	176	217	200
Other potatoes	203	203	203
Savoury snacks	77	91	85
Other soft drinks	1,999	2,153	2,092
Tap water	2,361	2,246	2,300
Meat pies/pastries	127	162	149

[a] foods consumed by 60 per cent or more of all children

listed in the survey, but only foods which were reported to be consumed by more than 60 per cent of children are included in the table. For the food types white bread, potato chips and meat pies/pasties, children in the manual social classes consumed at least 20 per cent more grams per week than children from non-manual social classes. Children in the manual social classes consumed 18 per cent fewer grams of other vegetables (not raw) than children from non-manual households. The report concluded that 'overall the pattern suggests a diet among children from a manual background with less emphasis on fruit and whole grain cereals; however the same subgroup of children were also less likely to be eating buns, cakes and pastries'.[10]

Teenage Conceptions

The *Health of the Nation*[9] target on teenage conceptions is to reduce the rate of conception amongst the under 16s by at least 50 per cent by the year 2000 from its 1990 base. Conceptions have several possible outcomes including stillbirths, abortions and live births. In 1994, 53 per cent of all conceptions to girls aged under 16 years were terminated by abortion. Data on abortion by social class are not available, therefore any analysis of social class variation in teenage conception could be open to misinterpretation if abortions and live births show different social class patterns.

Conclusion

A variety of measures of children's health and lifestyle by socio-economic status have been looked at in this chapter. The evidence presented suggest that children in the manual social classes are more likely to suffer from ill health and poorer dental health than children in non-manual social classes. Patient consulting ratios show that children in the manual social classes are more likely to have consulted with a GP for a whole variety of types and severity of condition than their non-manual counterparts.

The findings on health-related behaviours show that there is very little social class variation in the percentage of children who have ever smoked. However, children in manual social classes consumed more cigarettes per week than those in the non-manual classes. The evidence on alcohol consumption among children aged 9–15 years show that the percentage who have ever tried alcohol increases with increasing socio-economic status and twice as many children in the highest compared to the lowest socio-economic group reported being regular drinkers. However, more children in the lower than higher socio-economic group were reported to exceed the adult safe drinking limits, despite the fact only half the proportion in the lower socio-economic groups reported liking the taste of alcohol.

The reduction of these socio-economic variations in health status, health service utilisation and health-related behaviours among children would have a major long-term effect on health throughout life.

References

1   Woodroffe C, Glickman M, Barker M, and Power C. (1993) *Children, Teenagers and Health: The Key Data.* Open University Press. Buckingham, England.

2   Osteberg V, Vagero, D (1991) Socio-economic differences in mortality among children. Do they persist into adulthood? *Social Science and Medicine* 32: 403–10.

3   Office of Population Censuses and Surveys (annual) *General Household Survey.* HMSO, London.

4   O'Brien, M. (1994) *Children's Dental Health in the United Kingdom 1993.* HMSO, London.

5   Office for National Statistics (annual) *Congenital Anomaly Statistics: notifications.* HMSO, London.

6   McCormick, A Fleming, D and Charlton, J (1995) *Morbidity Statistics from General Practice - Fourth national study* 1991-1992. Series MB5 no 3. HMSO, London.

7   World Health Organisation (1977) *Ninth revision of the International Classification of Diseases.* WHO, Geneva.

8   Health Education Authority (1992) *Tomorrow's Young Adults.* Health Education Authority, London.

9   Department of Health (1992) *The Health of the Nation: A strategy for health in England.* London, HMSO.

10   Gregory J, Collins D, Davies P, Hughes J and Clarke P (1995) *National Diet and Nutrition Survey: children aged $1^1/2$ to $4^1/2$ years.* HMSO, London.

11   Foster K, Lader D and Cheesbrough S (1997) *Infant Feeding 1995.* The Stationery Office, London.

12   Department of Health and Social Security (1974) *Present Day Practice in Infant Feeding.* Report on Health and Social Subjects 9. HMSO, London.

15 Morbidity and health-related behaviours of adults – a review

Julia Bunting

Summary

- This chapter reviews data on the socio-economic differentials in adult morbidity, health service utilisation, and health-related behaviours. Data is derived from a number of sources including the General Household Survey.

- The proportion of adults reporting chronic sickness is higher among manual classes than non-manual. Men in manual classes are about 40 per cent more likely to report a long-standing illness that limits their activities than those in non-manual classes; the difference for women is slightly smaller.

- Acute sickness does not show a clear pattern by socio-economic status.

- There is a social class gradient in the prevalence of high blood pressure.

- In general GP consultations are higher among manual than non-manual classes, although the pattern varies by age group and sex. In contrast the use of preventive services, such as dental attendance and use of ophthalmic services, is higher among non-manual classes.

- The prevalence of smoking is higher among manual classes than non-manual; over twice the proportion of unskilled manual men and women smoke compared to professional. Among women alcohol consumption is twice as high among professional women as unskilled manual; the pattern for men is less clear.

- The consumption of fats and sugars is higher in low income households.

Introduction

This chapter provides a picture of the way in which health, health service utilisation and health-related behaviours vary by socio-economic status. It has been argued that, in developed countries, morbidity and general health status are increasingly becoming more important indicators of inequality than mortality. Blaxter suggests that although mortality is certainly a part of inequality in health, it may be that the lifelong experience of health and illness most clearly demonstrates the difference between social groups.[1]

The Department of Health's *Health of the Nation* White Paper, published in 1992, identified five key areas where there was both the greatest need and the greatest scope for making cost-effective improvements in the overall health of people in England.[2] These were: coronary heart disease and stroke, cancers, mental illness, HIV/AIDS and sexual health, and accidents. Difference in mortality by social class from these key areas are discussed extensively in Chapter 8 of this volume. The Variations Sub-Group of the Chief Medical Officer's *Health of the Nation* Working Group considered that health-related behaviours played some part in explaining the observed socio-economic differentials in morbidity and mortality. Risk factors such as smoking, drinking and diet, for example, explain around a third of the socio-economic gradient in coronary heart disease mortality and morbidity.[3] For this reason, variations by socio-economic status in health-related behaviours including diet, smoking, alcohol consumption and physical activity will be discussed.

Data used in this chapter are derived from a number of sources. This means that a number of different measures of socio-economic status are used including social class, socio-economic group and income group. Much of the analysis is based on data from the General Household Survey (GHS).[4] The GHS uses a collapsed version of the Registrar General's socio-economic grouping (SEG) to measure socio-economic status. The descriptive definition of the categories is shown in Table 15.1. More detailed information on this classification can be found in Appendix A. The definition of income groups used by the National Food Survey to measure socio-economic status is discussed in the section on nutrition in this chapter.

TABLE 15.1

Descriptive definition of Registrar General's socio-economic grouping used in General House-hold Survey

Source: Office of Population Censuses and Surveys [4]

Professional	health professionals; legal professionals; business and financial professionals etc.
Employers and managers	managers and proprietors in service industries; farm owners and managers etc.
Intermediate and junior non-manual	apprentices in health, teaching, accountancy; secretaries and personal assistants
Skilled manual and own account non-professional	foremen in the construction trade; self-employed workers without employees
Semi-skilled manual and personal service	apprentice in the textile industry; farm workers; waiters and bar staff
Unskilled manual	lift and car park attendants; window cleaners; kitchen porters and hands

Health

This section looks at patterns of health by socio-economic status using measures of chronic and acute sickness, mental health and blood pressure. The GHS defines chronic sickness as a long-standing illness, disability or infirmity. Acute sickness is defined by the GHS as the restriction of normal activities, as a result of illness or injury, during the two weeks prior to interview. Chronic and acute sickness are based on people's subjective assessment of their own health.[5] Comparisons of morbidity by socio-economic status must be interpreted with care because of varying expectations of health within subgroups of the population. Similarly, changes over time may result from changes in people's expectation of their own health as well as changes in the incidence or duration of sickness. Despite the difficulties in interpretation, self-perceived health status may be more meaningfully related to the demand for health services than objective or clinical measures of health.[6]

Chronic sickness – long-standing illness

The trends in the prevalence of long-standing illness for males and females, all ages, by socio-economic group from 1979 to 1994, are shown in Figures 15.1 and 15.2. The data are shown as three-year moving averages because of the year-to-year fluctuations associated with measures of self-perceived health. In general, the prevalence of chronic sickness is slightly higher for females than for males. Around 33 per cent of females and 31 per cent of males reported a long-standing illness over the period. This

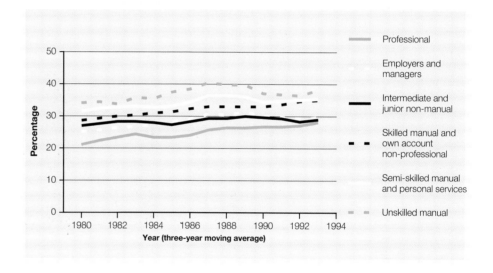

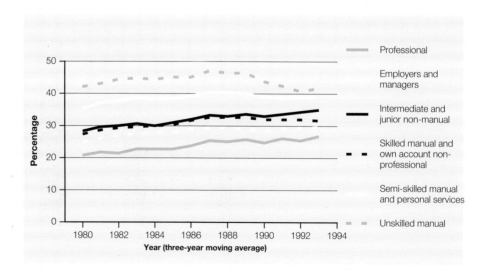

male/female differential does not occur if the age-band is restricted to adults under 75 years old,[7] because the prevalence of chronic sickness increases with age and a much higher proportion of women than men is aged 75 years and over. In 1995 there were estimated to be nearly twice as many women as men aged over 75 years in Great Britain, 2.6 million and 1.4 million respectively.

For both sexes, the percentage who reported long-standing illness is consistently higher in the manual than the non-manual group. Among males, there is a clear manual/non-manual difference. For females, the intermediate and junior non-manual group has a higher prevalence than the skilled manual group. For males, the ratio in the reported prevalence of long-standing illness between the top and bottom socio-economic groups has been about one and a half over the 16-year period. The corresponding ratio for females is nearer to two. However, for both males and females there has been a gradual decline in the differential over time. This narrowing has been more pronounced for females, declining from an average ratio of two between the top and bottom socio-economic groups for the years 1979–81 to an average of one and a half for 1992–94. For males, the narrowing in the differential has been much smaller: that between the top and bottom groups was just above one and a half at the beginning of the period and just below one and a half at the end.

FIGURE 15.3

Prevalence of reported long-standing illness by socio-economic group, men, by age group
Great Britain, 1994

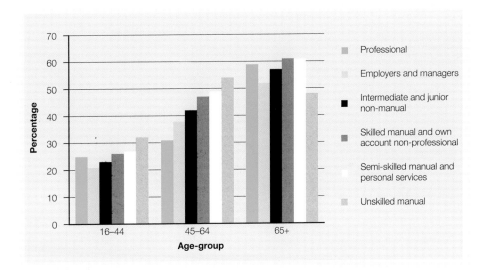

FIGURE 15.4

Prevalence of reported long-standing illness by socio-economic group, women, by age group
Great Britain, 1994

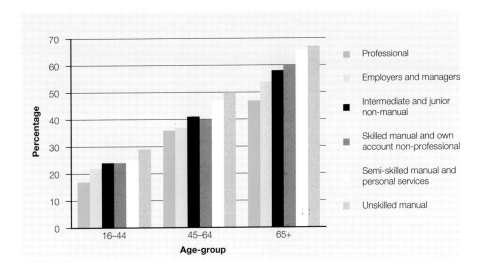

The percentage of adults reporting long-standing illness by age, sex and socio-economic group in 1994 are shown in Figures 15.3 and 15.4. As expected, the percentage reporting some form of chronic disease increases with age. At ages 16–44, 23 per cent of men and 24 per cent of women reported a long-standing illness. By age 65, this had increased to 58 per cent of men and 60 per cent of women. For men, the unskilled manual group has the highest prevalence of chronic illness at ages below 65 years. Above 65 years the unskilled manual group has the lowest reported prevalence, 48 per cent, compared to 59 per cent among the professional group. The trend for women by age group is different from that for men. Among women, the general pattern of increasing prevalence with decreasing socio-economic group persists in all age groups. Among men, there is a clear socio-economic gradient for 45–64 age group and to a lesser extent for the 16–44 age group. For men, the 65+ age group has no clear pattern by socio-economic status.

Chronic sickness – limiting long-standing illness

People with a long-standing illness were also asked whether this limits their activities in any way. Trends in limiting long-standing illness show a similar pattern to long-standing illness with very little change over time. A slightly higher percentage of females than males reported that their long-standing illness limited their activities, 20

FIGURE 15.5

Prevalence of reported limiting long-standing illness by socio-economic group, men, by age group
Great Britain, 1994

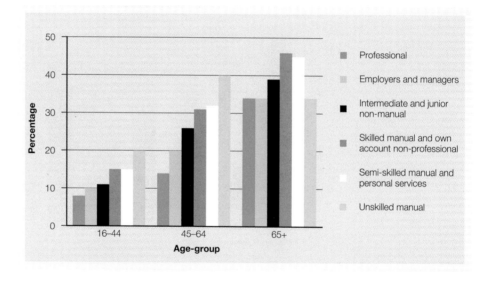

FIGURE 15.6

Prevalence of reported limiting long-standing illness by socio-economic group, women, by age group
Great Britain, 1994

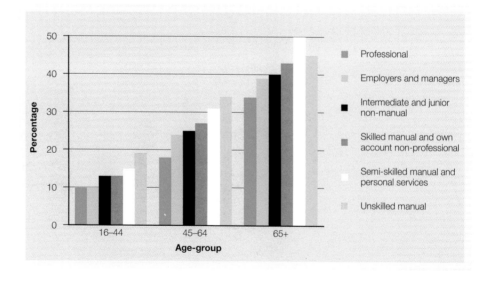

per cent and 18 per cent respectively. The socio-economic gradient exists for both males and females. Males in the manual group are about 40 per cent more likely to report a limiting long-standing illness than those in the non-manual group. The manual/non-manual difference is smaller among the females at about 30 per cent. Figures 15.5 and 15.6 show the breakdown by age and socio-economic group for men and women in 1994. For men and women aged under 65 years, the pattern is of increasing prevalence of self-reported limiting long-standing illness with decreasing socio-economic group. For women 65 years and over, the pattern is the same with the exception that women in the unskilled manual group have a lower prevalence than those in the semi-skilled manual and personal services group. For men aged 65 years and over, the prevalence of self-reported limiting long-standing illness is highest in the skilled manual group, 46 per cent. The professional and employers and managers groups have the same reported prevalence as the unskilled manual group, 34 per cent.

Acute sickness

The reported prevalence of acute sickness for males and females from 1979 to 1994 has remained almost constant. Over time, a higher percentage of females than males have reported acute illness, 14 per cent and 11 per cent respectively. Acute illness does

FIGURE 15.7

Prevalence of reported acute sickness by socio-economic group, men, by age group
Great Britain, 1994

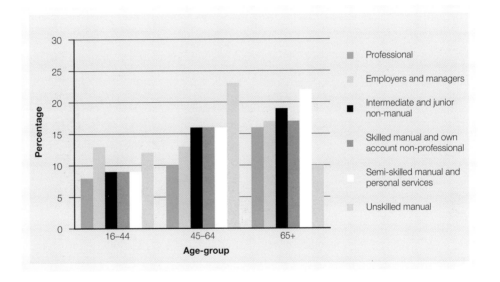

FIGURE 15.8

Prevalence of reported acute sickness by socio-economic group, women, by age group
Great Britain, 1994

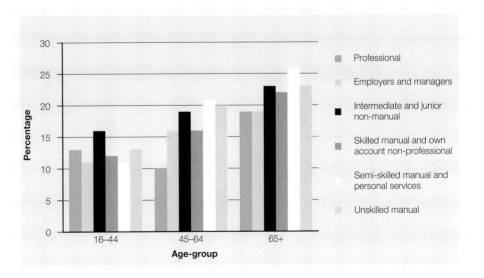

not show the clear differential seen for chronic sickness. For males, there has been no difference by socio-economic group in the prevalence of self-perceived acute sickness since 1989, remaining at 11 to 12 per cent. Among females socio-economic differences exist. Females in the lowest two socio-economic groups are about 30 per cent more likely to report acute sickness than those in the top two groups. This differential has not changed over the 16 years. The 1994 data on acute sickness by age, sex and socio-economic group are shown in Figures 15.7 and 15.8. For men and women aged 16–44 there is no obvious pattern by socio-economic group. At older ages, men and women in the manual groups generally have higher levels of acute sickness than the non-manual groups. The exception is for men aged over 65 years where the unskilled manual group has the lowest reported level of acute sickness, 10 per cent. This is in comparison to 16 per cent in the professional group and 22 per cent in the semi-skilled and personal services group.

Mental health

Information on mental health is derived from the OPCS survey of psychiatric morbidity among adults living in private households in Great Britain, carried out between April 1993 and August 1994.[8] The survey assessed the prevalence of neurotic disorders, functional psychoses and drug and alcohol dependence in the population in the week before the survey, based on the presence, frequency, severity and duration of various self-reported symptoms. The socio-economic classification used is the Registrar General's Social Class (based on occupation). Interesting results are found both by social class and by sex.

Table 15.2 shows the prevalence of any neurotic disorder by sex and social class as rates per 1,000 men and women. Women are one and a half times more likely than men to report having suffered from any neurotic disorder, 195 and 123 per 1,000 respectively. The differential in the prevalence of any neurotic disorder between men and women varies by social class. In Social Class I, women are more than two and a half times as likely to have reported suffering from symptoms in the previous week than men (155 and 60 per 1,000 respectively). For Social Class II, the rates for men and women are similar at 135 and 154 per 1,000 respectively. Among women, the trend is of increasing prevalence of any neurotic disorder with decreasing social class. The rate for women in Social Class V is 60 per cent more than in Social Class I (247 and 155 per 1,000 respectively). Among men, Social Class I has the lowest prevalence (60 per 1,000) but there is little variation in the rates for the other social classes, which range between 124 and 139 per 1,000.

TABLE 15.2

Prevalence of any neurotic disorder by social class, men and women aged 16+,

Great Britain, 1993–94

Source: Meltzer et al.[8]

Social class	Men	Women	Women/Men
	(per 1,000 population)		ratio
I	60	155	2.6
II	135	154	1.1
IIIN	139	213	1.5
IIIM	124	198	1.6
IV	124	235	1.9
V	129	247	1.9
All	**123**	**195**	**1.6**

FIGURE 15.9

Prevalence of neurotic
disorders, by social
class, men aged 16–64
Great Britain, 1993–94

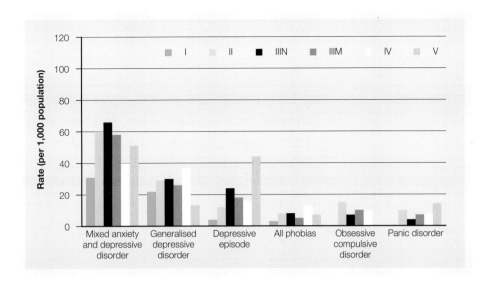

FIGURE 15.10

Prevalence of neurotic
disorders, by social
class, women aged 16–64
Great Britain, 1993–94

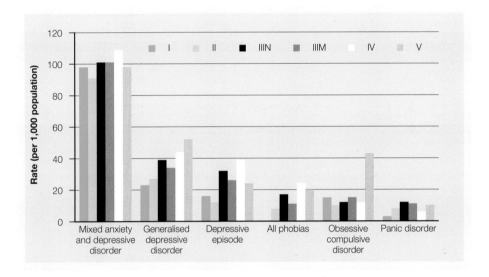

The breakdown of neurotic disorders by type, for men and women, is shown in Figures 15.9 and 15.10. The figures are drawn to the same scale to help comparison between the sexes. For both men and women, the most commonly reported condition is mixed anxiety and depression. However, nearly twice as many women as men reported such a condition, 99 and 54 per 1,000 respectively. Among women, there is very little social class difference in the prevalence of mixed anxiety and depression. Among men, however, the rate is much lower in Social Class I than the other social classes. For generalised depressive disorders there is very little difference in the rate between men and women for each social class. The exception is in Social Class V where women are four times as likely as men to have reported such a condition (52 and 13 per 1,000 respectively). For both depressive episodes in men and obsessive-compulsive disorders in women, individuals in Social Class V are much more likely to report symptoms than those in other social classes. Men in Social Class V are more than ten times as likely to have reported a depressive episode in the previous week than men in Social Class I (44 and 4 per 1,000 respectively). Women in Social Class V are nearly three times more likely than those in Social Class I to have reported experiencing an episode of obsessive-compulsive disorder in the previous seven days (43 and 15 per 1,000 respectively) and have more than four times the rate of women in Social Class II (10 per 1,000).

The pattern of a higher reported prevalence of neurotic disorders among women than men is reversed for drug and alcohol dependence, shown in Figures 15.11 and 15.12. For men, the rate of drug dependence is double that for women, 27 per 1,000 compared to 14 per 1,000. For alcohol dependence the difference is three and a half-fold, with 73 per 1,000 men and 21 per 1,000 women reporting dependence in the 12 months prior to the survey. For women, there is no clear pattern of drug or alcohol dependence by social class, the highest rates for both dependencies being seen in Social Class IIIN and V. The lowest rate for both dependencies for women is in Social Class II. For men, both drug and alcohol dependence show clear social class patterns with dependency increasing with decreasing social class. Men in Social Class V are two and a half times more likely to report alcohol dependency in the previous 12 months than men in Social Class I. For drug dependency, the differential between Social Class V and I is more than fifteen-fold, 73 and 5 per 1,000 respectively.

The other data shown in Figures 15.11 and 15.12 are for functional psychoses. This term covers experiences of mania, thought disorder, paranoia, delusions and auditory hallucinations in the past year. Although the reported level of functional psychoses in

FIGURE 15.11

Prevalence of psychiatric disorders, by social class, men aged 16–64
Great Britain, 1993–94

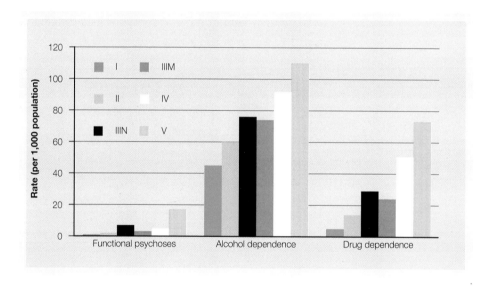

FIGURE 15.12

Prevalence of psychiatric disorders, by social class, women aged 16–64
Great Britain, 1993–94

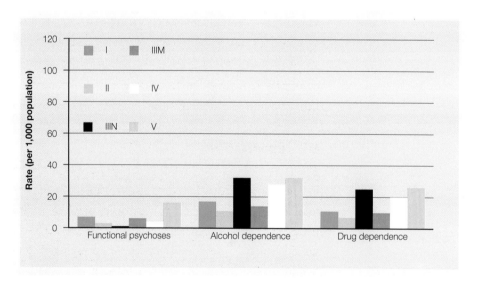

the population is low, with only 4 per 1,000 men or women reporting any experience, there are large differentials by social class. Among men, there is evidence of increasing reporting with decreasing social class, with the exception of Social Class IIIN which has the second highest rate. The difference between the reported prevalence for men in Social Class V and I is seventeen-fold (17 and 1 per 1,000 respectively). Among women there is no clear social class gradient, although Social Class V has the highest reported rate of 16 per 1,000.

Blood pressure

High blood pressure is a risk factor for several major diseases including coronary heart disease and stroke. Data on blood pressure by social class are derived from the 1995 Health Survey for England.[9] The prevalence of high blood pressure by social class for men and women is shown in Table 15.3. After adjustment for age using the direct age-standardisation method, the prevalence of high blood pressure increases with decreasing social class for both men and women. Among men, the age-standardised prevalence of high blood pressure increases from 16 per cent in Social Class I to 24 per cent in Social Class V. Among women, the age-standardised prevalence increases from 22 per cent in Social Class I to 26 in Social Class V. In every social class women have a higher prevalence of high blood pressure than men. Women in Social Class I are 40 per cent more likely to suffer from high blood pressure than their male counterparts, 22 and 16 per cent respectively.

TABLE 15.3

Prevalence of high blood pressure, by social class, men and women aged 16+

England, 1995

Source: Dong et al.[9]

| Social class | Men | | Women | |
	prevalence	standardised	prevalence	standardised
		percentage		
I	17.5	15.5	16.8	21.9
II	21.3	19.0	18.1	20.0
IIIN	23.8	21.2	27.8	23.4
IIIM	23.7	19.7	22.3	24.1
IV	23.9	20.3	27.0	25.4
V	29.9	24.2	34.6	26.0

Health service utilisation

This section presents evidence of differences in health service utilisation by socio-economic status derived from the GHS. Data are presented for GP consultations in the 14 days prior to the survey, regular attendance at a dentist and dental health and the percentage of the population wearing glasses or contact lenses and whether they have had a sight test in the previous 12 months.

GP consultations

The trend in GP consultations between 1979 and 1994, plotted as three-year moving averages, by sex and socio-economic group are shown in Figures 15.13 and 15.14. Across time, and in each socio-economic group, females have a higher level of consultation than males. In general, the professional group has the lowest level of consultation and the unskilled manual group the highest level of consultation, for both males and females. This finding masks considerable variation by age group.

FIGURE 15.13

GP consultations by
socio-economic group,
men, all ages
Great Britain, 1979–94

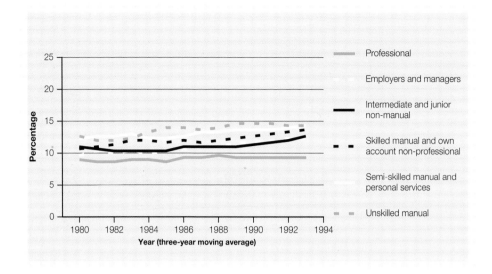

FIGURE 15.14

GP consultations by
socio-economic group,
women, all ages
Great Britain, 1979–94

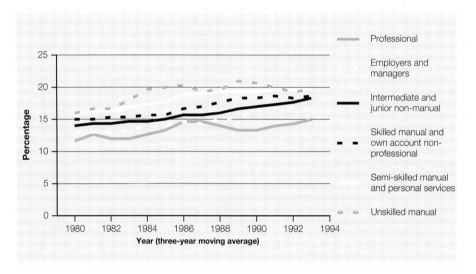

Figures 15.15 and 15.16 show the percentage of adults who consulted a doctor in the two weeks prior to the 1994 survey by sex and age group. In general, the percentage of individuals consulting increases with age. At each age women are more likely to consult a doctor than men. At ages 16–44, women are nearly twice as likely as men to have consulted a doctor, 17 and 9 per cent respectively. This large difference in consultation rates between men and women may not be a result of actual differences in health. The data on self-perceived morbidity presented earlier, show that this age is the healthiest stage in adults' lives. It is the age at which women consult GPs about reproductive health, especially contraception and pregnancy.[10] This helps explain why women's consultation rates are so much higher than men's despite only small variations in self-reported morbidity.

Very different patterns of socio-economic variation in the percentage consulting a GP are seen by age and sex. In men aged 16–44 and 45–64, consultation generally increases with decreasing socio-economic group, mirroring the pattern of self-reported morbidity. However, for men aged 65 years and over, the overall pattern is reversed, with men in the professional group more than 50 per cent more likely than those in the unskilled manual group to have consulted a GP in the previous two weeks, 20 and 13 per cent respectively. This pattern mirrors the self-reported prevalence of long-standing sickness. Among women, there is no socio-economic patterning at ages

FIGURE 15.15

GP consultations by
socio-economic group,
men by age-group
Great Britain, 1994

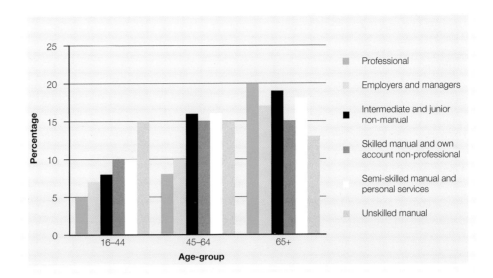

FIGURE 15.16

GP consultations by
socio-economic group,
women by age-group
Great Britain, 1994

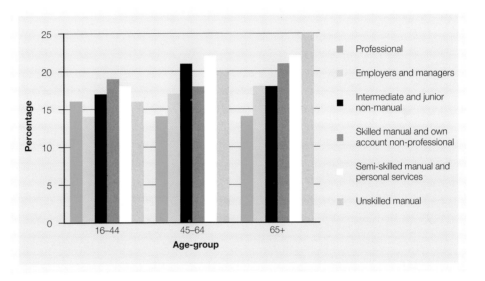

16–44. At 65 years and over the pattern is of increasing consultation with decreasing socio-economic group, the unskilled group being nearly twice as likely as the professional group to have consulted their GP in the previous two weeks, 25 and 14 per cent respectively.

Dental health

The GHS collected data on dental health in 1983, 1987, 1989, 1991 and 1993. Table 15.4 shows the percentage of adults without any natural teeth in 1989, 1991 and 1993. This percentage increases with decreasing socio-economic group. Over the five- year period there has been a decline in the percentage of people with no natural teeth from 19 per cent in 1989 to 16 per cent in 1993. Figure 15.17 shows the percentage of adults with no natural teeth by age and socio-economic group in 1993. With the exception of the youngest age group, where the numbers with no natural teeth are very small, there is a trend between the percentage of the population with no natural teeth and socio-economic group. Within the age group 75 years and over, 84 per cent of those classified in the unskilled manual group have no natural teeth, compared to 28 per cent in the professional group. This is a three-fold differential between the top and bottom of the scale. At younger ages the differential is even greater. For the age group 55–64 the difference between the top and bottom of the

TABLE 15.4

Percentage of adults with no natural teeth by socio-economic group

Great Britain, 1989, 1991, 1993

Source: Office of Population Censuses and Surveys.[4]

Socio-economic group	1989	1991	1993
		percentage	
Professional	5	5	3
Employers and managers	12	10	11
Intermediate and junior non-manual	14	14	12
Skilled manual and own account non-professional	22	20	19
Semi-skilled manual and personal services	30	25	23
Unskilled manual	37	34	33
All non-manual	12	11	10
All manual	26	23	22
Total 16+	**19**	**17**	**16**

FIGURE 15.17

Total tooth loss, by socio-economic group, men and women aged 16+

Great Britain, 1994

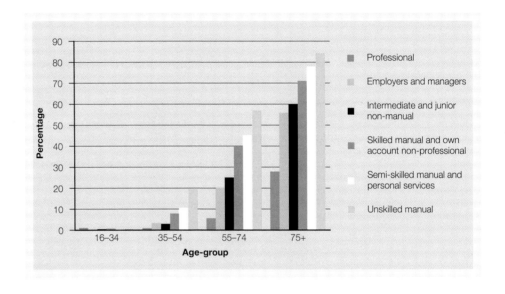

TABLE 15.5

Dental attendance pattern by socio-economic group, adults aged 16+

Great Britain, 1989, 1991, 1993

Source: Office of Population Censuses and Surveys.[4]

Socio-economic group	1989	1991	1993
	percentage who reported regular dental attendance		
Professional	62	63	64
Employers and managers	58	59	62
Intermediate and junior non-manual	56	54	55
Skilled manual and own account non-professional	40	41	44
Semi-skilled manual and personal services	39	37	41
Unskilled manual	29	36	38
All non-manual	58	57	59
All manual	39	39	43
Total 16+	**49**	**48**	**51**

The table includes only persons with some natural teeth

scale is nearly ten–fold, 4 per cent in the professional group and 39 per cent in the un-skilled manual group. The differential between the professional and unskilled groups is greatest at ages 45–54. At these ages, 2 per cent of those in the top socio-economic group have no natural teeth, compared to 30 per cent in the bottom group, a fifteen-fold differential.

The GHS asked people who had some natural teeth whether they went for regular dental check-ups. Again, there is a clear socio-economic gradient, Table 15.5. In 1989, those in the professional group were more than twice as likely as those in the unskilled manual group to report regular dental visits, 62 and 29 per cent respectively. Between 1989 and 1993 regular dental attendance increased for all socio-economic groups. The greatest increase, 30 per cent, occurred in the unskilled manual group, the percentage reporting regular attendance increasing from 29 per cent in 1989 to 38 per cent in 1993.

Ophthalmic health

The percentage of economically active adults wearing glasses or contacts lenses in 1994 by socio-economic group is shown in Table 15.6. Overall, more women than men wear either glasses or contact lenses, 59 per cent and 52 per cent respectively. The likelihood of wearing glasses or contact lenses has no socio-economic pattern for women. However, for men the percentage decreases with decreasing socio-economic group. In the professional group, 66 per cent of men wore either glasses or contact lenses compared to 40 per cent of men in the unskilled manual group. The GHS also collected data on the percentage of individuals who had been for a sight test in the past year, shown in Table 15.7. The pattern of the percentage of those who had been for a sight test in the past year, by sex and socio-economic group, is similar to that of the likelihood of wearing glasses or contact lenses. The difference in the percentage of individuals wearing glasses or contact lenses by sex and socio-economic group may result as much from the likelihood of the condition being spotted as actual differences in sight.

TABLE 15.6

Prevalence of wearing glasses or contact lenses by socio-economic group, economically active men and women aged 16+

Great Britain, 1994

Source: Office of Population Censuses and Surveys.[6]

Socio-economic group	Men	Women
	percentage	
Professional	66	63
Employers and managers	61	66
Intermediate and junior non-manual	57	59
Skilled manual and own account non-professional	46	58
Semi-skilled manual and personal services	44	55
Unskilled manual	40	66
Total	**52**	**59**

TABLE 15.7

Sight tests in previous 12 months by socio-economic group, men and women aged 16+

Great Britain, 1994

Source: Office for Population Censuses and Surveys.[6]

Socio-economic group	Men	Women
	percentage	
Professional	40	44
Employers and managers	35	40
Intermediate and junior non-manual	38	37
Skilled manual and own account non-professional	27	32
Semi-skilled manual and personal services	26	33
Unskilled manual	26	34
Total	**31**	**36**

Health-related behaviours

As mentioned earlier, health-related behaviours are an important part of the Department of Health's *Health of the Nation* strategy. This section presents data for *Health of the Nation* key areas for a number of health-related behaviours by socio-economic status.

TABLE 15.8

Definition of income
groups used in 1995
National Food Survey

*Source: Ministry of Agriculture,
Fisheries and Food.*[11]

Income group		Income range (weekly income)
Households with one or more earners	A	£570 and over
	B	£300 - £569
	C	£140 - £299
	D	under £140
Households without an earner	E1	£140 and over
	E2	under £140
	OAP	OAP

TABLE 15.9

Household consumption
of selected foods by
income group

Great Britain, 1995

*Source: Ministry of Agriculture,
Fisheries and Food.*[11]

	Income group (gross weekly income of head of household)						
	Households with one or more earners				Households without an earner		
	A	B	C	D	E1	E2	OAP
	£570+	£300-£569	£140-£299	under £140	£140+	under £140	
	grams per person per week[a]						
Milk and cream (ml)	1,992	2,073	2,097	2,227	2,648	2,251	2,502
Cheese	128	112	106	95	131	90	98
Meat	789	910	972	989	1,083	929	1,020
Fish	157	130	128	131	240	138	200
Eggs (number)	1.36	1.55	1.74	2.23	2.57	2.19	2.58
Fats	161	183	217	226	304	252	305
Sugar and Preserves	116	127	163	213	272	221	334
Vegetables	1,755	1,966	2,033	2,266	2,554	2,115	2,212
Fruit	1,283	1,073	846	723	1,533	828	1,078
Cereals	1,293	1,390	1,481	1,514	1,660	1,527	1,651
Beverages	48	52	53	64	110	69	115
Miscellaneous	574	432	394	353	443	335	348
Soft drinks (ml)	911	957	996	898	787	834	510
Alcoholic drinks (ml)	547	468	329	199	442	230	184
Confectionery	45	54	52	47	70	48	56

[a] except where otherwise stated

Nutrition

The National Food Survey is a continuing source of information on food consumption
and expenditure in Great Britain, which is carried out for the Ministry of Agriculture,
Fisheries and Food. Socio-economic status is measured by income groups. Summary
tables categorise households into seven income bands based on the gross weekly
income of the head of the household – the categories used are shown in Table 15.8.

Data on food consumption, expressed as grams per person per week (unless otherwise
stated) by income group are shown in Table 15.9. For households with one or more earners,
groups A–D, the consumption of most food groups was related to income. However, the
direction of the relationship varied for different food groups. The consumption of cheese,
fish, fruit and alcohol rose with income. In contrast, the consumption of milk and cream,
meat, eggs, fats, sugar and preserves, vegetables, cereals and beverages increased with
decreasing income. The consumption of soft drinks and confectionery showed no
pattern by income group. Tables 15.10 and 15.11 show the pattern in the consumption
of fats and sugars and fruit and vegetables by income group. The consumption of both
fats and sugars, in general, increases with decreasing income. Income group E1,

TABLE 15.10

Household consumption
and expenditure on fats
and sugar by income
group

Great Britain, 1995

Source: Ministry of Agriculture,
Fisheries and Food.[11]

Income group	Consumption (grams per person per week)		Expenditure (pence per person per week)	
	Fats	Sugar	Fats	Sugar
A	161	116	33.6	14.3
B	183	127	32.4	13.6
C	217	163	34.7	15.0
D	226	213	33.0	17.0
E1	304	272	56.2	29.8
E2	252	221	37.1	19.2
OAP	305	334	53.0	31.7

TABLE 15.11

Household consumption
and expenditure on fruit
and vegetables by
income group

Great Britain, 1995

Source: Ministry of Agriculture,
Fisheries and Food.[11]

Income group	Consumption (grams per person per week)		Expenditure (pounds per person per week)	
	Fruit	Vegetables	Fruit	Vegetables
A	1,283	1,755	1.58	2.50
B	1,073	1,966	1.19	2.29
C	846	2,033	0.89	2.09
D	723	2,266	0.75	1.97
E1	1,533	2,554	1.77	2.47
E2	828	2,115	0.85	1.83
OAP	1,078	2,212	1.15	1.84

households without an earner with an income of over £140 per week, consume on average 300 grams of fat per person per day, nearly twice that consumed by income group A, households with one or more earners and an income of over £570 per week. A similar pattern is seen for the consumption of vegetables. However, fruit consumption decreases with decreasing income. Income group D, households with one or more earners and an income of less than £140 per week, consume on average 65 per cent less fruit than income group A, 723g and 1,283g per person per week respectively.

Table 15.12 presents data for expenditure on food and drink, expressed as pounds per person per week, by income group. The overall trend in weekly expenditure on food and drink for households with one or more earners is of decreasing expenditure with decreasing income group. Households where the head of the household earns more than £570 per week gross spend on average £18.71 per week per head. Those in the lowest income group where the head of the household earns less than £140 per week spend on average £13.18 per person per week. This trend in expenditure is generally true of all food types, although expenditure on eggs and sugar and preserves increases with decreasing income. The types of products purchased within each food group may vary by income group so that expenditure patterns do not always reflect consumption patterns.[11] This is highlighted by the consumption and expenditure on vegetables (see Table 15.11). Households with one or more earners where the weekly income is more than £570 spend on average 27 per cent more money on vegetables than those earning less than £140, £2.50 and £1.97 per person per week respectively. However, those in the lowest income group actually eat more grams of vegetables per week than those in the highest income group, 2,266g and 1,755g per person per week respectively. This finding is also true for milk and cream, meat and meat products, cereals and beverages.

TABLE 15.12
Household expenditure
on selected foods, pence
per person per week by
income group
Great Britain, 1995
Source: Ministry of Agriculture,
Fisheries and Food [17]

	Income group (gross weekly income of head of household)						
	Households with one or more earners				Households without an earner		
	A	B	C	D	E1	E2	OAP
	£570+	£300-£569	£140-£299	Under £140	£140+	Under £140	
	pounds per person per week						
Milk and Cream	1.53	1.45	1.33	1.24	1.79	1.30	1.62
Cheese	0.68	0.52	0.45	0.39	0.64	0.39	0.44
Meat	3.71	3.77	3.58	3.22	4.26	3.07	3.69
Fish	0.99	0.69	0.60	0.59	1.31	0.64	0.98
Eggs	0.15	0.15	0.16	0.19	0.25	0.19	0.24
Fats	0.34	0.32	0.35	0.33	0.56	0.37	0.53
Sugar and Preserves	0.14	0.14	0.15	0.17	0.30	0.19	0.32
Vegetables	2.50	2.29	2.09	1.97	2.47	1.83	1.84
Fruit	1.58	1.19	0.89	0.75	1.77	0.85	1.15
Cereals	2.74	2.52	2.40	2.16	2.77	2.19	2.41
Beverage	0.43	0.40	0.40	0.39	0.76	0.44	0.70
Miscellaneous	0.92	0.76	0.67	0.60	0.84	0.54	0.57
Soft Drinks	0.63	0.55	0.51	0.43	0.43	0.40	0.26
Alcoholic Drinks	2.13	1.34	0.84	0.50	1.70	0.62	0.67
Confectionary	0.24	0.29	0.26	0.24	0.35	0.23	0.26
Total food and drink	**18.71**	**16.38**	**14.68**	**13.17**	**20.20**	**13.25**	**15.68**

Smoking

Questions about smoking have been included in the GHS every other year since 1974. Throughout the period a higher percentage of men than women have reported smoking cigarettes, although the difference in the prevalence of smoking between men and women has been declining over time. In 1974, 51 per cent of men aged over 16 years reported smoking cigarettes compared to 41 per cent of women. By 1994, the respective figures had declined to 28 and 26 per cent. Figure 15.18 shows the manual/ non-manual difference in the percentage of men and women smoking between 1974 and 1994 as three-year moving averages. There is a higher prevalence of smoking in manual than non-manual groups for both men and women. Within the manual group there has been a consistent trend of men being more likely to smoke than women. Between 1974 and 1980, the same pattern was observed for non-manual workers. However, since 1980 there has been a convergence in the percentage of men and women in the non-manual groups who smoke. In 1974, 45 per cent of men in the non-manual group smoked compared to 38 per cent of women. By 1980, the percentage of men smoking in the non-manual group had declined to 33 per cent, with the equivalent value for women declining to 32 per cent. Since 1980, the percentage of smokers among men and women in the non-manual groups has declined in tandem.

A decline in the percentage who smoke has been witnessed for both men and women in all socio-economic groups over the 20-year period. For men, the differential in the percentage smoking between the top and bottom of the socio-economic scale has fluctuated over time. In 1974 men in the unskilled manual group were just over twice as likely to smoke as those in the professional group. By 1994, this had increased to a two and a half-fold differential. Women have experienced an almost continual widening in the percentage smoking between the highest and lowest group. In 1974 women in the unskilled manual group were nearly twice as likely to smoke as women in the

FIGURE 15.18

Smoking prevalence by manual/non-manual socio-economic group, men and women aged 16+

Great Britain, 1974–94

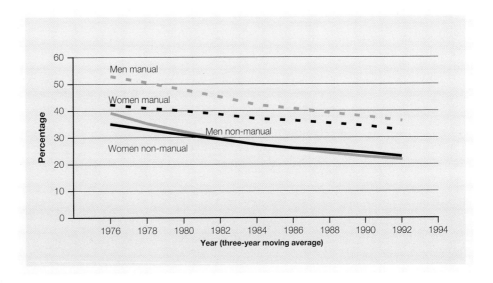

TABLE 15.13

Smoking prevalence by socio-economic group, men and women aged 16+

Great Britain, 1994

Source: Office of Population Censuses and Surveys.[6]

Socio-economic group	Men	Women
	percentage	
Professional	16	12
Employers and managers	20	20
Intermediate and junior non-manual	24	23
Skilled manual and own account non-professional	33	29
Semi-skilled manual and personal services	38	32
Unskilled manual	40	34
All	**28**	**26**

professional group. By 1994 this differential had increased to nearly three times.

The 1994 data on the percentage of smokers among men and women aged 16 years and over are presented in Table 15.13. Overall, and in each socio-economic group, men are more likely to be smokers than women. For both men and women the percentage of smokers increases with decreasing socio-economic group. Men in the unskilled manual group are two and a half times more likely to smoke than those in the professional group, 40 and 16 per cent respectively. The corresponding figure for women is nearer three times, 34 and 12 per cent respectively.

Data on the average weekly cigarette consumption for smokers by socio-economic group have also been collected since 1974. Between 1974 and 1994 there is no discernible pattern of cigarette consumption by socio-economic group. However, within every socio-economic group men smoke more cigarettes on average per week than women. Men on average smoked 114 cigarettes per week compared to 97 per week for women.

Alcohol

In December 1995 the Government published a review, based on scientific and medical evidence, on the health effects of alcohol consumption.[12] The report set benchmarks for sensible drinking levels, stating that the regular consumption of between three and four units of alcohol a day for men and two and three for women, will not accrue a significant health risk. Consistently exceeding these levels is not recommended, however, because of the progressive health risk this carries. The report also recognised

TABLE 15.14

Alcohol consumption by socio-economic group, men and women aged 16+

Great Britian, 1994

Source: Office of Population, Censuses and Surveys.[6]

Socio-economic group	Men	Women
	mean weekly number of units	
Professional	15.5	7.2
Employers and managers	16.5	7.0
Intermediate and junior non-manual	14.1	5.2
Skilled manual and own account non-professional	15.8	5.3
Semi-skilled manual and personal services	13.6	4.0
Unskilled manual	13.6	3.2
Total	**15.4**	**5.4**

FIGURE 15.19

Alcohol consumption, mean weekly number of units, by socio-economic group, men aged 16+

Great Britain, 1994

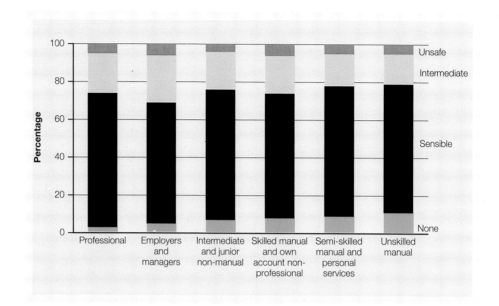

FIGURE 15.20

Alcohol consumption, mean weekly number of units, by socio-economic group, women aged 16+

Great Britain, 1994

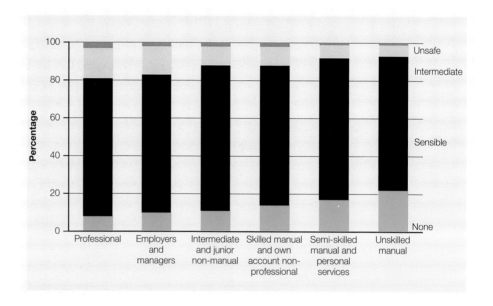

that alcohol can confer a benefit to health, mainly by giving protection from coronary heart disease. Since the data used in this review were collected before the new recommendations, the analysis is based on the previously recommended levels of 21 units per week for men and 14 units per week for women.

The GHS has included questions on drinking alcohol every other year since 1978. Prior to 1988, questions on alcohol consumption were only asked of those aged 18 and over.

Since 1988, respondents aged 16 and 17 have been asked the questions by means of a self-completed questionnaire. Respondents' answers are used to provide an estimate of their alcohol consumption level. However, because the measure is based on a person's estimate of the amounts 'usually drunk on any one day' the alcohol consumption rating is not a precise measure of weekly consumption.

The mean weekly number of units consumed by men and women by socio-economic group are shown in Table 15.14. For men, there is no clear pattern by socio-economic group. For women, the mean number of units consumed per week decreases with decreasing socio-economic group. Women in the unskilled manual group have under half the weekly alcohol consumption level of women in the professional group, 3.2 and 7.2 units per week respectively.

Figures 15.19 and 15.20 present the 1994 data for alcohol consumption levels for men and women by socio-economic group. For both men and women, the percentage who classify themselves as non-drinkers increases with decreasing socio-economic group. In all socio-economic groups approximately twice as many women as men report being non-drinkers. In the professional group 3 per cent of men and 8 per cent of women are categorised as non-drinkers. These figures increase to 11 per cent of men and 22 per cent of women in the unskilled manual group.

Among men, the percentage with an alcohol consumption rating above the Department of Health's 1994 recommendation of a maximum of 21 units per week shows no obvious pattern by socio-economic group. However, among women the percentage consuming above the recommended maximum of 14 units per week increases with increasing socio-economic group. Among women in the professional group 19 per cent exceed the recommended maximum. For women in the unskilled manual group, only 8 per cent consume more than the government recommendation.

The data on high alcohol consumption, from the GHS, do not show the same socio-economic patterning as alcohol dependency derived from the OPCS survey of psychiatric morbidity, shown in Figures 15.11 and 15.12. Among women, there is no clear socio-economic pattern for alcohol dependency but there is a clear pattern of increasing high alcohol consumption with increasing socio-economic status. For men, conversely, the prevalence of alcohol dependency increases with socio-economic status, but there is no socio-economic pattern for high consumption. This suggests that being a heavy drinker does not necessarily mean that an individual has the symptoms of alcohol dependency.

Obesity

In surveys carried out in England since 1980 there has been a trend towards increasing obesity in the adult population. This trend is of considerable importance given the established link between obesity and increased morbidity and mortality. The data on obesity, by social class, are derived from the 1994 Health Survey of England.[13] Obesity is measured using the body mass index (BMI) which is calculated by relating weight (kg) and height (m²). The measurement allows for differences in weight due to height. However, it does not differentiate from heaviness due to fatness and heaviness due to muscular physique.

TABLE 15.15

Age-standardised
prevalence of raised BMI
by social class, men and
women aged 16+

England, 1994

Source: Colhoun et al. [13]

Social class	BMI over 25		BMI over 30	
	Men	Women	Men	Women
	percentage			
I	55.3	43.3	9.6	11.7
II	57.5	44.7	12.9	13.0
IIIN	58.2	45.2	13.6	14.5
IIIM	58.9	50.1	14.1	19.1
IV	52.4	53.1	14.6	21.8
V	53.2	54.9	13.2	21.1
All	**56.8**	**48.0**	**13.3**	**16.9**

Table 15.15 presents data for the age-standardised prevalence of raised BMI by social class for men and women. For men, there is no clear pattern of being overweight or obese, BMI over 25, by social class. For women, the prevalence of being overweight or obese increases with decreasing social class. In Social Class I, 43 per cent of women are classified as overweight or obese, increasing to 55 per cent in Social Class V. For men, a clearer social class pattern is seen for BMI values of over 30, classified as obese. In Social Class I, 10 per cent of men are classified as obese, increasing to 15 per cent in Social Class IV. The difference between the top and the bottom of the social class scale is even greater among women classified as obese. Women in Social Class V are nearly twice as likely as those in Social Class I to be obese, 21 and 12 per cent respectively.

Physical activity

Data on physical activity are derived from the 1994 Health Survey for England.[14] Levels of activity are estimated from information on the time spent being active, the intensity of the activity and the frequency of participation. People are classified to one of six physical activity levels, 0–5, on the basis of their reported participation in different activities in the four weeks before interview. Table 15.16 presents the classification of activity levels used. For ease of interpretation in this discussion, the activity levels will be classified as 'none' (level 0), 'moderate' (levels 1–2) and 'high' (levels 3–5).

High	Level 5	12 or more occasions of vigorous activity (3 or more occasions a week)
	Level 4	12 or more occasions of a mixture of moderate or vigorous activity (3 or more occasions a week)
	Level 3	12 or more occasions of moderate activity (3 or more occasions a week)
Moderate	Level 2	5 – 11 occasions of at least moderate activity (more than 1, fewer than 3 occasions a week)
	Level 1	1 – 4 occasions of at least moderate activity (once a week or less)
None	Level 0	no occasions of even moderate activity

Data on physical activity levels by social class for men and women are presented in Figures 15.21 and 15.22. Overall, a greater proportion of men than women had high activity levels. More than half of men, 51 per cent, had activity level scores above 3, compared to 38 per cent of women. Roughly equal proportions of men and women, 16 and 19 per cent respectively, had no occasions of moderate activity in the previous four

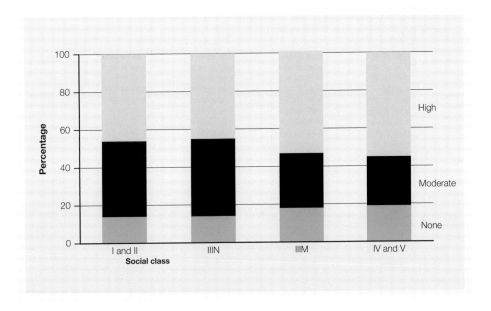

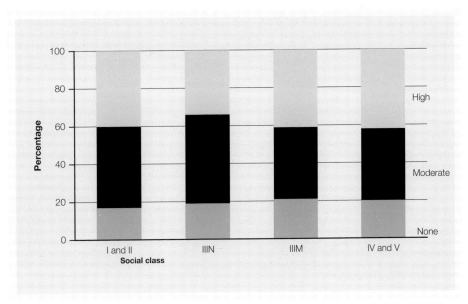

weeks. By social class, the proportion of both men and women with activity level scores of none increased with decreasing social class. Among men, those in Social Class I and II were more than one and a half times as likely as those in Social Classes IV and V to have moderate activity levels, 40 and 26 per cent respectively. For women, this differential by social class is smaller. In Social Class I and II, 40 per cent of women had moderate activity levels compared to 38 per cent in Social Class IV and V. For activity levels classified as high there is a manual/non-manual difference. About 55 per cent of men in the manual social classes have high activity levels, compared to about 45 per cent of men in the non-manual social classes. For women, there is very little social class difference for high physical activity levels.

Table 15.17 presents the age-standardised proportions of men and women active at the high level by activity type. Clear patterns are seen both by activity type and social class. For men, as would be expected, it is occupational activity which results in most of the social class differences. The incidence of high level work activity was much greater among the manual than non-manual social classes, 33 and 10 per cent respectively.

TABLE 15.17

Physical activity at high
level by own social class,
men and women aged
16+

England, 1994

Source: Gray.[14]

		(age-standardised proportions)			
Men	I and II	IIIN	IIIM	IV and V	Total
Occupation	9	13	31	32	20
Home	66	64	65	62	64
Walking	39	34	25	27	32
Sports	47	46	37	36	42
Women					
Occupation	13	5	16	18	11
Home	69	71	69	72	70
Walking	26	21	19	17	22
Sports	42	35	31	26	35

Among women, there was little variation in the incidence of high level work activity. However, Social Class IIIN has less than half the proportion in the other social classes, 5 per cent.

There was little variation by social class in the proportion of people doing high level home activity. However, in each social class the age-standardised proportion was higher for women than for men.

For both men and women, the age-standardised proportion of those doing high level walking and sports decreased with social class. For men, there are clear manual/non-manual differences. The age-standardised proportions for walking activity were 38 per cent for the non-manual group and 26 per cent for manual group. For sport, 47 per cent of men in non-manual occupations participated at a high level, compared to 26 per cent in the manual occupations. For women, the participation in sport was 38 per cent for Social Classes I to IIIN and 27 per cent for IIIM to V. The corresponding figures for walking were 23 per cent and 17 per cent respectively.

The data presented show that men and women in the non-manual social classes are more likely to take part in high level physical activities outside the workplace than those in manual occupations. However, within the work environment men in the manual social classes are more than three times as likely to have high physical activity than those in the non-manual classes.

Conclusion

A variety of different measures of morbidity, health service utilisation and health-related behaviours have been looked at in this chapter. In general, the proportion of adults reporting ill health increases with decreasing socio-economic status. The exception is acute sickness which shows no socio-economic pattern for men or women.

GP consultation, used here as a measure of health service utilisation, increases with decreasing socio-economic status. This trend has been found elsewhere.[15] However, the use of preventive services such as regular dental attendance and the use of ophthalmic services decreases with socio-economic status.[16,17] Such findings have prompted concern that an 'inverse care law' might be operating – that is, the availability of health services is less in areas where they are most needed.[18]

Alcohol consumption and smoking are both related to socio-economic status but the patterns go in different directions. The prevalence of smoking increases with decreasing socio-economic status for both men and women. The relationship between cigarette smoking and many diseases, especially lung cancer and other respiratory diseases, is now well established.[19] It is therefore predictable that differences in smoking habits by socio-economic status will contribute to socio-economic differences in mortality and morbidity. As with smoking, there is strong evidence that excessive alcohol consumption has a number of detrimental health consequences, including digestive cancers, cirrhosis of the liver and psychiatric disorders. However, with the pattern of excessive alcohol consumption increasing with socio-economic status for both men and women, it is not an explanatory factor for the differences in morbidity.

Overall, the socio-economic differences in health-related behaviours and health service utilisation are consistent with the patterns of morbidity and mortality. However, the differences in health-related behaviours by socio-economic status do not explain most of the observed differences in health. A number of studies show that even when behavioural differences are taken into account, social gradients in health still exist.[20,21] The question remaining is whether or not the behaviour of individuals can be separated from their social and material environment.

References

1 Blaxter, M (1989) A comparison of measures of inequality in morbidity. In: Fox, A J (ed.) *Health Inequalities in European Countries*. Aldershot, Gower Publishing Company Limited.

2 Department of Health (1992) *The Health of the Nation: a strategy for health in England*. London, HMSO.

3 Department of Health (1995) *Variations in Health : What can the Department of Health and NHS do?* London, Department of Health.

4 Office of Population Censuses and Surveys (annual) *General Household Survey*. London, HMSO.

5 Cleary, Paul D (1997) Subjective and objective measures of health: which is better when?, *Journal of Health Service Research Policy*, 1: 3–4.

6 Office of Population Censuses and Surveys (1996) *Living in Britain. Results from the 1994 General Household Survey*. London, HMSO.

7 Dunnell, K (1997) *Are we healthier?* In: Charlton, J (ed.) *The Health of Adult Britain 1841-1994*. ONS Series DS nos 12 & 13. London, The Stationery Office.

8 Meltzer, H, Gill, B, Petticrew, M and Hinds, K (1995) *The prevalence of psychiatric morbidity among adults living in private households*. London, OPCS/HMSO.

9 Dong, W, Primatesta, P and Bost, L (1997) Blood pressure. In: Prescott-Clarke, P and Primatesta, P (eds) *Health Survey for England 1995. Volume I: Findings*, London, HMSO.

10 McCormick, A, Fleming, D, and Charlton, J (1995) *Morbidity Statistics from General Practice : Fourth National Study 1991-1992*. OPCS Series MB5 no.3. London, HMSO.

11 Ministry of Agriculture Fisheries and Food (1996). *National Food Survey 1995*. London, The Stationery Office.

12 Department of Health (1995) *Sensible drinking : The report of an interdepartmental working group*. London, Department of Health.

13 Colhoun, H, Lampe, F, and Dong, W (1996) Obesity. In: Colhoun, H and Prescott-Clarke P (eds) *Health Survey for England 1994. Volume I: Findings*. London, HMSO.

14 Gray, R (1996) Physical activity. In: Colhoun, H and Prescott-Clarke P (eds) *Health Survey for England 1994. Volume I: Findings*. London, HMSO.

15 Blaxter, M (1984) Equity and consultation rates in general practice *British Medical Journal*, 288: 1963–7.

16 Eddie, S and Davies, J A (1985) The effect of social class on attendance frequency and dental treatment received in the general dental service in Scotland, *British Dental Journal*, 159: 370–72.

17 Todd, J E and Dodd, J (1985) *Children's dental health in the UK, 1983*. London, OPCS/HMSO.

18 Hart, J T. (1971) *The inverse care law, The Lancet*, i: 405–12.

19 Cancer Research Campaign (1996) *Lung cancer and smoking - UK. Factsheet no. 11*. Cancer Research Campaign, London.

20 Davey Smith, G, Shipley, M J and Rose, G (1990) The magnitude and causes of socio-economic differences in mortality: further evidence from the Whitehall study. *Journal of Epidemiology and Community Health*, 44: 265–270.

21 Woodward, M, Shewry, M, Smith W C and Tunstall Pedoe, H (1990) Coronary heart disease and socio-economic factors in Edinburgh and North Glasgow, *The Statistician*, 39: 319–329.

Part Four

Main findings and implications
for the future

16 Health inequalities : main findings and implications for the future

Margaret Whitehead and Frances Drever

Introduction

Before leaving the subject of inequalities in health, it is important to take an overview of the evidence presented in the various chapters of this volume, to draw out common themes and to look at implications for the future. In this chapter we single out the most striking findings concerned with the patterns and trends. The chapter ends by highlighting initiatives which have begun to address some of the issues in this area.

Substantial and consistent differences

The analyses in the volume are based on different, but nationally representative, data sources: cross-sectional data from the census and the full national deaths data; a 1 per cent representative sample of the population of England and Wales followed up in the ONS Longitudinal Study (LS); linked records on births and infant deaths; and morbidity from household interview surveys. These different sources allow specific aspects to be examined from a variety of angles, and also act as checks on the consistency of findings.

Although there is some variation in the absolute rates calculated from these different sources, the socio-economic patterns of health are remarkably consistent. All the sources show a marked socio-economic gradient in mortality and morbidity persisting into the 1990s. For example, using the full national deaths data, in 1991–93 the all-cause SMR for men aged 20–64 was almost three times higher among unskilled manual workers in Social Class V than among professional men in Social Class I. Furthermore, substantial differentials were not confined to the extremes of the social scale, but showed a step-wise increase with decreasing social class – men from Class IIIM and IV, for example, had nearly double the mortality of Class I. The LS, for the slightly earlier period of 1986–89 and for the wider age-range of 15–64, has reported a two and a half-fold difference in SMR between Class I and V, and a similar graded mortality across the social scale.[1]

In absolute terms, the standardised death rates for men aged 20–64 in 1991–93, calculated using the full national deaths data, ranged from about 290 deaths per 100,000 in Classes I and II to over 800 deaths per 100,000 in Class V. From the LS analysis of the latest period covering 1986–92, an older age-range (from age 35–64) was studied, so the two analyses are not directly comparable. However, what can be compared is the general pattern and this gave a consistent picture. In the LS, male death rates increased with declining social class, ranging from 455 deaths per 100,000 in Class I/II to 764 deaths per 100,000 in Classes IV/V. The social class gradient in mortality of women was slightly shallower than that for men, but still evident. Women's death rates ranged from 270 to 418 per 100,000 from Classes I/II to IV/V.

These represent serious, not trivial, differences in risk of death across society persisting into the 1990s. From the LS analysis in Chapter 6, for example, these differences translate into life expectancy at birth of 75 years for Class I/II men compared to just under 70 years for Class IV/V men – a gap of five years. For women, the equivalent figures are 80 and 77 years, a gap of three years. Infant mortality rates for births inside and outside marriage (jointly registered) showed an almost two-fold difference between Class V and I for 1993–95.

The review of international evidence in Chapter 4 shows that this situation is not confined to Britain, but that there is widespread concern across Europe and North America about the scale of social inequalities in health found within many countries.

Widening of relative differences between classes

The question of whether the observed social differentials in mortality have widened or narrowed over the past 20 years depends on the age group under consideration. The most encouraging evidence comes from infant mortality data detailed in Chapter 7. There have been declines in mortality for all social classes. From the early to the late 1980s, the ratio between the rates for Social Class V and I reduced from 2.0 to 1.7, and continued to decline in the 1990s, falling to a ratio of 1.6 for the period 1993–5 (see Figure 7.5). It should be noted that this conclusion only relates to births within marriage, as data on births both inside marriage and jointly registered outside have only been published routinely since 1993.

The story is not so positive, however, when other age-groups are considered. Indications of a deterioration in the relative position of adults in manual social classes comes from several distinct analyses. From Chapter 6, using LS data, the gap in life expectancy between Classes I/II and the other classes is seen to widen between the late 1970s and the late 1980s. For men, for example, the gap in life expectancy at age 15 between Classes I/II and IV/V widened from four to five years over this period (see Table 6.1). Similarly, for women at age 15, the gap widened from two to three years (see Table 6.5).

From the analysis using the full national deaths data comes evidence of a relative widening in the mortality differentials among men of working ages (see Chapter 8). The all-cause mortality rate of Class V men was nearly double that of Classes I and II men in 1970–72 and had increased to an almost three-fold difference by 1991–93. Even greater differentials between Classes I and II on the one hand and Class V on the other were found for lung cancer, and for external causes such as accidents and suicides, with these differences widening over time. This relative widening of mortality is confirmed by the LS analyses presented in Chapter 11, for men of older working ages. For example, the ratio of mortality in manual to non-manual men increased from 1.2 in the late 1970s to 1.5 in the period 1986–92 (see Table 11.6). This widening in the ratio between manual and non-manual mortality was seen for both employed and unemployed men (see Table 11.10).

For women aged 35–64, the LS provides evidence of a narrowing and then a widening of the differential between manual and non-manual classes from the late 1970s to 1986–92 (see Table 11.3). The alternative social classifications used in Chapter 13 provide further evidence of these trends. Using housing tenure as an indicator, differentials in women's mortality between local authority tenants and owner occupiers narrowed and then widened over the 22 years of follow-up in the LS.

Absolute mortality differences: improvements for some but not for others

Essentially, there are two main ways in which the observed widening of mortality across the various social groups could have occurred. The widening may have been a result of a general improvement in mortality rates for all groups, though at a more rapid pace for some. Alternatively the mortality gap could widen because of a stagnation in or worsening of mortality rates in one or more groups at the same time as improvements were occurring for other groups.

The evidence shows a complex picture, varying for different age-groups and for men and women. In some instances the gap appeared to be widening because of standstill or even deterioration in mortality for less advantaged socio-economic groups, while more advantaged groups have seen an improvement. For example, Table 6.6 shows that life expectancy for women aged 65 in Classes IIIM and IV/V did not improve at all over the period from 1977–91, while it increased by about ten months for women in Classes I/II.

For boys aged 10–14, there was an increase in death rates for the sons of unskilled manual workers (Class V) between the early 1980s and the early 1990s and little change for the sons of skilled manual workers. Over the same period, boys from non-manual classes experienced a marked decline in mortality. At younger ages and for girls at all ages from 1 to 15, however, mortality declined in all social classes, though at varying rates (Chapter 7). For men aged 20–64, the marked declines in mortality rates in most social classes over the 20 years since the 1971 Census contrasted with the marginal improvement in mortality for Social Class V (Chapter 8).

The LS analysis in Chapter 11 studied older adults, aged 35–64, and concluded that the widening social class differences in mortality in both men and women at these ages were due to general improvements across the board, but with larger declines in death rates among non-manual classes.

Picture confirmed with alternative measures of social circumstances

The analyses highlighted so far have been based mainly on social class, but alternative measures of socio-economic circumstances tell a similar story. In Chapter 13 housing tenure and car access have been used to explore mortality in more and less disadvantaged sections of the population. Both indicators show a gradient in mortality rising from the lowest mortality in owner occupiers, to private tenants at an intermediate level and local authority tenants with the highest mortality. Similarly, mortality also rose with decreasing car access. At working later ages, the gradient was as steep for women as for men. For women aged 35–59, the SMR for owner occupiers in 1981–92 was 83 rising to 126 for local authority tenants – almost identical to the values for men in the equivalent age and tenure groups. This contrasted with occupationally-based classifications, which often showed a less marked differential in mortality across the social groups for women than for men. These two alternative classifications were also able to demonstrate clear social gradients in mortality persisting after retirement in both men and women for the period 1981–92. In absolute terms, the differences in mortality were larger at post-retirement ages than at working ages.

Trends in mortality measured by these two indicators confirmed the evidence derived from the social class analyses. For both men and women at older working ages, and also for women over retirement, the gap in mortality between the most and least disadvantaged on both tenure and car access scales increased between the two periods covering the 1970s and the 1980s. These widening gaps resulted from declines in death rates for people in all the tenure and car access groups, but with the falls in mortality being larger for the most advantaged (see Chapter 13).

The contribution of specific causes of death

It is clear from the evidence that the social differentials in mortality cannot be attributed to just a few causes of death. As in previous decades, most of the major, and quite a few minor, causes of death exhibited a social class gradient in the 1990s, with higher mortality in Classes IV and V. There are a few exceptions to this general pattern, as well as some notable changes for specific diseases that have occurred over the decade.

The large number of deaths in the analysis using the full national deaths data has allowed social class analyses of many, even relatively rare, causes of death for men (Chapter 10). Very strong gradients were observed for tuberculosis, circulatory and respiratory diseases, diabetes, lung cancer, accidents, suicides, and mental disorders, such as alcohol and drug abuse. Clear but shallower gradients were found for other specific cancer sites. There was no clear gradient in some of the relatively rare diseases such as non-Hodgkin's lymphoma, septicaemia and motor neurone disease.

A few causes could be said to have the opposite gradient, with higher mortality in higher social classes: cancer of the brain, HIV infection and malignant melanoma. There are few deaths from malignant melanoma. However, the pattern of social class differences in mortality may have changed. There used to be higher mortality in all the non-manual classes,[2] but in the 1990s only Class I had raised mortality, all the others classes showed no difference from the national value of an SMR of 100.

From the LS analyses in Chapter 11, the smaller numbers in the sample mean that only the major causes of death can be investigated. However, from this source the strong social class gradients found elsewhere for men were confirmed for ischaemic heart disease, stroke, respiratory disease and lung cancer.

The LS has the advantage that it can study the major causes of death for women (Chapters 11 and 13). Clear social class gradients were found for ischaemic heart disease, stroke, respiratory disease and lung cancer, similar to the pattern found for men, but shallower.

In addition, breast cancer has been studied, which used to be one of the few causes of death which was higher in women in non-manual social classes[2]. For the latest period studied, 1986–92, there was no significant differential in breast cancer mortality between non-manual and manual women (Table 11.9). Furthermore, in absolute terms, death rates from breast cancer did not decline appreciably over the 22 years of follow-up for manual or non-manual women in this age-range. This pattern has been analysed further in Chapter 13 using alternative social indicators. With housing tenure and car access, there were no significant differences for breast cancer mortality in either 1971–81 or 1981–92 between the more and less disadvantaged groups on either scale, neither at ages 35–59 nor 60–74 (Figure 13.2).

Critical age groups

From the evidence presented in Chapter 8, critical age-groups can be identified when the health inequalities between the social classes are especially large. Over the whole age-range from 20–64, all-cause mortality is almost three times higher in Class V men than in Class I, but for the 30–34 age group it is four and a half times higher. For some of the major causes of death the mortality gap is even more pronounced and younger men again appear to be the most vulnerable. For suicides and undetermined injury, overall there is a four-fold difference in mortality between Class V and I, but at younger ages the differential is seven to eight-fold. This reduces to a five-fold difference at age 35–39 and a two-fold difference by age 55. For accidents, a five-fold difference between Class V and I at age 25–34 increases to a seven-fold difference by age 40–44, before levelling off at older ages.

These patterns have significant implications. First, it means that at ages when mortality is generally low, a large proportion of young lives are cut short by the high mortality associated with less advantaged social classes. The human wastage is considerable. At ages 25 to 34, about half the deaths are from accidents, suicide or homicide. The strong social class gradients in these causes of death mean that if all men had the same all-cause death rates as Classes I and II, then over 40 per cent of all deaths in that age group would be prevented.

Second, how can some of the national and international targets on improving health be reached in just a few years' time when the disparities are so great in the younger sections of the population? Clearly, there is a strong argument for a special focus on childhood and youth inequalities in any future strategies.

Migrant health and socio-economic status

One long-standing question in this field is whether the increased mortality risk observed in some migrant groups has more to do with their generally poorer socio-economic circumstances, rather than some feature of migrant status as such. In Chapter 9 the full national deaths data were used to examine this question for the years 1991–93, by comparing the social class pattern of mortality of men in the largest migrant groups with the social class pattern seen for all men in England and Wales for major causes of death.

The analysis showed that social class of selected migrant groups could account for some, but not all of the excess mortality observed. For stroke, higher than average mortality was observed in men from the Caribbean, West/South Africa, the Indian subcontinent and Ireland. Even after adjusting for the concentration of some of these migrants in manual classes, a substantial proportion of their excess mortality remained. After adjustment for social class, the mortality from stroke of Caribbean men came down from 69 per cent to 46 per cent above average. For Irish men, the excess mortality was reduced from 30 to 24 per cent (Table 9.9).

Overall, larger social class differences were seen for Scottish and Irish men. Among the non-white groups, social class gradients in mortality were evident for the migrant groups who had settled here the longest – from the Caribbean and Indian subcontinent. This contrasts with the findings of earlier analyses of the situation in the 1970s, when no social class differentials were observed among men from the Indian subcontinent and were almost reversed for Caribbeans.[3] Even though social class appeared to have become more important in this 1990s analysis, it could still not account for all the excess mortality observed.

Unemployment and social class

Another important question which the analyses in this volume have been able to address concerns unemployment and mortality. Several previous studies using the LS have found an excess of deaths among unemployed men and women compared to their employed counterparts during the 1970s[4,5] and the 1980s.[6] But, as unemployment is heavily concentrated among the less skilled social classes, is the excess mortality observed in the unemployed attributable to this underlying social class bias? Alternatively, is there something about the unemployed state itself which leads to higher mortality? Another possibility is that people with poor health may be more likely to drop out of employment because of their state of health. This selection of unhealthy people out of the workforce could lead to raised mortality rates among the unemployed group, unrelated to any adverse health effects of unemployment itself.

The analysis in Chapter 12 updates findings from the LS to 1992 and, as in the previous studies, finds raised mortality among both unemployed men and women persisting into the 1990s. While employed men had an SMR of 84, unemployed men in the study had an SMR of 132. The SMR for unemployed men was reduced to 125 after adjustment for the concentration of unemployment in less skilled social classes. This means that 25 per cent of the observed excess mortality was unexplained by the social class bias in unemployment among men. Very similar findings emerged from the equivalent analysis for women. Employed women had an SMR of 80, while that for unemployed women was 133, which reduced to 121 after social class adjustment.

Because people who were not in employment due to temporary or permanent sickness were excluded from the category containing people unemployed and seeking work, it is less likely that the observed excess mortality could be attributed to pre-existing ill health in the unemployed. As in previous decades, a sizeable proportion of the excess mortality of the unemployed is likely to be a consequence of the experience of unemployment itself.

The converse of the above question was posed in Chapter 11 – could the widening social class differentials in mortality be accounted for by higher mortality of unemployed people who tend to be concentrated in less skilled social classes? Trends in social class mortality differentials were examined for employed and unemployed groups separately. The conclusion was that unemployment was unlikely to explain the observed widening of social class differences in mortality.

Differentials in morbidity of growing importance

Chapters 14 and 15 bring together survey data from many different sources on morbidity and health-related behaviour for children and adults. The findings vary by age and gender, but in general show that in the 1990s the socio-economic pattern of increasingly poor health with declining socio-economic position was not confined to mortality, but was reflected in measures of self-reported chronic sickness, and for several major diseases and causes of disability. Evidence from consultations in general practice supported this interpretation. There were, for example, strong socio-economic gradients in consultations with GPs for conditions classed as serious for both boys and girls, particularly when children living in council housing were compared with those living in owner-occupied accommodation (see Table 14.2).

There was, however, a striking contrast with the observed socio-economic patterns of mortality. While the trend has been for mortality to decline overall and also for most socio-economic groups, the prevalence of self-reported morbidity in the population has tended to increase over the past two decades, both overall, and for each socio-economic group. This serves to flag up a major public health challenge which will be of growing importance in the future.

The data on health-related personal behaviour in the two chapters showed some diversity. Often, but not always, the socio-economic gradients in health-damaging and health-promoting behaviour went in the same direction as the socio-economic trends in morbidity and mortality. So, for example, there were progressively higher rates of smoking, poorer diet, and lower incidence of breast-feeding with declining socio-economic group. On the other hand, there was a higher prevalence of alcohol drinkers among professional and managerial socio-economic groups. The pattern of physical activity was complex. When only leisure time activity was counted, there was decreasing activity with decreasing socio-economic group. When work-related and domestic activities were also included, there was a higher prevalence of regular activity of a moderate intensity among men in all three manual social classes and very little variation in activity levels among women across the social scale.

From the available evidence, the conclusion is that the differentials in such behavioural risk factors could not account for the greater part of the observed differentials in morbidity and mortality.

Responding to the evidence

Why has the issue of socio-economic differentials in health been given such emphasis in this decennial supplement? The need for a thorough review is more pressing than ever as a new millennium approaches. As documented in Chapters 1 to 4, the socio-economic environment, and with it the key influences on health, have been changing profoundly over the past few decades, both in this country and abroad. The deterioration in some of the social and health indicators have focused renewed attention on the issue of inequalities in health and have led to a series of national initiatives during the 1990s.

One prominent initiative in 1995 was the setting up of a working group by the Chief Medical Officer for England. Their brief was to look at what the Department of Health and the NHS could do about variations in health[7]. This was an acknowledgement that the national health strategy, *The Health of the Nation*,[8] had lacked a focus on social inequalities in health when it was first formulated in 1992, and that some of the national goals and targets that had been set for health may not be met unless more attention was paid to the issue. This was acknowledged in the report setting out the conclusions of the Variations group, issued in October 1995:

> *'We welcome and endorse the Chief Medical Officer's recognition that action to tackle variations in health is central to the achievement of the government's Health of the Nation strategy. We conclude that tackling health variations is an aspect of a great deal of the work which the Department and the NHS is doing already, but one which is not being given sufficient emphasis. What is needed now is not a new initiative, isolated from mainstream work, but a much more explicit targeting of the issue within existing policies and activities.'* [7]

Selected recommendations of the Department of Health's Variations group are outlined in Box 16.1. Among them was the recommendation for a research programme focused on evaluation of interventions to address health inequalities, research to address the needs of particularly vulnerable groups in the population, and basic research into causal processes.[7] Also during 1995, both the Economic and Social Research Council (ESRC) and the Medical Research Council (MRC) announced that they were making social inequalities in health a priority area for research, and in spring 1997, the ESRC's five-year programme of research on health inequalities was officially launched.[9] The process of commissioning the Department of Health's recommended programme of research also began in spring 1997. The major statutory funders of health and social research in the country are therefore committed to taking forward monitoring and evaluation of this area.

Box 16.1 Recommendations of the Department of Health's Variations in Health Group [7]

- "An important way of achieving the *Health of the Nation* targets is to improve the health of the least healthy groups closer to the levels attained by the most healthy groups."
- Health authorities and GP purchasers should have a plan for identifying and tackling variations, and for evaluating interventions.
- Health authorities, GP purchasers and trusts should take steps to monitor access to services to safeguard equitable access.
- The Department of Health should work actively in alliance with other government departments and other bodies to encourage social policies which promote health.
- The MRC, ESRC and Department of Health should co-ordinate their programmes of research and commission research consultations to recommend priorities for research.

With echoes of the Victorian public health campaigns, several commissions and working parties have been set up in the 1990s to look at the evidence in specific policy areas, involving not only statutory bodies, but also the voluntary sector and professional associations. Prominent among these have been the Joseph Rowntree Foundation's two inquiries into *British Housing*[10] and *Income and Wealth,*[11] and the King's Fund initiative to draw up a policy agenda for action to tackle inequalities in health.[12] Some of the King's Fund proposals for the action needed are listed in Box 16.2.

Box 16.2 Selected King's Fund recommendations for wider policy to tackle inequalities in health[12]

- Income maintenance policies that provide adequate financial support for people who fall into poverty.
- Education and training policies that help prevent poverty in the long-term.
- More equitable taxation and income distribution policies.
- Targeted investment in new and improved housing.
- Investment in community development.
- Expansion of childcare and pre-school education, particularly for children living in disadvantaged circumstances.

Spring 1997 also saw the major medical and nursing journals putting their weight behind the call for a serious national commitment on the issue. A *Lancet* editorial in April 1997, for instance, declared 'Health inequality: the UK's biggest issue',[13] while a *British Medical Journal* editorial urged doctors to work together to reduce poverty's damage[14]. In July 1997, the government announced a new national inquiry into inequalities in health with the aim of identifying priority areas for future policy development.[15]

We hope this volume will provide some of the background analyses for the inquiry's deliberations. The volume also illustrates some of the gaps and defects in the routine information systems which have made certain analyses in this field difficult or even impossible. A more concerted effort to monitor trends and set targets for reduction of health inequalities will require more attention to the consistency and usefulness of the information collected over the long term.

What matters overall is that there is a serious commitment to carry on Britain's 150-year tradition of monitoring and reporting on health within our society. For the new millennium, the aim is not just to maintain, but to improve the way in which information is collected and analysed to inform policy-making in order to tackle these unacceptable inequalities in health.

References

1 Harding, S (1995) Social class differences in mortality of men: recent evidence from the OPCS Longitudinal Study, *Population Trends*; 80: 31-37.

2 OPCS (1986) *Occupational Mortality Decennial Supplement 1979–80,82–83.* Series DS, 6. London, HMSO.

3 Marmot, M, Adelstein, A, Bulusu, L, (1984) *Immigrant mortality in England and Wales 1970–78*, Studies in Medical and Population Subjects, 47; London, HMSO.

4 Moser, K, Fox, A J and Jones, D (1984) Unemployment and mortality in the OPCS Longitudinal Study, *The Lancet*, ii: 1324–28.

5 Moser, K, Fox, A J, Jones, D and Goldblatt, P (1986) Unemployment and mortality: further evidence from the OPCS Longitudinal Study, *The Lancet*, i: 365–7.

6 Bethune, A (1996) Economic activity and mortality of the 1981 Census cohort in the OPCS Longitudinal Study, *Population Trends*, 83: 37–42.

7 Department of Health (1995) *Variations in health: what can the Department of Health and the NHS do?* London, Department of Health.

8 Department of Health (1992) *The Health of the Nation. A strategy for health in England*. London, HMSO.

9 Economic and Social Research Council (1997) *Health Variations Programme: an outline of research awards*. London, ESRC.

10 Joseph Rowntree Foundation (1991) *Inquiry into British housing*. Second report June 1991, chaired by HRH The Duke of Edinburgh. York, Joseph Rowntree Foundation.

11 Joseph Rowntree Foundation (1995) *Inquiry into Income and Wealth*. Chaired by Sir Peter Barclay. York, Joseph Rowntree Foundation.

12 Benzeval, M Judge, K and Whitehead, M (eds) (1995) *Tackling inequalities in health: an agenda for action*. London, King's Fund.

13 Editorial (1997) Health inequality: the UK's biggest issue, *The Lancet*, 349: 1185.

14 Haines, A and Smith, R (1997) Working together to reduce poverty's damage: doctors fought nuclear weapons, now they can fight poverty, *BMJ*, 314: 529–30.

15 Department of Health. Terms of reference for the independent review of inaqualities in health to be conducted by Sir Donald Acheson. Issued 7 July 1997, London, Department of Health.

Appendices

Sources and methods

Julia Bunting

Introduction

This appendix discusses the data sources used by the authors of this volume. Statistical methods that are used widely in this volume are reviewed briefly. This appendix is not a comprehensive source of data sources or methodology. References to more detailed information are given in the headings to each section.

A wide variety of sources has been used in this Decennial Supplement. For the analysis of social class differentials in mortality, information comes from two main sources: the routine collection of occupation and the cause of death from death registrations and the ONS Longitudinal Study (LS). Every ten years death registration information is supplemented by an abundance of census data. Since 1971 these sources have been linked in the LS for a one per cent sample of the population. This is able to provide more accurate occupational data for study members because occupational information is given by the individual at census rather than by an informant at death.

Registrar General's Social Class (based on occupation)[1]

In 1911 the Registrar General established a classification of social class (based on occupation). The aim of this classification is to group together people who have similar levels of occupational skill. This is reviewed and up-dated each census. The present system is shown in Box A.1. Each occupation is assigned to a social class, though a person may be placed in a different social class if they are a foreman or manager. The basic guidelines used to assign a social class are shown in Box A.2.

Sources of data

Death registration data[2,3]

Under existing legislation, when a death occurs the attending doctor is required to complete a certificate of cause of death. This certificate must be returned to the local registrar of births

---

Box A.1   Registrar General's Social Class (based on occupation)

Class	Occupation type
I	Professional (e.g. accountants, electronic engineers)
II	Managerial and technical/Intermediate (e.g. proprietors and managers – sales, production, works and maintenance managers)
IIIN	Skilled non-manual (e.g. clerks and cashiers – not retail)
IIIM	Skilled manual (e.g. drivers of road goods vehicles, metal working production fitters)
IV	Partly skilled (e.g. storekeepers and warehousemen, machine tool operators)
V	Unskilled (e.g. building and civil engineering labourers, cleaners etc.)

Box A.2   Assignment of Social Class using the Registrar General's Social Class (based on occupation)

1. Each person is assigned to a social class depending on their stated occupation.

2. Those people in Social Class IV and V who are foremen are assigned to Social Class III.

3. In most cases those people who are managers are assigned to Social Class II.

4. Those in the Armed Forces are allocated to the group 'Occupied - other'.

5. Those people who are stated to have been employed but give insufficient details of occupation are allocated to the group 'Occupied - other'.

6. Those who give no information about occupation or who state they have never worked are allocated to the group 'Unoccupied'.

and deaths, usually within 5 days in England and Wales. For certain causes of death, procedures are different. In the case of a sudden death or where there is the possibility of an unnatural death, or when an industrial disease is suspected the case will be referred to a coroner in England and Wales. The coding of cause of death follows rules laid down by the World Health Organisation.[4,5]

The draft entry form, which is filled in by the registrar when a death is registered, is the source of information on the occupation of the deceased from which their social class is derived. The registrar tries to obtain sufficiently full details of the last occupation of those aged 16 years to 74 years so that the occupation and hence social class can be coded.

Birth registration data[6]

The social class of the father of a child can be derived from information on occupation which has always been collected when a birth is registered. This information is only available when a birth is within marriage or jointly registered by both parents. Prior to 1970, occupation was not coded. Since then it has been coded for a ten per cent sample of births. From 1980 to the mid-1990s, the proportion of births within marriage or jointly registered has been fairly constant at about 92 per cent of all births.

The occupation of the mother could be registered for births outside marriage from 1905 but this information was not coded. From 1986, registrars have been expected to ask if the mother had been in employment at any time before the baby was born. Higher status and full-time occupations are more likely to be recorded. This information is coded, when it is provided, for all stillbirths and for ten per cent of live births. However, mother's occupation was stated for only 31 per cent of live births in 1986. This increased to 58 per cent in 1995. In 1995 just 49 per cent of stillbirths had mother's occupation stated. The proportions of births with occupation of the mother, for live and stillbirths, varies with the mother's age and with whether the child is the first or subsequent child in a family.

Census data[7,8,9]

Data from the 1971, 1981 and 1991 Censuses are used in this volume to provide the population breakdown by age, sex and social class for the calculation of mortality rates and other demographic measures. The social class is derived from the data collected on occupation. In the 1971, 1981 and 1991 Censuses, questions were asked on the current job with details required for the last week. In 1971 and 1981, if a person was not working or was retired in the week before the Census, details of the last full-time job were requested. In 1991 if the person had not worked in the week prior to the census, questions referred to the previous job if it was within the last ten years.

ONS Longitudinal Study[10]

The ONS Longitudinal Study (LS) is a representative one per cent sample of the population of England and Wales containing linked census and vital events data for approximately 500,000 people. The LS was begun in the early 1970s by selecting everyone born on one of four particular days who was enumerated at the 1971 census. Subsequent samples have been drawn and linked from the 1981 and 1991 Censuses using the LS dates of birth. Population change is reflected by the addition of new sample members born on the LS dates together with the recording of exits via death or emigration. Routinely collected data on mortality, fertility, cancer registration, infant mortality, widow(er)hood and the migration of sample members are linked into the sample using the National Health Service Central Register (NHSCR) to perform the link.

The LS is a very rich source of data for mortality and health by social class. Social class is available for LS members based on the occupation questions at the 1971, 1981 and 1991 Censuses. The 1971 LS cohort were assigned to a social class according to their occupations at the 1971 Census. Similarly the 1981 cohort were assigned their social class at the 1981 Census.

Survey data

Data from a number of surveys have been used in the morbidity chapters in this volume. The major sources are described below and others are referenced in the chapters.

The General Household Survey (GHS)[11]

The General Household Survey (GHS) is a continuous survey which has been running since 1971. It is based each year on a sample of the general population resident in private, that is non-institutional households in Great Britain. Interviews are obtained from about 20,000 individuals aged 16 years and over residing in about 10,000 households. The GHS includes questions on population and fertility, housing, health, employment and education. Other subjects are covered periodically and new subjects are introduced from time to time.

The Health Survey for England (HSFE)[12]

In 1991, the Department of Health commissioned a new survey to be carried out by the Social Survey Division of the Office of Population Censuses and Surveys. Since 1994 the Health Survey for England has been carried out by the Joint Health Surveys Unit of Social and Community Planning Research and the Department of Epidemiology and Public Health, University College London. The survey aims to provide better and more regular information about various aspects of people's health, and to monitor some of the targets in the Department of Health's strategy *Health of the Nation*. The survey selects a nationally representative sample of adults, those aged 16 or over, living in private households in England. It is largely concerned with providing basic descriptive statistics for the variables measured and information on their association with demographic, social and behavioural characteristics of the sample. In its first four years, the survey focused on cardiovascular disease and associated risk factors. In 1995, focus moved from cardiovascular conditions to asthma, other atopic conditions, accidents and disability. For the first time children were included in the survey.

The Labour Force Survey (LFS)[13]

In non-census years the Labour Force Survey (LFS) provides valuable background information on the age, sex and occupation structure of the workforce. The LFS first took place in 1973. Since then it has expanded in frequency and sample size. It is now a quarterly panel survey of about 60,000 households in Great Britain, with one fifth of the households being replaced in each quarter. The employment questions refer to the last week for those working, or to the previous job in the last three years.

ONS Psychiatric Morbidity Survey[14,15]

These surveys aim to provide up-to-date information on the prevalence of psychiatric problems among adults in Great Britain as well as their associated social disabilities and use of services. Four separate surveys were carried out from April 1993 to August 1994.

Statistical methods

It is not the purpose of this section to provide full information on the standard statistical and epidemiological tools used in the analyses in this volume. Many excellent texts devoted to these subjects are available. Short summaries of some of the techniques used in this volume are, however, described.

Standardisation

The purpose of this volume is to highlight differences in health and mortality across the social classes. Different numbers of people make up each social class and therefore it is necessary to consider mortality rates rather than simply the number of

deaths. The simplest measure of mortality, the crude death rate, is the number of deaths divided by the total population. In order to compare differences in mortality across social classes it is necessary to allow for the different age structures within each social class. There are two main methods with dealing with this problem: direct and indirect standardisation.

Direct standardisation involves taking a standard age structure for a population and applying to this the deaths rates from each of the social class populations being compared. This gives an expected number of deaths. The European standardised rate (ESR) used in this volume is an example of direct standardisation. Indirect standardisation uses a set of national death rates and applies these to the population structure of each of the social classes to produce an expected number of deaths. The standardised mortality ratio (SMR) used in this volume is an example of indirect standardisation.

European standardised rates (ESR)

To calculate age-standardised mortality rates, a notional standard population is selected with a specified age structure. In this volume, the European standard population is used because it is the closest to the demographic profile of England and Wales, having a high proportion of population in the older age groups. ESRs are calculated by multiplying the age-specific death rates of each social class at each point in time by the standard population structure. This gives the expected number of deaths. The ESR is then the expected number of deaths divided by the number of people in the standard population. This is conventionally multiplied by 100,000 to give the number of deaths per 100,000 population.

$$ESR = \frac{\Sigma \text{ expected number of deaths in the study population}}{\Sigma \text{ standard population}} \times 100,000$$

The European standard population has the advantage of allowing international comparisons with other developed countries. It is also the standard that was used in setting the Department of Health's *Health of the Nation* targets.

Standardised mortality ratio (SMR)

The SMR is a measure of how much more or less likely a person is to die in the study population than someone of the same age and sex in the standard population. In this volume we are interested in deaths in the social classes (based on occupation) compared to the standard population of England and Wales. The SMR is the ratio of the actual number of deaths in the social class to the expected number of deaths in that class. This is usually multiplied by 100 to ease interpretation.

$$SMR = \frac{\text{observed number of deaths in the social class}}{\text{expected number of deaths if the age-sex specific}} \times 100$$
$$\text{rates were the same as those of England and Wales}$$

An SMR value of 100 means that the odds of dying are the same in both the social class and England and Wales as a whole. A value of less than 100 indicates that the chances of death are lower in the social class considered than in England and Wales as a whole. Conversely, an SMR of greater than 100 means that the individuals in that social class have higher mortality than the population of England and Wales as a whole.

Rate ratio (rr)

The rate ratio is a measure of the relative mortality between two groups. It is the ratio of the number of expected deaths in the groups whose mortality are of interest to the expected number of deaths in the baseline group. The expected number of deaths is calculated by applying the age-specific death rates of the groups to the age-specific populations of the standard population, in this case the European population. For example, when comparing the mortality of manual and non-manual workers, the calculation would be:

$$rr = \frac{\text{expected number of deaths in manual workers}}{\text{expected number of deaths of non-manual workers}}$$

Expectation of life using the LS data

Abridged life tables were prepared using the LS as a dynamic population sample allowing entry by birth and immigration into England and Wales, and exit by death and emigration. All LS members who had entered the study between 1971 and 1991 were used to provide a population for each calendar year from 1972 to 1991. Exact age was calculated in months. Five-year groups of data were used to calculate the mortality rates from which the life tables could be generated because of the small numbers of deaths occurring in a single year.

LS members were included in the sample if they had been traced at the National Health Service Central Register (NHSCR). LS members were excluded if they had never been traced at NHSCR, were traced but had joined at one census only to be lost to the LS without a valid exit before the next census, or were born or immigrated into the LS intercensally and missed the next census without a valid exit. A small number of LS members who were misclassified as present at the next census when other records had shown them to be dead or emigrated prior to that census were also excluded.

Out of a total sample of 821,681 traced LS members who entered the study between 1971 and 1991, 729,467 remained after the exclusions had been applied.

Once the sample had been selected, a set of rules was applied to allow an LS member only one exit and no re-entries to the population. Valid exits were considered to be emigration from England and Wales or deaths.

Derivation of social class used for LS life expectancy

Each member of the LS was assigned a social class (based on occupation) at entry which remained fixed throughout their inclusion in the study. Own social class was used where possible. However, individuals categorised as armed forces, inadequately described, students, retired, permanently sick, housewives and those with no social class assigned were reclassified. If information was available from their spouse or father or mother this was used and they were assigned into Classes I to V. If no additional information was available they were grouped as 'missing'. After reclassification, 11 per cent of men and 19 per cent of women were still allocated to the 'missing' group. No separate life tables were created for this group but the LS members in them were included in the all male and all female categories.

The methodology used in the construction of the abridged life tables is given in detail elsewhere.[16,17] The probability of dying (q_x) was calculated using the Reed-Merrell tables[18] to transform m_x to q_x. The variance and standard errors of the expectation of life were calculated using Chiang's method[19]. Expectations of life (e^o_x) were produced for each age group in the life table up to age 90 where they were truncated.

Statistical differences in e^o_x between social classes were calculated using the test for difference between means, as an expectation of life at age x is the *average* number of years expected to be lived after age x by any member of the synthetic cohort who has survived to age x.

References

1. Office of Population Censuses and Surveys (1991). *Standard Occupational Classification. Volume 3*. London, HMSO.

2. Office for National Statistics (1996). *Mortality statistics: cause.* Series DH2, 21. London, HMSO.

3. Noble, B, Drever, F and Shah, N (1995) *Sources and Methods.* In: Drever, F (ed.) *Occupational health – a Decennial Supplement.* Series DS, 10. London, HMSO.

4. World Health Organisation (1977). *Manual of the International Statistical Classification of Diseases, Injuries and Causes of Death.* Volume 1. Geneva WHO.

5. World Health Organisation (1978). *Manual of the International Statistical Classification of Diseases, Injuries and Causes of Death.* Volume 2. Geneva WHO.

6. Office for National Statistics (1996). *Mortality statistics: Childhood, infant and perinatal.* Series DH3, 27. London, HMSO.

7. Office of Population Censuses and Surveys (1972). *1971 Census. General Report.* London, HMSO.

8. Office of Population Censuses and Surveys (1982). *Census 1981 Definitions.* London, HMSO.

9. Office of Population Censuses and Surveys (1992). *1991 Census Definitions Great Britain.* London, HMSO.

10. Hattersley, L and Creeser, R. (1995) *Longitudinal Study 1971-1991 History, organisation and quality of data.* Series LS, 7. London, HMSO.

11. OPCS (annual). *General Household Survey.* London, HMSO.

12. Joint Health Surveys Unit (annual). *Health Survey for England.* London, HMSO.

13. ONS (quarterly). *Labour Force Survey Quarterly Bulletin.* London, ONS.

14. Meltzer, H, Gill, B, Petticrew, M and Hinds, K (1995) *OPCS Surveys of Psychiatric Morbidity In Great Britain. Report 1: The prevalence of psychiatric morbidity among adults living in private households.* London, HMSO.

15. Meltzer, H, Gill, B, Petticrew, M and Hinds K (1995) *OPCS Surveys of Psychiatric Morbidity In Great Britain. Report 2: Physical complaints, service use and treatment of adults with psychiatric disorders.* London, HMSO.

16. Newell, C (1994) *Methods and Models in Demography.* Chichester, John Wiley and Sons.

17. Shyrock, H S and Siegel, J S (1976) *The Methods and Materials of Demography.* Abridged edition. New York, Academic Press.

18. Reed, L J and Merrell, M (1977) *A short method for constructing an abridged life table.* Re-printed in Smith, D and Keyfitz, N *(eds) Biomathematics Volume 6. Mathematical Demography: Selected Papers.* Berlin, Springer-Verlag.

19. Chiang, C L (1993) *The life table and its construction.* Reprinted in Bogue, D J, Arriaga, E E and Anderton, D L.(eds) *Readings in Population Research Methodology Volume 2. Mortality Research.* New York, United Nations.

How were the census based mortality rates calculated?

Frances Drever

Introduction

This appendix examines possible sources of bias in the calculations using the primary deaths database records for 1991–93 by social class, and populations from the 1991 Census. It also discusses the comparability of the 1990 SOC revision of the Registrar General's Social Class (based on occupation) with the previous classification.

Definitions of social class

The calculations of standardised mortality ratios (SMRs) and European standardised mortality rates (ESRs) use two sources of data, mortality information from the primary deaths database and populations from the economic activity ten per cent sample from the 1991 Census. These sources use slightly different coding systems. Both use occupational and economic activity information, but in different ways. The resulting codes are slightly different.

Mortality data

Mortality data for the three-year period 1991–93 were extracted from the primary deaths database. The social class of the deceased is ascertained from the last occupation and employment status stated on the deceased's death certificate. There are nine possible codes for social class:

1   Class I
2   Class II
3   Class IIIN
4   Class IIIM
5   Class IV
6   Class V
7   Armed forces
8   Inadequately described occupation (not enough information to code, and employment status not economically inactive)
9   Full-time care of home and/or dependent relative, housewife/husband, full-time student, independent means, permanently sick, no previous occupation or not stated (economically inactive or no information at all)

Census

Data from the ten per cent economic activity sample of the 1991 Census were used to provide base population data for the calculations. This sample is not one in ten people but a sample of one in ten households who completed a form. This means that there are slightly less than ten per cent of the people included in census tables. There are nine possible codes for social class in the census :

1   Class I
2   Class II
3   Class IIIN
4   Class IIIM
5   Class IV
6   Class V
7   Armed forces
8   Inadequately described and not stated (economically active, but not enough information to code)
9   No social class (i.e. those unemployed, retired or permanently sick for over ten years and also those on a government scheme, economically inactive)

Mortality calculation

As the two sets of social class data have to be used in conjunction, standard definitions of the codes are required. Codes 1 to 6 in the census data match codes 1 to 6 in the mortality data and allocate people to a social class. For both mortality and census data, people coded 7 or 8 have been working at some time but have given insufficient details to be assigned a social class. Those with these codes have been placed in the category 'unclassified'. Those coded 9 are classified as 'unoccupied', because no last occupation was given at death registration (mortality data), or they have not been working in the last ten years (census data). So, the codes used in these analyses in Chapters 8 and 10 are:

1	Class I	5	Class IV
2	Class II	6	Class V
3	Class IIIN	7/8	Unclassified
4	Class IIIM	9	Unoccupied

Other definitional issues

Years of data to be analysed

It is best to use as many years as possible around a census year for the mortality data when calculating SMRs or ESRs by social class to ensure sufficient numbers of deaths in each age and cause grouping. Unfortunately, the longest span possible in the

1990s is three years, 1991–93. This is not centred on the census year. A new revision of the occupational classification, and thus social class based on it, was introduced in 1991. The 1989 and 1990 data would require recoding to permit their inclusion in the analysis and so are omitted.

Age-range and age groups

Looking at the age distribution across social classes, it was decided to restrict the analysis to ages 20 to 64 years (see Table B.1 and Figure B.1). More than 40 per cent of those aged 16–19 have no class allocated at census. For ages over 65, those with no class allocated rises from 25 per cent in the 65–69 group to 55 per cent in the group 70–74. No class is coded on mortality records at ages 75 and over. Calculations of SMRs and ESRs for the period 1991–93 used five-year age groups. The data available from previous censuses have two ten-year age groups, 35–44 and 45–54. In the trend analyses, data for 1991–93 were grouped into the same age groups.

Underenumeration in the 1991 Census

The problems with underenumeration of the 1991 Census have been well documented.[1] A number of different methods of grossing were considered. For these analyses, the final mid-1991 population estimates at England and Wales level and by five year age groups are the populations to which the census data were grossed.

The grossing assumed that the census age distribution within social class was applicable across the population as a whole. This means that the social class distribution was applied to the 1991 population estimates, in five-year age groups. This assumption is examined in a sensitivity analysis of the SMRs.

Classification changes

Changing the rules within the classification

Each time the classification is changed it does, of course, introduce problems. However, one way to quantify the difficulties arising from the classification change is to look at how the *same*

individuals fare under the different classifications. Tables B.2 and B.3 do this. Just under 70,000 men in employment at the 1971 Census were allocated a social class using both the 1970 and 1980 classifications. This information was then grossed to the full ten per cent sample. Table B.2 shows, for each 1980 class, the proportion of men in each 1970 class. For example, of those allocated to Social Class I in the 1980 classification, 91 per cent would have been in Social Class I using the 1970 classification, six per cent would have been in Social Class II, two per cent in Social Class IIIN and so on. Table B.3 shows an equivalent comparison for over 70,000 men in employment at the 1981 Census. Again the data were grossed up to the full ten per cent sample. Together these tables indicate that the classification changes did not affect the vast majority of men, 91 per cent did not change class in the 197/81 comparison. The 1981/91 comparison has an astonishing 99 per cent of men staying in the same class.

The 1980 revision had not only a greater overall effect than the 1990 revision, but also a more widespread one. Men moved not just to neighbouring classes but right across the spectrum. The 1990 revision was much less drastic. Very few men changed class. Those who did change tended to move to neighbouring classes.

Occupations within classes – changes between 1981 and 1991

To see if the change in classification of occupations into social classes together with the changes in numbers of people in occupations could affect any comparisons of deaths rates over time, an analysis of the numbers in each occupation in each class in 1981 and 1991 was undertaken. Overall, the proportions of men aged 20–64 in each class has changed slightly (see Table B.4). Classes I and II have slightly higher proportions in 1991 than in 1981. The other classes have correspondingly smaller proportions in 1991 than in 1981.

The numbers of men assigned to each occupation at the 1981 and the 1991 Censuses were examined. The data for 1981 were from an unpublished table prepared for the decennial

Table B.1: 1991 Census (10% sample). Number of men aged 16+ by social class, England and Wales

Class	16-19	20-24	25-29	30-34	35-39	40-44	45-49	50-54	55-59	60-64	65-69	70-74	75+
I	26	7,137	13,761	13,286	12,305	13,336	10,515	8,545	7,266	6,641	5,069	2,349	1,058
II	4,993	26,765	43,480	48,091	50,568	59,190	48,426	37,537	32,623	28,405	22,276	10,965	3,066
IIIN	17,409	26,634	21,673	17,563	14,108	14,863	12,197	10,351	10,417	10,342	9,222	4,973	1,285
IIIM	25,220	49,760	57,692	53,993	48,836	54,634	46,524	42,285	37,942	33,432	25,169	11,595	1,571
IV	17,692	31,597	28,763	23,180	19,606	20,890	18,442	19,139	19,241	19,261	15,633	7,041	1,443
V	7,250	11,913	10,452	7,888	6,284	6,614	6,028	6,352	6,591	6,689	5,264	2,480	762
Unclassified	3,835	6,764	5,839	4,890	3,920	3,369	2,602	2,085	1,721	1,396	1,146	592	345
Unoccupied	54,690	20,872	9,041	6,799	6,085	6,801	6,427	8,017	9,936	15,187	29,229	45,688	109,701
Total	**131,115**	**181,442**	**190,701**	**175,690**	**161,712**	**179,697**	**151,161**	**134,311**	**125,737**	**121,353**	**113,008**	**85,683**	**119,231**

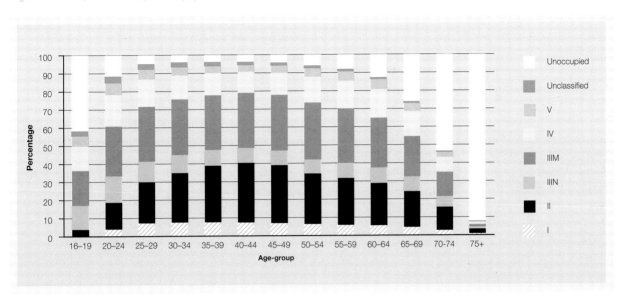

Table B.2: Proportions of the 1971 population in 1970 groups included in each 1980 group, men in employment, England and Wales

		1980 Social Class							
		I	II	IIIN	IIIM	IV	V	Not classified	Number
									grossed to 10% total
1970	I	**91.1**	5.1	0.1	0.1	0.1	0.0	0.2	72,168
Social	II	6.1	**89.3**	2.7	1.2	1.1	0.1	0.3	246,443
Class	IIIN	1.7	2.7	**88.0**	0.6	0.5	0.2	0.1	163,315
	IIIM	0.7	2.3	5.7	**94.2**	10.9	2.1	1.3	520,976
	IV	0.4	0.5	3.4	3.0	**85.7**	8.4	2.1	233,816
	V	0.0	0.0	0.1	0.9	1.7	**89.1**	0.3	100,004
	Not classified	0.0	0.1	0.0	0.0	0.0	0.1	**95.7**	31,423
Number grossed to 10% total		63,580	256,383	171,786	506,045	235,948	102,057	32,346	1,368,145

Table B.3: Proportions of the 1981 population in 1980 groups included in each 1990 group, men in employment, England and Wales

		1990 Social Class							
		I	II	IIIN	IIIM	IV	V	AF etc.	Number
									grossed to 10% total
1980	I	**98.1**	0.5						77,582
Social	II	1.9	**99.5**	1.3	0.0	0.1			307,937
Class	IIIN		0.0	**98.6**					157,440
	IIIM		0.0		**98.8**	0.4			480,049
	IV			0.1	1.1	**98.6**			227,946
	V				0.0	1.0	**100.0**		86,191
	Not classified							**100.0**	70,731
Number grossed to 10% total		77,550	305,903	159,493	484,814	225,604	83,781	70,731	1,407,876

supplement dealing with mortality data for the years 1979–80, 1982–83.[2] The allocation to occupation was made on the basis of the information on the 1981 Census forms. The classification was that in use at the time. It is commonly known as the '550 groups' because there are 550 different occupation codes. This coding maps easily on to the occupational units given in the *Classification of Occupations 1981*.[3] Information from Appendix B1 of the classification was used to allocate a social class to a particular occupation. Some occupations could belong to two or more classes. A cross-tabulation of occupation against social class was created from the ½ per cent subsample of 1981 Census records. Although some multiclass occupations were too small to be allocated in this way, overall less than 0.1 per cent of men aged 20–64 in England and Wales with occupational information at the 1981 Census were unable to be allocated to a class.

During 1991 Census coding, occupation was coded so that tabulations both by the new occupation codes and by the previous coding could be undertaken. Tables for men aged 21–64 in England and Wales were commissioned on both classifications. Again a social class was assigned to each of the 550 codes, this time using the 1991 rules, of which occupations belonged to which social classes. This was possible by comparing mappings of the old classification with the new one together with information in volume 3 of the *Standard Occupational Classification* (SOC).[4] There were several mismatches and multiclass occupations. To help resolve these, again a cross-tabulation was produced, this time from the 1991 ½ per cent subsample. Another source of help was the individual *Sample of Anonymised Records*. From this, a cross-tabulation of occupation, SOC main group codes, against social class and

socio-economic group was created. Many of the problems were resolved leaving overall less than 0.4 per cent of men aged 21–64 who had occupational information at the 1991 Census unable to be allocated to a social class.

Table B.5 shows the proportion of men allocated to each class using the method as described earlier. Together with Table B.4, we can see how successful this allocation method was. Unfortunately, for 1991 the age-range is slightly different. The 1981 match is very good indeed. In 1991 a slightly higher proportion have been allocated to Social Class IIIM and a slightly lower proportion to Class IV. The differences are too small to invalidate any analysis of these data.

Changes in main occupations within classes

The largest occupations within each class are remarkably similar at the 1981 and 1991 Censuses. There are differences of course, but these are not of a size to introduce occupational bias to mortality trends by social class carried out using the 1991 Census populations. Tables B.6–B.11 summarise the main occupations within each class in 1981 and 1991. The tables give the main occupations in 1991, together with the equivalent proportions for 1981. Any occupations which could have been considered 'main' in 1981, or which had similar proportions to occupations listed as 'main' in 1991, are also listed. The total numbers of men allocated to the social class tabulated using this occupational method, are also shown. Short statements about the main occupations within classes for 1971 are also included. As it was not possible to have the 1971 data on the 1981 classification, it could have been misleading to show these on the tables.

Table B.4: 1981 and 1991 Censuses (10% sample). Proportion of men aged 20–64 by social class, England and Wales

Social class (based on occupation)		1981 (per cent)	1991 (per cent)
I	Professional, etc. occupations	5.6	6.5
II	Managerial and technical occupations	22.0	26.4
IIIN	Skilled occupations (non-manual)	10.8	9.7
IIIM	Skilled occupations (manual)	33.4	29.9
IV	Partly skilled occupations	15.3	14.1
V	Unskilled occupations	5.5	4.8
Number of men		1,363,383	1,421,804

Table B.5: 1981 and 1991 Censuses (10% sample). Proportion of men by social class, England and Wales

Social class (based on occupation)		1981 (20–64) (per cent)	1991 (21–64) (per cent)
I	Professional, etc. occupations	5.6	6.6
II	Managerial and technical occupations	21.8	26.7
IIIN	Skilled occupations (non-manual)	10.7	9.3
IIIM	Skilled occupations (manual)	33.6	30.5
IV	Partly skilled occupations	15.2	13.6
V	Unskilled occupations	5.5	4.6
Number of men		1,363,383	1,385,470

Social Class I – professional occupations

Accountants, doctors and engineers are the main occupations at both the 1981 and 1991 Censuses, making up about 42 per cent of Social Class I (see Table B.6). The mix across the engineering specialities has changed with mechanical and aeronautical becoming a smaller group and design and development, and electronic increasing in size. The class was slightly larger at the 1991 Census compared to the 1981 Census.

In 1971, the large occupations within this group, using the 1970 classification, were very similar to those given in the table for 1981 and 1991. Accountants, doctors and engineers made up about 40 per cent of the class in 1971.

Social Class II - managerial and technical occupations

Managers still make up about 35 per cent of Social Class II (see Table B.7). Not surprisingly, the numbers of office managers and marketing and sales executives have increased. The proportion of teachers (not elsewhere classified) has dropped from seven and a half to five per cent. The class was somewhat larger at the 1991 Census than at the 1981 Census.

This group was also dominated by managers in 1971. The changes in the classification make it more difficult to sort out the different types of manager. However, sales managers and proprietors and managers (sales) made up over 22 per cent of

Class II. Farmers were a larger proportion of this group in 1971, making up over eight per cent of the group.

Social Class IIIN – skilled occupations (non-manual)

The slight drop in numbers allocated to this class was apparent in the 20–64 age group as well as comparing the two age groups given in the table. This class is still dominated by clerks and cashiers, being about two fifths of the class (see Table B.8). The other major occupation is still sales representatives. In 1971, clerks and cashiers made up over half of this class.

Social Class IIIM – skilled occupations (manual)

The slight drop in numbers allocated to this class was apparent in the 20–64 age group as well as comparing the two age groups given in the table. There is a large number of occupations within this class. Most individual occupations account for less than one per cent of the class as a whole. However, about a quarter of the class is made up of drivers of goods vehicles, metal production fitters and carpenters (see Table B.9).

Although exact comparability is difficult because of the large size of this group and the wide variety of occupations within it, the largest occupations were very similar in 1971 to those given in the table. Drivers of road goods vehicles, carpenters and joiners and fitters (not elsewhere classified), machine erectors, etc, made up about 20 per cent of the group.

Table B.6:   1981 and 1991 Censuses (10% sample). Proportion of men in occupations within Social Class I, England and Wales

Description	1981 Census (per cent)	1991 Census (per cent)
Chartered and certified accountants	10	8^1/$_2$
Medical practitioners	7	6^1/$_2$
Civil, structural, municipal, mining and quarrying engineers	6	6
Mechanical and aeronautical engineers	12	6^1/$_2$
Design and development engineers (mechanical)	1^1/$_2$	6
Electronic engineers	4^1/$_2$	7^1/$_2$
Physical and geological scientists, mathematicians	6	4
Building, land and mining surveyors	5^1/$_2$	5^1/$_2$
	(20-64)	(21-64)
Number of men allocated to this class in analysis	76,170	91,949

Table B.7:   1981 and 1991 Censuses (10% sample). Proportion of men in occupations within Social Class II, England and Wales

Description	1981 Census (per cent)	1991 Census (per cent)
Marketing and sales managers and executives	5	6^1/$_2$
Production, works and maintenance managers, works foremen	11	10
Office managers nec	5	7
Other proprietors and managers (sales)	13^1/$_2$	12
Teachers nec	7^1/$_2$	5
Farmers, horticulturists, farm managers	5^1/$_2$	4
	(20-64)	(21-64)
Number of men allocated to this class in analysis	296,920	369,976

Table B.8:   1981 and 1991 Censuses (10% sample). Proportion of men in occupations within Social Class IIIN, England and Wales.

Description	1981 Census (per cent)	1991 Census (per cent)
Other clerks and cashiers (not retail)	41	37½
Shop salesmen and assistants	6	8
Sales representatives	12½	13
Policemen (below sergeant)	6	7½
Number of men allocated to this class in analysis	(20-64) 146,507	(21-64) 128,505

Table B.9:   1981 and 1991 Censuses (10% sample). Proportion of men in occupations within Social Class IIIM, England and Wales

Description	1981 Census (per cent)	1991 Census (per cent)
Carpenters, joiners	4½	6
Metal working production fitters and fitter/machinists	9½	8
Drivers of road goods vehicles	10½	11
Electricians, electrical maintenance fitters	4½	4½
Number of men allocated to this class in analysis	(20-64) 458,202	(21-64) 422,558

Social Class IV – partly skilled occupations

This class makes up a smaller proportion of the males aged 20–64 in 1991 than in 1981. Increases in numbers of security guards etc, and in postmen (see Table B.10) have compensated for decreases in the numbers in manufacturing occupations, for example machine tool operators.

As with Class II, the major change in this group from 1971 to the information in the table, is in the proportion of this class in the agricultural industry. In 1971 about seven per cent of this group were classified as agricultural workers (not elsewhere classified). Warehousemen, storekeepers and assistants was the largest individual occupation in the class in 1971 at 13 per cent.

Social Class V – unskilled occupations

The drop in numbers allocated to this class was apparent in the 20–64 age group as well as comparing the two age groups given in the table. The majority of this class is still made up of labourers and cleaners – well over half. The proportion of general labourers in engineering and allied trades has dropped echoing the comments earlier about the changes in the manufacturing industries (see Table B.11).

The increase in the service sector can be seen by the fact that less than six per cent of this class in 1971 was made up of charwomen, office cleaners, chimney sweeps and road sweeps. The majority of the class in 1971, 56 per cent, were in the labouring and unskilled workers – other and labouring and unskilled workers – building and engineering occupations.

Changing age structure of the England and Wales population by social class

The social class structures of the 16–19 and 65 and over age groups in the 1991 Census were so different from the social class structures of the 20–64 age groups, that the calculations used only men aged 20–64 (see Figure B.1). A comparison of the age structures of the 1971, 1981 and 1991 Census populations shows interesting changes. Figure B.2 shows the proportions of each age group in each class at each of these three censuses. At each age group, the proportion in Class II has risen over the two decades. In general, the proportion in Class IIIM has dropped over the same period. Class V may have a cohort effect - it appears to be getting younger. The age structure of the base population greatly affects the SMR calculations. If the age structures of the different substrata are very different from each

FIGURE B.2
Percentage in each age group
by social class, men
England and Wales, 1971,1981,1991

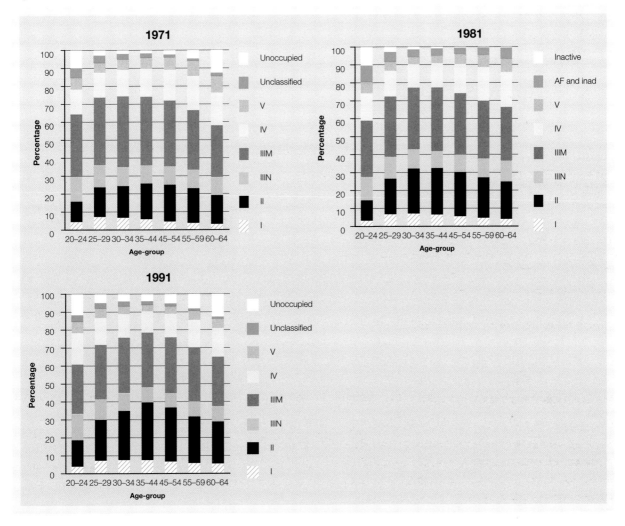

Table B.10:   1981 and 1991 Censuses (10% sample). Proportion of men in occupations within Social Class IV,
England and Wales

Description	1981 Census (per cent)	1991 Census (per cent)
Postmen, mail sorters	5	$6^1/_2$
Security guards and officers, patrolmen, watchmen	4	$5^1/_2$
Gardeners and groundsmen	4	$5^1/_2$
Machine tool operators	11	$7^1/_2$
Other metal, jewellery, electrical production workers	6	5
Storekeepers, warehousemen	10	$8^1/_2$
Inspectors, viewers (metal, electrical goods)	5	$3^1/_2$
Farm workers	4	$3^1/_2$
	(20-64)	(21-64)
Number of men allocated to this class in analysis	207,277	188,941

Table B.11:   1981 and 1991 Censuses (10% sample). Proportion of men in occupations within Social Class V, England and Wales

Description	1981 Census (percent)	1991 Census (percent)
Cleaners, window cleaners, chimney sweeps, road sweepers	13	19
Building and civil engineering labourers	21	23½
General labourers - other	20½	16½
General labourers - engineering and allied trades	13½	8
Number of men allocated to this class in analysis	(20-64) 75,366	(21-64) 64,170

Table B.12:   Summary of sensitivity analysis – individual classes altered: SMRs, all causes, men aged 20–64, England and Wales, 1991–93

	Changing IIIN					Changing IIIM			
	Standard	5%	10%	25%	50%	5%	10%	25%	50%
I	66	66	67	67	69	67	69	73	82
II	72	72	72	73	75	73	74	79	88
IIIN	100	96	92	82	69	102	104	111	124
IIIM	117	117	118	119	122	112	107	95	81
IV	116	117	117	119	122	119	121	128	143
V	189	190	191	193	198	193	196	209	233
E&W	100	100	100	100	100	100	100	100	100

	Changing IV					Changing V			
	Standard	5%	10%	25%	50%	5%	10%	25%	50%
I	66	67	67	69	72	66	66	67	68
II	72	72	73	74	78	72	72	72	73
IIIN	100	101	102	104	109	101	101	102	103
IIIM	117	118	119	122	127	117	117	118	120
IV	116	111	107	95	80	117	117	118	119
V	189	191	192	197	205	181	173	154	130
E&W	100	100	100	100	100	100	100	100	100

other, then the standardisation will not overcome these difficulties.

Looking at proportions within each class, as opposed to each age group, further emphasises the fact of Class V becoming younger. Class II is becoming more grouped in the 35–44 age group. The two ten-year groups in the middle mask some of the changes which could affect SMRs. Nearly 60 per cent of deaths in the men aged 35–44 group are of men aged 40–44. The same unevenness is true in the 45–54 group, 60 per cent of deaths in this group are of men aged 50–54 (see Figure B.3).

Sensitivity analysis

When grossing up the census populations to the population estimates, it was assumed that the age distribution of social class within the census was also the age distribution within the whole population. There is no hard evidence either way. There is an age bias in the underenumeration of the 1991 Census. This has been taken into account by grossing, not the whole population regardless of age, but using five-year age groups within which to gross. However, is this assumption reasonable? How sensitive are the SMRs to such an assumption?

To try to answer this, a sensitivity analysis using the 1991–93 all-cause SMRs was undertaken. A variety of different scenarios of social class distributions was examined to see how they affected the SMRs. The number of people in each age group to be assigned a class was known. For example, about 2 million males aged 20–24 had to be assigned to a social class. In the original analysis, these were distributed across the social classes in the same proportion as in Table B.1.

Altering a single class with subsequent changes to the other classes

For the first sensitivity calculations, the numbers allocated to each of the individual classes was changed by fixed amounts:

FIGURE B.3
Percentage per social class by
age group, men aged 20-64
England and Wales, 1971, 1981, 1991

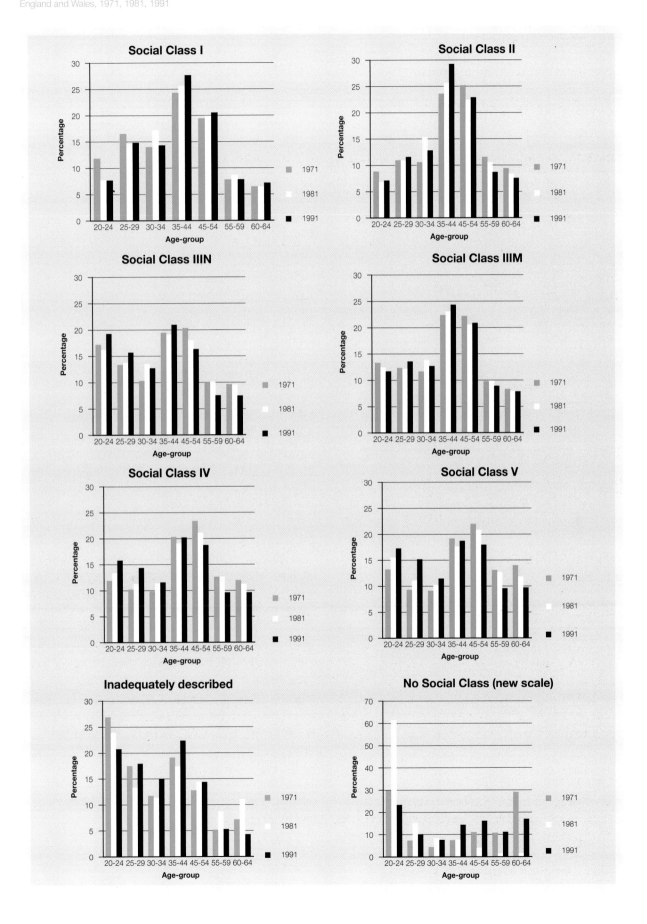

Table B.13: Summary of sensitivity analysis – combination of classes altered: SMRs, all causes, men aged 20–64, England and Wales, 1991–93

	Standard	Changing IIIM, IV, V unocc and unclass				Changing IV, V unocc and unclass			
		all 5%	all 25%	5/10/10/ 25/25	10/25/25/ 5/5	all 5%	all 25%	5/10/ 25/25	25/25/ 10/5
I	66	71	97	81	76	67	73	71	69
II	72	76	105	87	82	73	79	77	75
IIIN	100	107	149	123	116	102	111	108	105
IIIM	117	112	95	107	112	119	129	126	123
IV	116	111	95	95	107	111	95	95	111
V	189	181	154	154	173	181	154	154	173
E&W	100	100	100	100	100	100	100	100	100

	Standard	Changing V, unocc and unclass			
		all 5%	all 25%	25/ 10/5	5/ 10/25
I	66	67	69	67	68
II	72	72	74	73	73
IIIN	100	101	104	102	103
IIIM	117	118	122	119	120
IV	116	117	121	119	120
V	189	181	154	154	181
E&W	100	100	100	100	100

5 per cent, 10 per cent, 25 per cent, 50 per cent. The rest of the men in the age group were assigned to a social class in proportion to the remainder of that age group. By pro rata grossing, about 133,000 men aged 20–24 were allocated to Class V. This left about 1.9 million to be allocated elsewhere. If we increased the amount in Class V by say five per cent to nearly 140,000, we have 4,000 fewer men to allocate elsewhere. The remaining men were then allocated in proportion to how they were distributed across the social classes in the 20–24 age group in Table B.1. Table B.12 summarises the changes to the SMRs using these new populations.

Altering a combination of social classes

The problem is even more complex than this. If underenumeration is biased by social class, it is unlikely that only one class is affected. A second analysis was carried out using combinations of different classes changing by different amounts. Again the SMRs are affected, but fairly large changes to the proportions have to be made to make big changes to the SMR values. Few combinations changed the overall pattern. Table B.13 shows a summary of the second sensitivity analysis.

Conclusion

The analyses carried out indicate that the possible sources of bias are not of a sufficiently large nature to affect unduly the conclusions drawn when using mortality data and census data together around the 1991 Census.

The classification revisions leave the vast majority of people in the same classes, 91 per cent in the 1980 revision and 99 per cent in the 1990 revision. The occupations making up the classes have changed over time. However, it is the lack of change in the largest occupations within classes which is most remarkable. The age distribution of the classes has changed over the last 20 years. This may contribute to the different patterns emerging in SMRs for some causes.

The 1991–93 SMRs are sensitive to assumptions about the social class distribution of the census underenumeration. However, fairly large changes in the distribution are needed to make big differences in the pattern of SMR values. With no other evidence, it would be unreasonable to assume a different social class distribution from that in the ten per cent sample from the 1991 Census. The known age distribution of the undercount has been taken into consideration in the calculations.

References

1 OPCS (1995). *1991 Census, General Report, Great Britain*. London, HMSO.

2 OPCS (1986). *Occupational mortality Decennial Supplement 1979-80*, 82-83. Series DS, 6. London, HMSO.

3 OPCS (1980). *Classification of Occupations 1980*. London, HMSO.

4 OPCS (1991). *Standard Occupational Classification. Volume 3*. London, HMSO.

External Referees

We appreciate greatly the help we received from our independent referees. Each chapter was reviewed by a minimum of four external referees. They made very valuable comments about chapters at draft stage. Many of these comments helped us as editors to clarify points with the authors and to ensure that the volume tells its story coherently. The overall responsibility for each chapter rests with the chapter authors. No responsibility for the contents or comments within a chapter rests with the referees.

Dr Andrew Boddy
Director, Public Health Research Unit
University of Glasgow
1 Lilybank Gardens
Glasgow G12 8RZ

Professor Hilary Graham
Programme Director, ESRC Health Variations Programme
Department of Applied Social Science
Lancaster University
Cartmel College
Lancaster LA1 4YL

Professor Dr Louise J Gunning-Schepers
Professor of Public Health
Universiteit van Amsterdam
Instituut voor Sociale Geneeskunde
Academisch Medisch Centrum, GEB.J
Meibergdreef 15
1105 AZ Amsterdam
The Netherlands

Dr Bobbie Jacobson
Director of Public Health
East London and The City Health Authority
Tredegar House
97–99 Bow Road
London E3 2AN

Professor Sally Macintyre
Director, MRC Medical Sociology Unit
6 Lilybank Gardens
Glasgow G12 8RZ

Professor J N Morris
Emeritus Professor
London School of Hygiene and Tropical Medicine
Keppel Street
London WC1E 7HT

Index

standardised mortality ratios (SMRs) 96–7
    see also standardised patient consulting
        ratios
    economic activity *159*, **160**, 161–4, **162**,
        163
    housing tenure/car access **170**
        changes 180–3, **182**
        men 173-6, *175*, **176**, *178*
        women 170–5, *171*, **172**, *174-5*
    immigrants **112**, 113
        men 115, *116*, **116**, **119**
    men
        all-causes **98**
        migrant *114*, **114**
        social class *98*, *100*
    social class effects **140**, 224
    Spanish study 52, *53*
    unemployment **164**
standardised patient consulting ratios
    (SPCRs) 190–2, **191**
standards of living, mortality effects (19/20C.)
    20–1
stillbirth rate
    definition 84
    England and Wales 85, **85**
stroke mortality
    men 99, **100**, 105
    migrants 228–9
Sudden Infant Death Syndrome 88, *88*
suicides 96
    male mortality 99, **100**, 101
        age-specific 102, *104*
        European standardised rates 105
    migrant mortality 117, **119**
    SMR (1991–93) **140**
    unemployment **164**, 167
summary chapter 224–33
Sweden
    mortality 53, **54**, 166
    socio-economic health differences 50–1,
        51–2, 53, **54**
    women's health 55

teenagers, conception 196
tooth decay *see* dental health
transport systems, improvements (18C.) 11,
    14
tuberculosis, mortality 227

unemployment
    see also employment
    definition 158
    growth 36–7, *37*, *38*
    monitoring 54–5
    mortality 156–67
        causes 163–4, **164**
        explanations 165–7
        men 151–4, *152–3*, **152–4**
        social class 159–62, *160–1*, **160**
    psychiatric conditions 167

United States of America (USA)
    data collection resurgence 60–1, *61*
    health inequalities 63, 64
    minorities and class 56–8, **57**
    mortality 52, 56–8, **57**
    Multiple Risk Factor Intervention Trial 58
    National Longitudinal Mortality Study
        (1979–89) 57

Variations group *see* Department of Health

wages, poverty (19C.) 19
West Africa migrants, male mortality 111, **112**,
    113, **113**
White Americans
    health 56–8
    health status **57**
Whitehall study 169
Whitehead, Margaret 2–28, 44–72, 224–33
WHO *see* World Health Organisation
Whyman, Steve 29–43
women
    see also adults
    international health inequalities 55–6
    labour force changes 37, *38*
    life expectancy *46–7*
        social class 77–81, *78*, **78–81**
    Longitudinal Study analyses 71
    mortality
        differentials 225–6, 227–8
        economic activity **160**, 163
        housing tenure/car access 170–5, *171*,
            172–3, *174-5*
            changes 177–9, **179**
        mothers 53, *54*, 90–1
        social class 145–7, **146–7**, **148**, **150–1**
        unemployment **164**, 229
    social class distribution *161*
work, changing nature 37–8
workhouses, New Poor Law Act 1834 18
World Health Organisation (WHO)
    European Health For All Strategy 2
    European Region health trends 45
    European Standard Population 144, 172

young people
    see children; infant mortality
    mortality **13**, 228

Compiled by INDEXING SPECIALISTS, Hove.

Printed in the United Kingdom for The Stationery Office
J23265 C15 9/97 078166